STATISTICAL PHYSICS

STATISTICAL PHYSICS

A. F. BROWN

Professor of Physics at the City University
London

1968

NEW YORK

American Elsevier Publishing Company, Inc.

© A. F. Brown 1968
EDINBURGH UNIVERSITY PRESS
22 George Square, Edinburgh 8
North America
American Elsevier Publishing Company, Inc.
52 Vanderbilt Avenue
New York, New York 10017

Library of Congress Catalog Card Number 67-31343

Printed in Great Britain

582192

PREFACE

This book is based on lectures given at the University of Edinburgh to a class composed mainly of students of chemistry in their second year of a Scottish four-year honours course. Several circumstances prompted me to give them. First, complete recasting of the physics course for these students made it possible to get away from the traditional division of elementary physics into heat, light, properties of matter and so on, and to try to base a selection of useful topics on a single mathematical technique, in this case the elementary theory of probability. Secondly, I had come to the conclusion that there were some – surprisingly few – physical concepts which were so important as to merit a great deal of trouble in making them understood as distinct from merely learnt; among these is the Boltzmann factor, exp ($-$ energy$/kT$), and all it implies; another is the estimation of the accuracy of a measurement.

The presentation is intended to be elementary and accessible to students in the transition years between school and university. Arguments from the general to the particular are always avoided. However neat such arguments may be, the student usually finds it easier to have the complete proof of a simple case of a law, then to try to generalise it; then, if the generalisation is seen to work in practice, to proceed to further generalisations. Using this method and asking the student to make the effort to acquire a very few mathematical techniques (mainly associated with the integrals $\int_0^\infty x^n e^{-x^2} dx$), it is rarely necessary to use the off-putting phrase 'it can be shown that . . .'. Where this phrase does occur in this book it has the meaning 'the student should now be able to show that . . .'.

Application of these principles has produced a rather long book covering only a small part of physics. The length has been further increased because I have never hesitated to labour a point which any of my students has ever found difficult, or to give alternative proofs of important results. The student who finds the going easy can readily find faster paths through the book and try the problems, which are meant to be read as part of the text.

My thanks are due to the Director of the Postgraduate Education Centre at Harwell for making it possible for me to complete the manuscript in the stimulating, yet peaceful, atmosphere of the Harwell library, and to Mr A. H. Seville and Mr C. J. Shaddock, who read the typescript and proofs and corrected many of my errors.

A. F. Brown
Edinburgh, April 1967

CONTENTS

INTRODUCTION

When we are dealing with the interaction of a small number of bodies, we can write down equations which exactly describe their behaviour. For example, using the laws of conservation of energy and momentum we can describe the collision of two billiard balls. Inevitably we make some simplifying assumptions: we neglect the effect of irregularities in the structure of the table and the balls and simply write down a few equations – one for conservation of energy and one or two more, depending on whether we are playing one-dimensional or two-dimensional billiards, for conservation of momentum.If we are dealing with the collision of only a few particles of atomic scale – for example an electron and an atom – we may be more conscious of the simplifications we make but we shall still require four equations – one for energy, three for momentum conservation – to describe each two-body collision.

When the number of interacting particles is large it is not possible to describe their motion in this way. For example one cubic centimetre of a gas at N.T.P. contains about 10^{19} molecules. Even if we knew where each molecule was at any instant, how fast it was going and in what direction and could write down the equations describing its fate in the next collision, we would have to write down a new set of 10^{19} equations after each collision. We shall see later that each molecule in a gas at N.T.P. makes about 10^9 collisions per second. Even if it were possible to write down and solve all these equations, the results would be of no interest since all that we want or can observe is the averaged-out effect of the collisions of molecules with the walls of the container and with each other.

The processes whereby we determine the average or most probable behaviour of a large assembly of particles are an example of the use of statistical methods in physics. We shall first illustrate the methods by reference to a gas of real material particles, but it will be seen later that these methods are applicable to entities which are not material particles as we usually think of them – packets of energy and vibration and even less tangible concepts such as errors and missing atoms. To begin with we shall use the word particle, atom or molecule rather than introduce a more general term (such as 'enton') for something which is so general that it has no property other than existence.

The most elementary application of statistics to physics is the kinetic theory of gases. We shall first derive a few results in this theory to show how the behaviour of large numbers of bodies can be predicted by simple statistical methods. The statistical concepts themselves will be examined later.

Chapter 1

KINETIC THEORY OF GASES

§ 1.1 Models

In physics we can derive laws that relate directly observable quantities. One example is Boyle's law, $pV = $ constant, which relates the pressure and volume of a gas at constant temperature; another is Ohm's law, which states that the electrical current through a conductor is proportional to the potential difference between its ends. Physics, however, attempts to go beyond these phenomenological relations and discover the reason for them in terms of the structure of matter, that is, in terms of atoms, molecules, and the particles which make them up. To do this we set up a *model* of the system considered and attempt to calculate the consequences of our assumptions. If the calculations agree with experiment and enable us to predict as yet unobserved phenomena then we say the model is a good one.

In the kinetic theory of gases our first model is that the gas can be thought of as consisting of small, hard, mass points moving within the container and colliding only with the walls. We further assume that collisions with a wall are such that the molecule is reflected as in a mirror; its component of velocity normal to the wall is reversed, but the other components are unaltered. The final assumption is that all directions of motion are equally probable. We realise that this is only a model since we know that atoms and molecules are certainly not mass points, but we suspend our disbelief in the model until we see what we can derive from it. Thus, if the model is good we can calculate the pressure on the walls by calculating the number of molecules which strike each wall and the change of momentum when each is reflected. Our model can in fact explain the equation of state for a gas and enable us to calculate the specific heat of the simplest gases.

We can then add complications to our model: first, we can allow the molecules to have some sort of internal structure and to exchange their translational energy for internal energy, for example rotational energy. This variation enables us to predict the specific heats of more complex gases.

Adding further complexities, we can give the atoms and molecules a finite size so that they can collide with each other. With this extra assumption we shall be able to explain the various transport phenomena: transfer of heat from the more energetic molecules to the less energetic (thermal conductivity); transfer of momentum from the faster moving molecules in a stream to the slower (viscosity); transport of matter whereby molecules of different kinds become mixed (diffusion).

While we have to be sure that as we add complications we do not give the model self-contradictory properties, the principle is that the model should be the simplest which enables the observed phenomenon to be explained. The test of a model is in what we can deduce from it.

§ 1.2   The simplest model

Consider a gas consisting of mass points, that is, of particles whose only properties are mass and velocity, contained in a rectangular

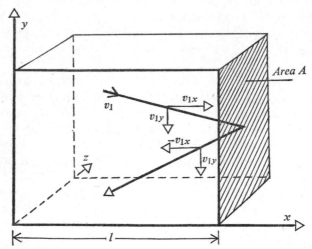

Figure 1.1. *Collision of a molecule with a wall. For simplicity the drawing shows only the x- and y-components of motion.*

vessel of length l and cross-sectional area A. We assume that the particles all have the same mass but do not all have the same velocity. Consider first one particle of mass m and velocity v_1 making a collision with the plane at right angles to the x-axis, as shown in *fig.* 1.1. Let the particle's x-component of velocity be v_{1x}. Since we are assuming elastic collisions, with specular reflection from the wall, this component of velocity will be reversed, the other components will be unchanged.

Thus the change of momentum of this one particle is $2mv_{1x}$. This momentum is imparted to the wall. A particle travelling with velocity v_{1x} will take a time $2l/v_{1x}$ to make the return trip, distance $2l$, to the other end of the box and back; so the number of impacts on the wall in time t is $v_{1x}t/2l$, provided $t \gg 2l/v_{1x}$, and the total momentum given to the wall in this time is mv_{1x}^2t/l.

Suppose there are N particles in the container and that their x-components of velocity are $v_{1x}, v_{2x}, \ldots, v_{Nx}$, where the quantities v_{rx} need not be all different. We call the set of all the v_{rx} a velocity *distribution*. Then we can go through the same argument for each particle, treating them all separately, since we have assumed that the molecules do not interact in any way. We find that the change of momentum in time t at the wall is given by

$$\frac{mt}{l}(v_{1x}^2 + v_{2x}^2 + \ldots + v_{Nx}^2).$$

The quantity in brackets is $N\overline{v_x^2}$, where

$$\overline{v_x^2} = \frac{v_{1x}^2 + v_{2x}^2 + \ldots + v_{Nx}^2}{N}, \qquad 1.2.1$$

that is, $\overline{v_x^2}$ is the average of the squares of the velocities of all the particles. Thus, the total change of momentum in time t is

$$\frac{mt}{l}N\overline{v_x^2}$$

and the rate of change of momentum is

$$\frac{m}{l}N\overline{v_x^2}.$$

The change of momentum in unit time or the rate of change of momentum is, by Newton's second law, the force on the wall. It is likewise an average, being the average force obtained by adding up the momenta imparted to the wall by all the impacts over a time t long compared with the time for which each molecule is in contact with the wall and dividing by the time t. Thus, the average force $\overline{F}$ on the wall is

$$\overline{F} = \frac{m}{l}N\overline{v^2}. \qquad 1.2.2$$

If impacts were rare events or if we had very sensitive measuring apparatus we might be able to detect that F was not a constant force but was made up of a rain of small impacts. This is examined in §11.5. Normally we can only record a steady pressure p on the wall given by

$$p = \bar{F}/A ,$$

where A is the area of the wall. Thus

$$p = \frac{m}{lA} N \overline{v_x^2}$$

$$= \frac{m}{V} N \overline{v_x^2} , \qquad\qquad 1.2.3$$

since $lA = V$, the volume of the vessel containing the gas. Now the square of the speed of any particle is

$$v^2 = v_x^2 + v_y^2 + v_z^2 . \qquad\qquad 1.2.4$$

The average of the square of the speed v^2 is

$$\overline{v^2} = \overline{v_x^2} + \overline{v_y^2} + \overline{v_z^2} , \qquad\qquad 1.2.5$$

while, if we add to the properties of our model the assumption that the velocity distributions are the same in any direction, we have

$$\overline{v_x^2} = \overline{v_y^2} = \overline{v_z^2} . \qquad\qquad 1.2.6$$

We shall not digress at the moment to give formal proofs of assertions 1.2.5 and 1.2.6, though 1.2.5 is obvious from 1.2.1 and 1.2.4 and the truth of 1.2.6 could be demonstrated physically by using the knowledge that the pressure given by 1.2.3 is the same in any direction.

So $\qquad \overline{v_x^2} = \tfrac{1}{3}\overline{v^2} ,$

or $\qquad p = \tfrac{1}{3}\dfrac{mN}{V}\overline{v^2} \qquad\qquad 1.2.7$

and $\qquad pV = \tfrac{1}{3}mN\overline{v^2}. \qquad\qquad 1.2.8$

Compare this with the equation of state for a perfect gas,

$$pV = nRT , \qquad\qquad 1.2.9$$

where n is the number of kilogram-molecules of gas in the sample occupying volume V at pressure p. R is the universal gas constant (8·3 kJ/kg-mole deg) and T is the absolute temperature in °K. It should be noted in passing that our model gas has all the attributes of a perfect gas; there are no forces between molecules nor between molecules and walls, and each single molecule has no volume.

We now rewrite 1.2.7, expressing the number of particles in the sample in terms of the number of molecules in a kg-mole, where N_0 is Avogadro's number and, like R, is a universal constant, and obtain:

$$pV = \tfrac{1}{3}mnN_0\overline{v^2} = \tfrac{1}{3}nM\overline{v^2}, \qquad 1.2.10$$

where M is the (kilogram) molecular weight.

Comparing 1.2.9 and 1.2.10

$$\tfrac{1}{3}mnN_0\overline{v^2} = nRT,$$

or $\qquad\qquad m\overline{v^2} = 3(R/N_0)T.$

The quantity R/N_0 is also a universal constant, being the quotient of two universal constants. It is called *Boltzmann's constant* k and (as shown in § 1.12) has the value $1{\cdot}4 \times 10^{-23}$ joule deg^{-1}. Thus

$$\tfrac{1}{2}m\overline{v^2} = \tfrac{3}{2}kT. \qquad 1.2.11$$

Equation 1.2.11 tells us that the mean translational kinetic energy of a gas molecule is $\tfrac{3}{2}kT$. From this the root-mean-square speed can be calculated for any given gas:

$$(\overline{v^2})^{\frac{1}{2}} = (3kT/m)^{\frac{1}{2}} = (3RT/M)^{\frac{1}{2}}. \qquad 1.2.12$$

For example, for hydrogen H_2, we have $M = 2$ kg, which with $R = 8{\cdot}3 \times 10^3$ J/kg-mole deg and $T = 290°K$ (room temperature) gives

$$(\overline{v^2})^{\frac{1}{2}} = 1{\cdot}9 \times 10^3 \text{ m/s.}^*$$

Alternatively $(\overline{v^2})^{\frac{1}{2}}$ may be obtained from 1.2.7 since mN is the mass of the gas in volume V. Thus mN/V is the density, so

$$p = \tfrac{1}{3}\rho\overline{v^2}. \qquad 1.2.13$$

For H_2 at 0°C and pressure 1000 mb ($= 10^6$ dynes/cm$^2 = 10^5$ Nw/m^2), tables give $\rho = 0{\cdot}09$ gm/litre $= 0{\cdot}09$ kg/m^3, so

$$(\overline{v^2})^{\frac{1}{2}} = 1{\cdot}8 \times 10^3 \text{ m/s.}$$

The mean or average speed $\bar{v}$, as we shall see in § 5.9, is about 10% less than this.

---

* We shall use M.K.S. units throughout this book. Molecular weights will thus be numerically the same as in the c.g.s. system as used in most books of tables but the units will now be kilograms. The gas constant R is thus 10^3 times the c.g.s. value, i.e., $R = 8{\cdot}3 \times 10^3$ J/kg-mole deg. Avogadro's number N_0 is then the number of molecules in a kg-mole and is consequently 10^3 times larger than the number in a gram-mole. Energies, including thermal energies, will be in joules and speeds in m/s.

2

§ 1.3   Equipartition of energy

Again, using 1.2.5 to rewrite 1.2.11, we obtain

$$\tfrac{1}{2}m(\overline{v_x^2}+\overline{v_y^2}+\overline{v_z^2}) = \tfrac{3}{2}kT,$$

and, remembering that

$$\overline{v_x^2} = \overline{v_y^2} = \overline{v_z^2},$$

we have

$$\tfrac{1}{2}m\overline{v_x^2} = \tfrac{1}{2}m\overline{v_y^2} = \tfrac{1}{2}m\overline{v_z^2} = \tfrac{1}{2}kT. \qquad\qquad 1.3.1$$

This is the famous *law of equipartition of energy* which appears to have been first enunciated by J. C. Waterston in 1845. It tells us that the mean value of each of the three terms in the expression for the kinetic energy of a point particle is $\tfrac{1}{2}kT$.

Anticipating the extension of the law to more complex systems, we may re-express it in the more usual form: if we call each term which occurs as the square of a velocity in the expression for the energy of a particle *a degree of freedom*, then to each degree of freedom corresponds a mean energy $\tfrac{1}{2}kT$. It must be stressed that $\tfrac{1}{2}kT$ (or $\tfrac{3}{2}kT$ for the total kinetic energy) is the mean value averaged over all the particles in the gas. The energy of an individual particle can have any value.

The above 'proof' of the law has been obtained by the use of a very simple model. It is natural to see if the result can now be extended. Let us make the hypothesis that the law is of more general validity, and try to apply it to more complex cases. If it works, and if we obtain results which are confirmed by experiment, we may assume that the law has general validity.

§ 1.4   Equipartition (i) : a mixture of gases

If we have a mixture of N_A molecules or n_A kilogram-molecules of gas A each with mass m_A, and N_B molecules or n_B kilogram-molecules of gas B each with mass m_B occupying volume V then, applying our equipartition principle to molecules with different masses, we have

$$\tfrac{1}{2}m_A\overline{v_A^2} = \tfrac{3}{2}kT, \qquad\qquad 1.4.1$$

$$\tfrac{1}{2}m_B\overline{v_B^2} = \tfrac{3}{2}kT,$$

or multiplying by N_0 throughout

$$\tfrac{1}{2}M_A\overline{v_A^2} = \tfrac{3}{2}RT, \qquad\qquad 1.4.2$$

$$\tfrac{1}{2}M_B\overline{v_B^2} = \tfrac{3}{2}RT.$$

Now from 1.2.9:

$$p_A V = \tfrac{1}{3} n_A M_A \overline{v_A^2} = n_A RT ,$$ 1.4.3

$$p_B V = \tfrac{1}{3} n_B M_B \overline{v_B^2} = n_B RT .$$

This means that the pressures of each of the components are in the ratio of the amounts of each present: each behaves as if the other were not there. This rather trivial demonstration is the substance of Dalton's law of partial pressures. It is also the form in which Waterston first gave the law. Again, from 1.4.2:

$$\overline{v_A^2}/\overline{v_B^2} = M_B / M_A .$$ 1.4.4

Without going for the moment into the mechanism of diffusion or into the relationship between $\overline{v^2}$ and $(\bar{v})^2$, it is clear that the rate of diffusion, for example the rate at which gas A passes out of a porous container relative to rate for gas B, will be directly related to their molecular speeds–the faster will diffuse faster. Equation 1.4.4 expresses Graham's law of diffusion of gases, which states that the rates of diffusion of gases are inversely proportional to the square roots of their molecular weights. The consequences of 1.4.4 will be considered in more detail in § 1.16, where it will be used to derive a method of separating gaseous mixtures.

§ 1.5 Equipartition (ii): specific heats of monatomic gases

The specific heat C of a substance is defined as the amount of heat Q required to raise the temperature of unit mass of the substance by unit amount in a reversible manner. Thus

$$C = \frac{dQ}{dT} ,$$

while in a reversible change the first law of thermodynamics tells us that

$$dQ = dU + p\, dV ,$$

where U denotes the internal energy of the substance. In our model of a monatomic gas, U is simply the sum of the kinetic energies of all the particles; $p\, dV$ is the work done by expansion.

It is customary to define two principal specific heats. First, there is the specific heat at constant volume C_V given by

$$C_V = \left(\frac{\partial U}{\partial T}\right)_V ,$$

where the subscript V indicates that V is to be kept constant in the differentiation. Secondly, there is the specific heat at constant pressure C_p given by

$$C_p = \left(\frac{\partial U}{\partial T}\right)_p + p\left(\frac{\partial V}{\partial T}\right)_p,$$

where the subscript p reminds us that in these differentiations p is to be kept constant.

We shall assume throughout that the mass of substance with which we are dealing is the kilogram-atom or kilogram-molecule of the substance depending on whether it is an element or a compound. For both we shall use the term kg-mole or just mole. In this case the specific heat is the heat to raise one mole of the substance by unit temperature and is called the molar specific heat or just *molar heat*. It will be written with a small c, thus:

$$c_V = \left(\frac{\partial U}{\partial T}\right)_V, \qquad\qquad\qquad 1.5.1$$

$$c_p = \left(\frac{\partial U}{\partial T}\right)_p + p\left(\frac{\partial V}{\partial T}\right)_p.$$

For one mole of a perfect gas we have the equation of state

$$pV = RT.$$

Also the internal energy of a perfect gas like ours depends only on the kinetic energy of its molecules. Thus U is a function of temperature only and does not depend on p or V. So in equation 1.5.1

$$\left(\frac{\partial U}{\partial T}\right)_V = \left(\frac{\partial U}{\partial T}\right)_p, \qquad\qquad\qquad 1.5.2$$

whence, for a perfect gas:

$$c_p - c_V = R.$$

To use 1.5.1 and 1.5.2 for even a monatomic gas, the model requires slight modification in order that heat can be given to the gas; for, as it stands, the model assumes that when a particle strikes the wall it rebounds without any change in its (kinetic) energy. We now introduce the idea that if the temperature of the wall is raised by a *small* amount ΔT above the temperature of the gas then the particles which strike this wall will *on the average* take away additional kinetic energy $\frac{3}{2}k\,\Delta T$ each. The total energy U of a gas of N_0 particles is thus increased by ΔU given by

$$\Delta U = \tfrac{3}{2}N_0 k\,\Delta T, \qquad\qquad\qquad 1.5.3$$

while its temperature is increased by ΔT. Since the vessel containing our model gas is of constant volume we have

$$c_V = \frac{\Delta U}{\Delta T} = \tfrac{3}{2}N_0 k = \tfrac{3}{2}R , \qquad\qquad 1.5.4$$

assuming that we can use the quantities ΔU and ΔT as differentials. In fact, heat given at constant volume to the model gas is directly proportional to temperature, so c_V is simply the constant gradient of the relationship between ΔU and ΔT.

From 1.5.2 we have that for a monatomic gas

$$c_p = c_V + R = \tfrac{5}{2}R$$

and $\qquad \gamma \equiv c_p/c_V = \tfrac{5}{3} = 1{\cdot}67 .$

Experiment (table 1) shows that the calculated values of c_V and γ are almost exact for the monatomic gases He, Ne, Ar, etc., at all temperatures for which the gases can be considered perfect; that is at temperatures not too near to those at which they become liquid.

The procedure whereby we allow a weak interaction with the walls but still persist in the assumption that there are no forces between the particles and the walls or between the particles themselves is basic to the statistical models we shall be discussing. It will be clear that the new hypothesis does not affect the earlier results. We may now proceed to try further modifications to our model.

§ 1.6   Equipartition (iii): polyatomic molecules

Still retaining the idea of atoms as mass points let us now assemble them into simple chemical molecules. For example we might make a model of a diatomic molecule such as H_2 or O_2 in the form of a dumb-bell where two point masses are held rigidly at a fixed distance

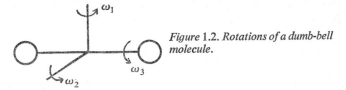

Figure 1.2. Rotations of a dumb-bell molecule.

apart (*fig.* 1.2). We can still assume that this distance is so small that the complete molecule can be treated as a mass point. The total (kinetic) energy of such a model molecule is made up of the translational energy of its centre of gravity plus the rotational energy round each of two axes mutually perpendicular and at right angles to the line joining the atoms. That is

$$U = \tfrac{1}{2}mv_x^2 + \tfrac{1}{2}mv_y^2 + \tfrac{1}{2}mv_z^2 + \tfrac{1}{2}I_1\omega_1^2 + \tfrac{1}{2}I_2\omega_2^2 , \qquad 1.6.1$$

where m is the mass of the whole diatomic molecule, I_1 and I_2 are the moments of inertia round each of the two axes (I_1 and I_2 are, of course, equal in a diatomic molecule) and ω_1 and ω_2 are angular velocities of rotation round the respective axes.

Equation 1.6.1 does not include a term for energy ($\tfrac{1}{2}I_3\omega_3^2$) of rotation round the axis joining the atoms. In our model, where the atoms are represented by mass points, this term is zero, since $I_3 = 0$. Similarly we did not include energy terms for the spin of the monatomic gas particles. We know that atoms are really not mass points, so that our model, while self-consistent, does not agree with other experience. We shall discuss the discrepancy in § 9.9.

We now try to use the principle of equipartition on this system by giving an average of $\tfrac{1}{2}kT$ to each of the terms in the expression for the energy of a molecule, including the two involving the square of an angular velocity. Then the mean energy of a molecule in a diatomic gas at temperature T is

$$U = \tfrac{5}{2}kT ,$$

and the additional energy which has to be added at constant volume to raise the temperature of a gas of N_0 molecules by a small amount ΔT is

$$\Delta U = \tfrac{5}{2}N_0 k \, \Delta T = \tfrac{5}{2}R \, \Delta T . \qquad 1.6.2$$

This step is not trivial, since it involves a further change in our original model. We now have to arrange for the rotational degrees of freedom to receive extra energy and this we can do by devising some mechanism whereby rotational energy, like translational energy, can be obtained in collisions with the walls. Alternatively we can postulate some weak interaction between the molecules themselves—so weak that none of our earlier conclusions are invalidated but just strong enough to allow energy to be transferred from translational modes to rotational modes.

As before, 1.5.1 gives for the molar heat at constant volume:

$$c_V = \frac{\Delta U}{\Delta T} = \tfrac{5}{2}R .$$

If the gas is still assumed to be ideal, $c_p = \tfrac{7}{2}R$ and $\gamma = \tfrac{7}{5}$. As table 1 shows, these values are in pretty good agreement with experimental values for the 'permanent' gases H_2, N_2, O_2 at normal temperatures. Agreement is not so good for the less stable halogens.

TABLE 1 : molar heats of gases in kJ/kg-mole deg

gas	temp.	c_V calc.	c_V obs.	c_p calc.	c_p obs.	$\gamma \equiv c_p/c_V$ calc.	$\gamma \equiv c_p/c_V$ obs.
He	room	12·4	12·4	20·7	20·7	1·67	1·66
Ne	room	12·4	—	20·7	—	1·67	1·64
Ar	room	12·4	12·9	20·7	21·3	1·67	1·67
Hg	360°C	12·4	—	20·7	—	1·67	1·67
Na	800°C	12·4	—	20·7	—	1·67	1·68
H_2	−200°C	20·7	14·0	29·0	22·2	1·40	1·60
H_2	room	20·7	20·3	29·0	28·9	1·40	1·41
O_2	room	20·7	20·7	29·0	29·0	1·40	1·40
N_2	room	20·7	20·7	29·0	29·0	1·40	1·41
Cl_2	room	20·7	24·8	29·0	37·0	1·40	1·36
CO	room	20·7	20·8	29·0	29·0	1·40	1·40
NO	room	20·7	22·2	29·0	30·5	1·40	1·38
HCl	room	20·7	21·4	29·0	29·8	1·40	1·39
CO_2	room	24·9	29·1	33·2	37·3	1·33	1·30
H_2O	100°C	24·9	22·4	33·2	28·8	1·33	1·28
NH_3	room	24·9	27·9	33·2	36·6	1·33	1·31
CH_4	room	24·9	27·3	33·2	35·8	1·33	1·31

§ 1.7 More complex molecules

For triatomic and more complex molecules we should expect a sixth term in the expression for the energy of a molecule, corresponding to rotation about a third axis perpendicular to the other two. Thus

$$\Delta U = \tfrac{6}{2} R \, \Delta T ,$$

$$c_V = 3R ; \qquad c_p = 4R ; \qquad \gamma = \tfrac{4}{3} .$$

As table 1 shows, the molar heats of the more complex molecules are larger than for diatomic molecules, but numerical agreement between theory and experiment is not very good.

§ 1.8 Specific heats of real gases

Table 1 gives experimental values of c_V and γ for a few gases at various temperatures. It is clear that reasonable agreement with equipartition theory is obtained only for monatomic and some diatomic gases. For other gases, not only are the experimental values of c_V generally too high but also they would have to be explained by invoking fractional degrees of freedom. Moreover the specific heats of gases, even simple ones like H_2, are not independent of temperature.

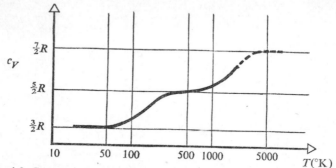

Figure 1.3. *Constant volume molar heat of hydrogen gas at various temperatures.*

Fig. 1.3 shows the temperature dependence of the molar heat c_V of hydrogen. From the curve it appears as if two degrees of freedom—presumably the rotational ones—become progressively inoperative below room temperature until at temperatures below about 70°K, H_2 behaves as a monatomic gas. At temperatures near to 1000°K the specific heat of H_2 rises above the equipartition value, the curve suggesting that two additional degrees of freedom are becoming operative.

We shall return to these points in § 9.9.

§ 1.9 Equipartition (iv): specific heats of solids

A crystalline solid consists of a regular three-dimensional array of atoms, ions, or molecules. We might make up a model sufficient for our purpose by supposing that we have to deal with a lattice of independent, non-interacting mass points held in position by springs as shown in *fig.* 1.4. Each mass point can vibrate about its position of equilibrium without affecting its neighbours and this vibratory motion is the origin of all the thermal energy of the 'crystal'.

The energy of a mass m vibrating in one-dimensional simple harmonic motion is a function of its distance x from the point of equilibrium and its velocity $\dot{x}$ at that point:

$$U = \tfrac{1}{2}m\dot{x}^2 + \tfrac{1}{2}\lambda x^2,$$

1.9.1

where λ is a spring constant, the force to produce unit extension of the spring holding the particle to its point of equilibrium. Since the particle can also vibrate in the y and z directions there will be two further similar expressions in $\dot{y}$ and y, $\dot{z}$ and z. Thus the total energy of each of the N_0 particles in our crystal model requires six terms to express it, three for kinetic energy and three for potential energy.

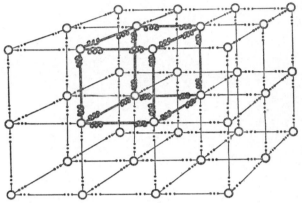

Figure 1.4. Model of a crystalline solid. In this model each atom is held to its position of equilibrium by springs of strength λ. It can vibrate about its position of equilibrium independently of its neighbours.

We now postulate that the equipartition rule can be extended in two ways: first, to include co-ordinates as well as velocities and secondly to include both velocities and co-ordinates which are not constant for a given particle. In fact the latter extension of the principle is not really necessary since, as is well known, the kinetic and potential energies averaged over a complete cycle of oscillatory motion are constant.

With these assumptions, the mean energy of a particle vibrating about its point of equilibrium in one dimension is $2 \times \frac{1}{2}kT = kT$ and in three dimensions is $6 \times \frac{1}{2}kT = 3kT$. If the model crystal contains N_0 particles—that is a kilogram-atom of a substance consisting of only one kind of atom—we have

$$U = 3N_0kT,\qquad\qquad 1.9.2$$

which is the same as if we had given energy kT to each of $3N_0$ linear harmonic oscillators and by the same reasoning as before

$$c_V = 3R.\qquad\qquad 1.9.3$$

To obtain this we have to assume, as in § 1.6, that although the oscillators are non-interacting for the purpose of reckoning the total energy there is still a weak interaction between them which allows thermal energy introduced at one side of the crystal to become distributed throughout the whole $3N_0$ oscillators.

§ 1.10 Dulong and Petit's law

The result that the molar heat of a monatomic substance is $3R$ or 24·9 kJ/kg-mole deg would, if correct, explain the empirical law of Dulong and Petit. This law, first enunciated in 1819, said that the specific heat of solid elements multiplied by the atomic weight was almost constant, the average value being about 27 kJ/kg-mole deg.

TABLE 2 : molar heats of solids in kJ/kg-mole deg
(at room temperature unless otherwise stated)

chemical formula	c_p (measured)	c_V (calculated from the measured c_p and equation 1.10.1)
elements – metals		
Al	24·3	23·5
Au	26·7	25·5
Bi	27·0	26·6
Fe	26·8	26·3
Hg (solid −43°C)	28·3	—
Li	27·6	26·4
W	26·2	25·8
elements – non-metals		
B	10·9	—
C (diamond)	5·7	5·7
C (diamond 1000°C)	23·1	23·1
compounds		
NaCl	50·3($=2\times25\cdot2$)	
PbO	46·8($=2\times23\cdot4$)	
PbO_2	62·3($=3\times20\cdot7$)	
$AlCl_3$	106 ($=4\times26\cdot5$)	
$AgNO_3$	85 ($=5\times17$)	

Now the measured value of the molar heat is c_p since it is not practicable to prevent a solid specimen from expanding; but our calculated value is c_V because, in our model crystal, we took no account of thermal expansion. Since work has to be done to produce expansion, c_p must be larger than c_V which is in qualitative agreement with our theory based on equipartition.

Table 2 gives values of the molar heat of some solids chosen for their variety of crystal types, melting points, and atomic weights. Column 2 gives the measured value of c_p and column 3 the value of c_V calculated from this and the thermodynamic formula, valid for solids:

$$c_p - c_V = (\beta^2 V_m/\kappa)T,\qquad\qquad 1.10.1$$

where β is the coefficient of linear thermal expansion, V_m is the molar volume and κ is the compressibility. $c_p - c_V$ for solids at room temperature is generally about 1 kJ/kg-mole deg.

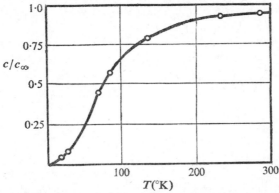

Figure 1.5. *Specific heat c of copper at various temperatures: c_∞ is the value of c extrapolated to high temperatures.*

Table 2 shows that room temperature measurements of the molar heat c_V of metals are in good agreement with the value 24·9 kJ/kg-mole obtained from equipartition. Agreement for non-metals at room temperature is not good while, for diamond, the law is a complete failure. If, however, we measure the molar heats of solids at temperatures other than room we find that c_p for all solids falls with temperature, tending to zero as the temperature approaches absolute zero. The theoretical value, based on equipartition, as *fig.* 1.5 shows, is an asymptotic value reached at high temperatures. Thus the agreement of theory and experiment for metals is due to the fortunate chance that measurements were made at room temperature and that room temperature is a high temperature for metals. Apparently room temperature is a low temperature for diamond and to a lesser extent for boron.

We shall be discussing the specific heats of solids in more detail in §§ 9.6 – 8.

§ 1.11 The law of Neumann and Kopp

The method used above to calculate the specific heats of monatomic solids can be extended to crystals containing more than one kind of atom. An example is NaCl where the lattice consists of a three-dimensional alternation of sodium and chlorine ions. Considering each ion as a mass point constrained by springs to oscillate around its point of equilibrium, we can carry out the same calculations as above, applying them to a kilogram-molecule of the substance containing N_0 sodium and N_0 chlorine ions. It is easy to see that the molar heat at constant volume of such a crystal should be $6R$. In the general case where the chemical molecule contains n atoms the molar heat should be $3nR$. This is the theoretical basis of the law of Neumann and Kopp (1823). A few examples of measured values of c_p for compounds are given in table 2. The same comments as were made for monatomic solids are relevant here.

§ 1.12 Determination of Boltzmann's constant

In the previous sections we have had no need to know a numerical value for Boltzmann's constant k since it has always occurred in the form $N_0 k$ or R, where N_0 is Avogadro's number, the number of molecules in a kilogram-molecule of any substance, and R is the gas constant. Since R is known, k can be calculated if N_0 is known.

Nowadays N_0 can be found by methods which do not depend on statistics. For example, one might find the crystal structure and interatomic spacing of a solid by means of X-rays. Hence one could calculate the number of atoms in the solid and knowing its mass could then calculate the number of atoms in a mass equal to the kilogram-molecular weight.

It is, however, instructive, and an interesting application of equipartition, to study a statistical method of measuring N_0. This was the first reasonably accurate determination and was made by the French physicist Jean Perrin in 1908. To understand Perrin's method we need a formula from elementary hydrostatics.

The barometer formula. The density of the atmosphere falls off with height. Let us find a formula which tells us the number of air molecules per unit volume as a function of height z.

The variation of pressure with height is given by the hydrostatic formula

$$dp = -\rho g\, dz, \qquad\qquad 1.12.1$$

where dp is the pressure exerted by a column of fluid of height dz and density ρ; g is the gravitational acceleration and the minus sign indicates that the pressure falls as the height z increases.

Assuming that the atmosphere behaves as a perfect gas we can apply to it the equation

$$pV = nRT,$$

where n is the number of kilogram-molecules in volume V. The density ρ is

$$\rho = nM/V = pM/RT,$$

where M is the molecular weight. Thus equation 1.12.1 becomes

$$\frac{dp}{p} = -(Mg/RT)dz.$$

Integrating this, on the assumption that the temperature is constant throughout the atmosphere, gives

$$p = p_0\, e^{-(Mg/RT)z}. \qquad\qquad 1.12.2$$

This is the barometer formula originally derived by Laplace. It gives the variation of pressure p with height z. Putting in the usual value, $M = 29$, for the mean molecular weight of air consisting of one-fifth oxygen ($M = 32$) and four-fifths nitrogen ($M = 28$) with $T \sim 290°K$, we see that at height $z = 8 \cdot 3$ km the atmospheric pressure is reduced to e^{-1} of its value at the Earth's surface.

We now write $M = N_0 m$, where m is the mass of a single molecule, and so obtain

$$p = p_0 \exp\left(-N_0 mgz/RT\right). \qquad\qquad 1.12.3$$

At constant temperature, the pressure p is proportional to the number n of molecules per unit volume. In fact

$$n = N/V = N_0(p/RT). \qquad\qquad 1.12.4$$

n is a quantity we shall require frequently. The bold character serves to remind us that n is not a pure number but has dimensions $(\text{length})^{-3}$. Equation 1.12.3 thus becomes

$$n = n_0 \exp\left(-N_0 mgz/RT\right), \qquad\qquad 1.12.5$$

where $n(z)$ and n_0 are the numbers of molecules in unit volume at height z and height $z = 0$ respectively.

If we have a mixture of perfect gases, then we saw before in § 1.4 that it was a consequence of the law of equipartition of energy that the partial pressure of each is the same as if the others were not present. Thus equation 1.12.5 can be used for each gas of a mixture separately. For example, we might use it to calculate how the ratio of the numbers of oxygen ($M = 32$) and nitrogen ($M = 28$) molecules varies with height in the atmosphere.

Perrin's experiment. Here it was assumed that equipartition need not be restricted to particles of atomic size but could be used for particles large enough to be observed in the microscope. If this is correct then a suspension of large particles in air could be treated as a mixture of gases and the variation of the density of the 'gas' of large particles with height can be obtained from 1.12.5. Rewriting this equation with $m = m_p$ the mass of a large particle and $R/N_0 = k$ we obtain

$$n = n_0 \exp\left(-m_p g z/kT\right), \qquad\qquad 1.12.6$$

from which we see that a plot of $\ln (n/n_0)$ against z should give a straight line the slope of which is $-m_p g/kT$. If m_p can be measured, then k can be calculated.

Apart from the possibility that m_p can be measured and n/n_0 counted, the use of particles of visible size has two other advantages: first, the large mass m_p so increases the magnitude of the coefficient of z in the exponential that a relative change of n which would require kilometres of height difference with gas molecules will now occur in a distance of the order of millimetres. Secondly, we expect from equipartition that the large particles will move about in the mixed gas with root-mean-square speed $(\overline{v_p^2})^{\frac{1}{2}}$ given by

$$\overline{v_{p]}^2} = (3kT/m_p).$$

The larger m_p, therefore, the slower the random motion of the particles and the more easily will they be watched individually. This point will be reconsidered in § 1.13.

Perrin further assumed that the results obtained for an atmosphere of molecules could be extended to colloidal particles in suspension in a liquid. This could easily be tested by verifying that the variation of number of particles n with depth z obeyed a law of the form of 1.12.6, that is that

$$\ln n = A - Bz,$$

where A and B are constants. Apart from this, the only modification required to the equipartition theory was to alter the gravitational force mg acting on the colloidal particle to take account of hydrostatic upthrust in the liquid. Thus, if the particles were uniform spheres of radius r, m_p in equation 1.12.6 is replaced by

$$m_p = \tfrac{4}{3}\pi r^3(\rho_p - \rho_l),$$

where ρ_p, ρ_l were the densities of the particle and liquid respectively.

Perrin used colloidal suspensions of gum in water, centrifuging to obtain particles of uniform size. The radius of the particles was determined by direct measurement, by weighing, and by use of Stokes's law, and was about $\tfrac{1}{2}\mu$ ($\equiv \tfrac{1}{2} \times 10^{-3}$ mm). The variation of number with height was determined by differential focusing of a microscope. Perrin's result was that N_0 lay between $6 \cdot 5 \times 10^{26}$ and $7 \cdot 2 \times 10^{26}$ per kilogram-molecule.

The best modern value of N_0 determined by X-ray methods is

$$N_0 = 6 \cdot 0254 \times 10^{26} \text{ molecules/kg-mole};$$

and knowing that the modern value of R is

$$R = 8 \cdot 3170 \text{ kJ/kg-mole deg}$$

we have the value of k:

$$k = 1 \cdot 3803 \times 10^{-23} \text{ J deg}^{-1}$$
$$= 8 \cdot 6166 \times 10^{-5} \text{ eV deg}^{-1}.$$

Finally, using the result observed from chemistry that the kilogram-molecule of any gas occupies $22 \cdot 4 \text{ m}^3$ at standard temperature (0°C) and pressure (760 mm Hg) we have that the number of molecules per cm³ at N.T.P. is

$$n \simeq 3 \times 10^{19} \text{ molecules cm}^{-3}$$
$$\simeq 3 \times 10^{25} \text{ molecules m}^{-3}.$$

§ 1.13 Brownian motion

We saw in the last section that equipartition of energy need not be restricted to particles of atomic size but could be applied to particles large in comparison with atoms. If this is a general rule then we would expect that a large particle of mass m suspended in a gas would move with a mean-square velocity $\overline{v^2}$ given by

$$\tfrac{1}{2}m\overline{v^2} = \tfrac{3}{2}kT ; \qquad\qquad 1.13.1$$

and since m is much greater than the mass of an atomic particle its speed should be much less – possibly small enough to be measured by watching the particles through a microscope. In fact, smoke or pollen particles suspended in air are observed to be in continuous motion, and small crystals which have reflecting facets are observed to be in continuous oscillation.

These phenomena, known as *Brownian motion*, are tested theoretically by assuming that each of these relatively large particles receives $\frac{1}{2}kT$ for each of its three degrees of translational freedom and for each of its three degrees of rotational freedom. Now a typical particle observed in Brownian motion might have a diameter of about $0\cdot 1\,\mu$ (10^{-7} m). If the particle is assumed to be roughly spherical and to have a specific gravity of about one, then its mass is about 10^{-18} kg or roughly 10^8 times the mass of the H_2 molecule. Its root-mean-square speed at room temperature is thus (using 1.4.4) about 10^{-4} that of the H_2 molecule or about 20 cm/sec. This would perhaps be observable, but in fact the observed speed is usually much less than 1 cm/sec. It is further observed that a Brownian particle does not travel in a straight line but follows an erratic path.

The conclusion to be drawn from this is that large particles move in Brownian motion because they have the same mean kinetic energy as the gas molecules. Since they need never go near the walls of the container in their erratic path, their kinetic energy is obtained from collisions with gas molecules and since these collisions are random, the path of each particle is erratic. The mean speed of the particle between collisions is correctly given by 1.13.1; but the average speed obtained by timing the particle over macroscopic distances is less than the true average speed. This is because the particle, following an erratic path from collision to collision, as shown in *fig.* 1.6, covers a distance much larger than what we observe.

Figure 1.6. Brownian motion. The true path from A to B is much longer than the distance AB.

The particles which Perrin used for his measurement of k had a diameter of about $1\,\mu$ or 10^{-3} mm. Their mass was thus some thousand times greater than the value used in the calculation above, and their root-mean-square speed would be less than 1 cm/sec. Again, the observed speed was much less than this, so that the particles were almost motionless. It was this fact which made Perrin's experiments possible.

Similarly the angular velocity of rotation about some axis is given by

$$\tfrac{1}{2}\overline{I\omega^2} = \tfrac{1}{2}kT \,,$$

where ω is the moment of inertia about this axis. We could use this equation to calculate $\overline{\omega}$ but once again we would find that the frequency of the twinkling produced when light is reflected from the crystal facets is much less than $\overline{\omega}$.

We have not yet introduced the idea that the particles of our model gas make collisions other than with the wall of the vessel; we shall therefore delay a fuller consideration of Brownian motion until we have done so, returning to the subject in § 6.9.

§ 1.14 The limitations of equipartition

The above discussion stressed the successes of the principle of equipartition of energy as an example of the application of simple statistical ideas to large assemblies of particles. It is necessary now to draw attention to the limitations of the principle.

First, our models gave results exact for monatomic gases and in very good agreement with experiment for diatomic gases. Thus, given that our model of a diatomic model is two mass points joined by a rigid weightless bond, the calculation that there are just five degrees of freedom is correct. However, we know that atoms are not mass points but have a finite extension: thus, we should surely have included another degree of freedom for rotation about the bond. Again, we know that the bond is not rigid and that the atoms vibrate towards and away from each other—in fact we postulated that they did so in our model of a solid; we ought, therefore, to have included two more degrees of freedom for the kinetic and potential energies of vibration. Finally, we saw that the specific heats of gases and solids are not constant: for example, c_V for a diatomic gas at low temperatures falls below the value $c_V = \tfrac{5}{2}R$ and tends to the value corresponding to a monatomic gas: $c_V = \tfrac{3}{2}R$. At high temperature c_V rises above $\tfrac{5}{2}R$. The complete curve for hydrogen was shown schematically in *fig.* 1.3.

The explanation of these departures from simple kinetic theory is to be found in the quantum theory, according to which only discrete values of rotational and vibrational energy are allowed. Thus, a certain minimum amount or *quantum* of energy has to be given to a

3

molecule before it can rotate at all. If the quantum required to excite it to such a state is much less than kT then all the molecules will rotate and the mean value of the rotational energy will be the equipartition value. If the energy required is much greater than kT then rotation will not occur at all and rotational kinetic energy will be missing from the expression for the energy. At intermediate temperatures, when kT is of the same order of magnitude as the energy to excite rotation, some of the molecules will rotate, but the mean energy will be less than the equipartition value. This is the temperature range ($100-250°K$) corresponding to the first rise in the specific heat curve shown in *fig*. 1.3. The second rise ($1000-2500°K$) corresponds to the excitation of vibrations.

By the same argument we can understand that, at low temperatures, vibrations are only partly excited in solids so that the equipartition value corresponding to Dulong and Petit's law is really observed only if the temperature is high enough.

Again, quantum theory tells us that energies much greater than any kT are normally required to excite the inner structure of an atom to higher energy states. This is why we can ignore such inner structure and treat the atoms as mass points. On the other hand, translational energy is not divided into discrete quanta, so our calculations on monatomic gases and on the translational part of the energy for polyatomic gases are exact at any temperature at which the gas exists.

We shall return to the problem of calculation of the mean energy of internal degrees of freedom as a function of temperature in § 9.9 and meantime conclude this chapter with a practical application of equipartition. For this we require one further result.

§ 1.15   Frequency of impacts with a wall

In the second paragraph of § 1.2 we obtained the result that the number of impacts made by a single particle in time t was $v_{1x}t/2l$, where v_{1x} was the component of velocity of the particle in the direction normal to the wall and t was assumed to be long compared to the time $2l/v_{1x}$ between successive impacts. The total number of impacts by all the N particles in time t is then

$$\frac{t}{2l}\{|v_{1x}|+|v_{2x}|+ \ldots +|v_{Nx}|\},$$

where the vertical bars on each $|v_x|$ in the sum show that each term is to be taken positive. This is necessary, since the number of impacts is essentially a positive quantity although, at any given moment, some v_x will be positive, some negative. It was not, of course, necessary to make such a proviso in a sum of squares such as occurred in 1.2.1. The quantity in brackets is then

$$|v_{1x}| + |v_{2x}| + \ldots + |v_{Nx}| = N|\overline{v_x}|, \qquad 1.15.1$$

where $|\overline{v_x}|$ denotes the average of the speeds in the x-direction of all the particles, or the average of the x-components of velocity all taken positive.

Denoting the number of impacts with unit area of the wall in unit time by Γ we have

$$\Gamma(At) = \frac{1}{2l} N |\overline{v_x}|, \qquad 1.15.2$$

whence $\qquad \Gamma = \tfrac{1}{2}\frac{N}{V}|\overline{v_x}| = \tfrac{1}{2} n |\overline{v_x}|. \qquad 1.15.3$

Here n is the number of particles per unit volume, as defined by 1.12.4. Once again heavy type for n reminds us that n is not a pure number but has dimensions (length)$^{-3}$.

The quantity $|\overline{v_x}|$ which was introduced by 1.15.1 is not so readily dealt with as was $\overline{v_x^2}$, introduced by 1.2.1, since we cannot at present express $|\overline{v_x}|$ in terms of $\bar{v}$, the mean speed of all particles. We may, however, take the expedient of arguing as follows: The sum on the left hand side of 1.15.1 includes terms where v_x is positive and others where v_x is negative. Our assumption that all directions of motion are equally probable further suggests that for every particle going in one x-direction with a given speed there is another going in the opposite direction with the same speed. Thus the mean x-component of velocity

$$\bar{v}_x = 0, \qquad 1.15.4$$

and moreover

$$|\overline{v_x}| = 2\vec{v}_x, \qquad 1.15.5$$

where $\vec{v}_x$ denotes the sum of the x-components of velocity of those particles which happen to be going in one of the two x-directions at any given time divided by the total number of particles; $\vec{v}_x$ is not a true average. The factor $\tfrac{1}{2}$ in the expression 1.15.3 for Γ therefore arises because there are two x-directions. So far the argument is essentially rigorous.

We now extend the argument by noting that there are six possible directions of motion, two in each of the three axes of co-ordinates, so that 1.15.3 becomes

$$\Gamma = \tfrac{1}{6}n \mid \bar{v} \mid , \qquad\qquad 1.15.6$$

where $\mid \bar{v} \mid$ is the mean speed of all particles. $\mid \bar{v} \mid$ is usually written simply $\bar{v}$ and is called the mean speed, though strictly $\bar{v}$ should indicate the mean velocity and with this meaning would be zero.

The argument which produced the factor $\tfrac{1}{6}$ is not rigorous nor is the result quite correct. We shall, however, use result 1.15.6 until, in §§ 4.10 and 5.10, we obtain a better one. When we first use the formula for Γ in the next section, the numerical factor will cancel out.

§ 1.16 Application of equipartition to separation of a gas mixture

We have seen above (§ 1.4) that in a mixture of gases with different molecular weights the different components have different translational speeds. We may also recall (§ 1.14) that since translational energy is not subject to quantum considerations the result is quite rigorous no matter how complex the molecules may be. We now show that the different speeds can be used as the basis of a method of separation.

To do this, we note from § 1.15 that the faster molecules make more collisions with the walls of the containing vessel than do the slower molecules. If the walls have holes in them the faster molecules will have a greater chance of escape, leaving behind them a gas enriched in the slower, heavier molecules. We recall that the molecules are still considered as mass points and cannot collide with each other.

From 1.15.6 the number of collisions in unit time with unit area of wall is

$$\Gamma = \tfrac{1}{6}n\bar{v} . \qquad\qquad 1.16.1$$

Now consider a gas consisting of a mixture of n_A, A-type and n_B, B-type molecules, each per unit volume, in a container with a porous wall. We assume that the container is either very large or that the gas in it is replenished so that the numbers of A- and B-type molecules in it both remain constant when molecules are leaving through the pores. We also assume that the pressure on the outside of the porous wall can be kept so low that there is no need to take account of molecules returning to the vessel from outside.

We then define the concentration c of A-type molecules inside the container as

$$c = \frac{n_A}{n_A + n_B} = \frac{n_A}{n},$$ 1.16.2

where $n \equiv n_A + n_B$ is the number per unit volume of molecules of both kinds. The concentration of B-type molecules is then

$$1 - c = \frac{n_B}{n_A + n_B} = \frac{n_B}{n}.$$ 1.16.3

From 1.16.1 the number of A-type molecules hitting the porous wall per second is

$$\Gamma_A = \tfrac{1}{6} n c \bar{v}_A$$ 1.16.4

with a similar expression for Γ_B.

We assume that a fraction γ of the molecules hitting the barrier pass through it. γ is obviously a measure of the ratio of the area of the pores to the total area. We further assume that γ is the same for both types of molecule, that is, that the action of the porous wall is not to sieve the molecules by size. In fact this assumption is already covered by the specification of our model in which the molecules were represented as mass points.

Using the same definition of concentration as in 1.16.2 we have that the concentration c' of A-type molecules on the low-pressure side of the porous wall is

$$c' = \frac{\tfrac{1}{6} \gamma n c \bar{v}_A}{\tfrac{1}{6} \gamma n c \bar{v}_A + \tfrac{1}{6} \gamma n (1 - c) \bar{v}_B}$$

or $$\frac{1}{c'} = 1 + \frac{1 - c}{c} \frac{\bar{v}_B}{\bar{v}_A}.$$ 1.16.5

Using 1.4.3, which was obtained by the assumption of equipartition, we have

$$\overline{v_A^2} / \overline{v_B^2} = M_B / M_A,$$

where $M_B(= N_0 m_B)$ and $M_A(= N_0 m_A)$ are the molecular weights of the respective types of molecules. Then, assuming that there is a simple ratio relating $\overline{v^2}$ and $(\bar{v})^2$ (proved in § 5·10) we have

$$\bar{v}_B / \bar{v}_A = (M_A / M_B)^{\frac{1}{2}}.$$ 1.16.6

Separation of isotopes. A further simplification of formula 1.16.5 is possible if we assume that M_A and M_B are not very different. This would certainly be true for a mixture of isotopes, which is probably the only sort of mixture one would try to separate in this way, since there are generally easier methods of separating mixtures of chemically different gases. Then

$$(M_A/M_B)^{\frac{1}{2}} = (1 - \Delta M/M_B)^{\frac{1}{2}} \simeq 1 - \Delta M/(2M),$$

where $\Delta M = M_B - M_A \ll M_B$

and we have taken $M_B > M_A$.

M is the mean molecular weight of the element and to this approximation can be written indiscriminately for M_A or M_B. Equation 1.16.5 then simplifies to

$$\Delta c = c' - c = c'(1 - c)\Delta M/(2M). \qquad 1.16.7$$

Since $\Delta M/(2M) \ll 1$ and c' and $c < 1$, equation 1.16.7 shows that $(c' - c) \ll c$. Thus we may replace c', on the right-hand side of 1.16.7, by c.

The classic example of the use of this method is the separation of the uranium isotope U^{235} ($c = 1/140$) from U^{238} which is $139/140$ of natural uranium. The gaseous compound used is said to have been UF_6 with molecular weight 352. In this case we put $M = 352$, $\Delta M = 3$ and obtain the relative enrichment of the U^{235} as

$$\Delta c/c = 3/704 .$$

This enrichment is very small and it is clear that even in the ideal case considered the process would have to be repeated many times over to increase c to even a few per cent. In practice ideal conditions cannot be obtained; for example, if a reasonable amount of gas has to be processed, γ has to be large and this contradicts the assumption that we can maintain the pressure on the low-pressure side of the porous wall low enough to ignore gas going in the wrong direction. Diffusion through a porous barrier is not a method to be adopted if others are available.

The above calculation is an application of elementary kinetic theory to a practical problem and shows how a very simple model and theory can give an indication of the practicability of an industrial process.

§ 1.17   Problems

1. Find an expression for the temperature at which the root-mean-square speed of gas molecules is just equal to the velocity of escape

from the Earth. Show that for hydrogen H_2 this temperature is 9400°K while for oxygen O_2 it is $1\cdot5 \times 10^4$ °K.

Given that gravitation at the surface of the moon is $0\cdot16$ as strong as at the surface of the Earth show that the corresponding temperatures for the moon are 470°K and $7\cdot5 \times 10^3$ °K.

2. A porous barrier divides a gas-filled vessel into two parts. Initially the system is in equilibrium at temperature T_1 with the pressures on either side of the barrier equal. The gas on one side of the barrier is now warmed to temperature T_2 while that on the other side of the barrier is kept at T_1. By considering the numbers of molecules of gas striking either side of the barrier in unit time show that in equilibrium

$$p_1 / p_2 = (T_1 / T_2)^{\frac{1}{2}} \qquad\qquad 1.17.1$$

so that the higher pressure is on the hot side.

This phenomenon, known as *thermal transpiration*, is the basis of the Knudsen absolute manometer for measuring very low pressures. The instrument consists basically of a metal plate P (*fig.* 1.7)

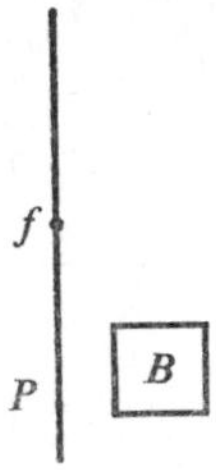

Figure 1.7. Principle of Knudsen's 'absolute manometer'.

suspended at f by a fine torsion fibre. Near to the plate is a fixed block B maintained at a temperature T_B which is greater than T_g, the temperature of the gas and the plate P. The theory of the instrument assumes that the temperature in the region between plate P and block B is the mean $\frac{1}{2}(T_g + T_B)$ so that, by 1.7.1, the pressure on the plate p_P is given by

$$p_P = p_g [\tfrac{1}{2}(T_g + T_B)/ T_g]^{\frac{1}{2}} ,$$

where p_g is the pressure in the unheated remainder of the gas. The net outward force per unit area on the part of the plate opposite B is thus

$$\Delta p = p_P - p_g = \tfrac{1}{4}(T_B - T_g)(p_g / T_g) ,$$

provided

$$T_B - T_g \ll T_g . \qquad\qquad 1.17.2$$

Δp is measured by observing the rotation of the plate by an optical reflection system. In fact, the apparatus does not obey equation 1.17.2 accurately and has to be calibrated: it is therefore not an absolute manometer though the name has stuck.

§ 1.18 Further reading

Two classical texts on the kinetic theory of gases are

L. B. Loeb *The Kinetic Theory of Gases* McGraw-Hill, New York and London, 1934.

E. H. Kennard *The Kinetic Theory of Gases* McGraw-Hill, New York and London, 1938.

These books include extensive discussions of refinements to the theory and its experimental verification. A modern short text is

P. D. Present *The Kinetic Theory of Gases* McGraw-Hill, New York and London, 1958.

Chapter 2

TRANSPORT AND FREE PATH PHENOMENA

§ 2.1 Intermolecular collisions

We saw in § 1.2 that kinetic theory predicted the mean speeds of gas molecules to be of the order of 1000 metres per second. An early objection to this theory was that a gas with a distinctive smell, released in one part of a room, might take many seconds to reach a point a few metres away, indicating a speed of the order of metres or even centimetres per second for the gas molecules.

The explanation of the discrepancy is, of course, that the molecules should not be treated as mass points: each has a finite size and in consequence suffers collisions with other molecules. So, even if the mean speed of a molecule is as large as calculated in § 1.2, the molecule does not travel far before having its direction of flight changed. Its path between two points of observation is thus a zig-zag one many times longer than the straight-line path, and the apparent speed between the end points is much less than the true speed. The problem of the path taken by a body which suffers random changes of direction is that of the *random walk* and is treated in chapter 6. The variation of the distance between collisions is a problem of *distribution* and is treated in chapter 4. In the meantime we shall show that from the elementary idea of a mean distance between collisions or mean free path we can derive a series of useful formulae.

§ 2.2 Hard sphere model

We modify the kinetic model of a gas introduced in § 1.2 by giving particles a finite size, in particular by assuming them to be hard spheres of diameter d and calling them molecules. Two such spherical molecules will then collide if their centres approach within a distance d of each other. We retain the assumption of non-interacting molecules by assuming that, for central distances greater than d, the flight of neither is affected.

The path followed by a typical molecule is shown in *fig.* 2.1; the distances between collisions are called free paths and the average of these, the total distance travelled divided by the number of collisions, is the *mean free path*. To obtain the number of collisions, we begin by assuming that we can calculate a quantity $\bar{v}_r$, which is

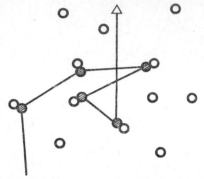

Figure 2.1. *Path of a particle in a gas of similar particles. The mean free path is the total path length divided by the number of collisions.*

the average of the speeds of the molecules relative to each other. We shall later (§§ 2.3 and 4.10) find how $\bar{v}_r$ is related to $\bar{v}$, the mean speed as defined in § 1.15. The problem of the relative motions of the various molecules is then treated by considering the path of a single molecule moving with speed $\bar{v}_r$ through a gas of similar randomly-spaced motionless molecules.

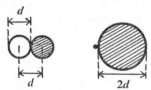

Figure 2.2. *A particle with diameter d moving through a gas of similar particles makes the same number of collisions as one with diameter 2d moving through a gas of mass points.*

actual collision   equivalent collision

From *fig.* 2.2 we can see that the moving particle for which the free paths are indicated would make the same number of collisions if its diameter were $2d$ and if all the motionless particles were reduced to mass points. This single molecule of diameter $2d$ moving with speed $\bar{v}_r$ sweeps out in time t a cylinder of volume $\pi d^2 \bar{v}_r t$ through the gas, the cylinder having the form of a jointed pipe with an angle joint at every collision. Within this cylinder there are n point masses per unit volume or $n\pi d^2 \bar{v}_r t$ in all, and our molecule collides with every one of these, so that in time t it makes $n\pi d^2 \bar{v}_r t$ collisions. The number of collisions Z in unit time is thus

$$Z = n\pi d^2 \bar{v}_r. \qquad\qquad 2.2.1$$

Now in time t a molecule goes, on the average, a distance $\bar{v}t$, where $\bar{v}$ is the mean speed; and in this time it makes Zt collisions. The mean distance between collisions or mean free path Λ is thus given by

$$\Lambda = \bar{v}t / Zt = \bar{v} / Z \qquad 2.2.2$$

or $\qquad \Lambda = \dfrac{\bar{v}}{\bar{v}_r} \cdot \dfrac{1}{n\pi d^2}.$ $\qquad\qquad\qquad 2.2.3$

Until we have more information, it seems reasonable to put $\bar{v}_r = \bar{v}$ so that we have the simplest formula

$$\Lambda = \frac{1}{n\pi d^2}. \qquad 2.2.4$$

To obtain estimates of Z and Λ we already have from § 1.12 that $n \simeq 3 \times 10^{25}$ molecules m^{-3}. For $\bar{v}$ we may for the moment use $(\overline{v^2})^{\frac{1}{2}}$; it will be shown in § 5.10 that there is only 10% error in so doing. Thus, from 1.2.12, we have for H$_2$ at room temperature

$$\bar{v} \simeq (\overline{v^2})^{\frac{1}{2}} \simeq 2 \times 10^3 \text{m/sec}.$$

The only missing quantity is our newly-introduced atomic diameter d and we may estimate this as follows: if, as we assumed, the molecules are incompressible spheres then a knowledge of the density of the substance in a condensed state, when the molecules are permanently in contact with each other, gives an estimate of d. Thus the density of liquid hydrogen is about 90 kg/m^3 and, since the kilogram-molecular weight is 2, a cubic metre of condensed hydrogen contains 45 moles or $45N_0$ molecules where N_0 is Avogadro's number. Taking (§ 1.12) $N_0 \simeq 6 \times 10^{26}$ we see that each molecule occupies a volume of $\simeq 1/(45 \times 6 \times 10^{26})$ m^3 and that its diameter is $\frac{1}{3} \times 10^{-9}$ m or about 3 Å.

Using these estimates we find that for hydrogen at N.T.P. Z and Λ are:

$\qquad Z \simeq 2 \times 10^{10}$ collisions/sec,

$\qquad \Lambda \simeq 10^{-7}$ m, or 1000 Å or about 300 atomic diameters.

The corresponding estimates for oxygen ($M = 32$) are:

$\qquad \rho \text{ liquid} \simeq 1 \cdot 2 \text{ kg/litre} = 1 \cdot 2 \times 10^3 \text{ kg m}^{-3}$,

$\qquad d \simeq 3 \text{ Å}$,

$\qquad \bar{v} \simeq 5 \times 10^2 \text{ m/sec}$,

$\qquad Z \simeq 5 \times 10^9 \text{ sec}^{-1}$,

$\qquad \Lambda \simeq 10^{-7} \text{ m}$.

The variation of Λ with pressure is obtained by noting that n is proportional to p. In fact, for a perfect gas, 1.12.4 gives

$$n = N_0 \cdot \frac{p}{RT} = \frac{p}{kT},$$ 2.2.5

so that

$$\Lambda = \frac{kT}{p \pi d^2}.$$ 2.2.6

Thus, at a given temperature, Λ is inversely proportional to pressure.

§ 2.3   Refinement of the hard sphere model

Retaining the hard sphere model we can make as many refinements as we wish: for example, we may, as a preliminary exercise in statistics, investigate the accuracy of writing $\bar{v}$, the mean molecular speed, in the equations for Z and Λ when what we really needed was $\bar{v}_r$, the mean speed of molecules relative to each other.

Consider two molecules with the same speed v. Their mean speed $\bar{v} = v$. To obtain an estimate of their mean relative speed we simplify by allowing them to travel only in directions parallel to the axes, that is, we apply much the same simplification as we did in § 1.2. If motions parallel to only one axis are allowed, that is if we are dealing with a one dimensional gas, then four possibilities occur: in two the molecules are moving in the same direction and have relative velocity zero; in two the molecules are moving in opposite directions and have relative velocity $2v$. The mean speed averaged over all four possibilities is thus

$$\bar{v}_r = \tfrac{1}{4}(0 + 0 + 2v + 2v) = v.$$

In two dimensions, with the same restrictions, one molecule has four ways of moving, that is, in either direction parallel to either axis. For each of these possibilities the other molecule has also four possibilities. The total number of ways in which the two molecules can move relative to each other is thus sixteen. Of these, four are cases where both are moving parallel to one axis and four are where both move parallel to the other. Of these eight we have already seen that four have $v_r = 0$ and four have $v_r = 2v$. In all the remaining eight cases the molecules move each on a different axis and by elementary composition of velocities $v_r = \sqrt{2}v$. Adding all these velocities up and dividing by the number of cases gives

$$\bar{v}_r = \tfrac{1}{16}(4 \times 0 + 4 \times 2v + 8 \times \sqrt{2}v)$$
$$= \tfrac{1}{2}(1 + \sqrt{2})v \simeq 1 \cdot 21v.$$

A similar argument for the $6 \times 6 = 36$ possibilities in tri-axial motion gives six with $v_r = 0$, six with $v_r = 2v$ and 24 with $v_r = \sqrt{2}v$. From this

$$\bar{v}_r = \tfrac{1}{3}(1+2\sqrt{2})v \simeq \frac{3\cdot83}{3}v.$$

The accurate value, averaging over all directions of motion, not only over those parallel to the axis is

$$\bar{v}_r = \tfrac{4}{3}v. \tag{2.3.1}$$

This is shown in § 4.10, equation 4.10.14.

The next refinement would be to take account of the fact that not all molecules travel with the same speed. An exactly similar argument to that above but giving the two colliding molecules different speeds, say v and $2v$, will serve to show that we cannot obtain the mean relative speed from equation 2.3.1 by writing $\bar{v}$ for v on the right-hand side. Since, however, we have as yet no information on how the speeds are distributed among the molecules we shall simply quote the final result that, taking account of the distribution of molecular speeds,

$$\bar{v}_r = \sqrt{2}\bar{v} \tag{2.3.2}$$

and that a formula for Λ better than 2.2.4 is

$$\Lambda = \frac{1}{\sqrt{2}n\pi d^2} = \frac{kT}{\sqrt{2}p\pi d^2}. \tag{2.3.3}$$

The former is the formula usually quoted for Λ.

Formula 2.3.3 enables us to understand why the mean free path is different for molecules in different ranges of speed. Thus, molecules with speeds much higher than the mean would see most of the other molecules as being at rest. The free path of these high-speed molecules is given by the simple formula 2.2.4, namely

$$\Lambda_{v \to \infty} = \frac{1}{n\pi d^2} = \sqrt{2}\Lambda,$$

where Λ is the mean free path for all molecules assuming 2.3.3 to have been proved. At the other extreme, molecules at rest have zero free path, so that

$$\Lambda_{v \to 0} = 0.$$

Free paths, therefore, vary with speed within the limits zero to $\sqrt{2}\Lambda$.

These and other refinements were worked out in the nineteenth and early twentieth centuries. The mathematical processes involved form an elegant piece of theory but do not necessarily give physically accurate formulae since they are carried out within the limitations of the hard sphere model. Nowadays we know that atoms and molecules are not hard spheres, so that these mathematical refinements have rather gone out of fashion, though there is continued interest in other refinements designed to allow the spherical molecules a certain degree of elasticity (§ 2.11).

We shall press these refinements no further than is necessary to obtain formulae sufficiently accurate for practical use. We shall console ourselves for our inability to face the mathematics involved by noting that the resulting formulae, for example for Λ, are not sufficiently different to be distinguished experimentally.

§ 2.4   Are the formulae derived assuming point masses consistent with the spherical particle model?

In § 1.1 it was mentioned that we had to reassure ourselves that successive complications added to a model to explain additional phenomena did not invalidate the results obtained by the simpler model.

For the derivation of the formula for pressure in § 1.2 we can bring in the idea of free path by simply assuming that all the action takes place within a distance l much less than Λ, from the wall, so that the probability of a collision in distance l is negligible. We note that l does not occur explicitly in any of the final formulae. Alternatively, in a one-dimensional elastic collision of like particles, the particles simply exchange velocities or, what is the same thing, momenta. Thus, momentum is carried from end to end of a container of length $l (\gg \Lambda)$ in exactly the manner described in § 1.2. A given particle of mass m does not necessarily make the round trip in time $v/2l$ but a piece of momentum of size mv does.

In later parts of chapter 1 we had already begun to assume that there existed some mechanism whereby the particles could transfer momentum to each other while at the same time retaining the property of being 'non-interacting'. The hard sphere model is all that is required: we allow collisions between particles which approach each other within a distance given by the mean of their diameters; otherwise there is no interaction whatever.

§ 2.5   Transport phenomena

If the properties of the molecules of a gas vary with position in the container, then the random motions assumed in chapter 1 will tend to even out the variation. Thus, in the example mentioned in § 2.1, a batch of molecules of a different kind, introduced at one point in a gas, will spread out until the composition of the mixed gas is uniform. This is the phenomenon of diffusion or transport of matter by random movement. Again, a batch of molecules having more energy (higher temperature) will spread out amongst their less energetic neighbours, exchanging energy by collisions with them, until the temperature of the whole mass of gas is uniform. This is the phenomenon of thermal conductivity. These, together with momentum transport (viscosity) are the three transport phenomena. The concept of mean free path enables us to calculate the rate at which each takes place, the method in each case being almost the same.

We imagine a plane P dividing the gas into two parts, as in *fig.* **2.3a.**

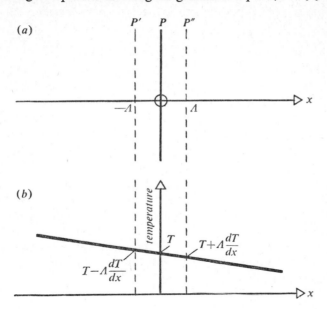

Figure 2.3(*a*). *The mean-free-path method for transport phenomena.*
Figure 2.3(*b*). *Temperature gradient in a gas, with temperatures at three planes perpendicular to the gradient.*

We then assume that the average molecule crossing the plane in either direction made its last collision, prior to crossing, on a plane at a distance Λ away and that it has, in consequence, the properties corresponding to the mass of gas on that plane. Since we know

(§ 1.15) that the number of molecules crossing unit area of the plane P per second in one direction is $\frac{1}{6}n\bar{v}$, we can then calculate the rate of transport of whatever property is non-uniformly distributed in a direction normal to P. We can then compare the calculated transport with the phenomenological equations for diffusivity, viscosity or thermal conductivity, as the case may be.

Although the method is the same for all, it is easier to treat each separately. Discussion of all three formulae follows in § 2.11.

§ 2.6   Thermal conductivity

If a temperature gradient dT/dx is maintained in a material, then the rate of transport of heat Q/t per unit area in the direction of the temperature gradient is proportional to the temperature gradient. The constant of proportionality is the *thermal conductivity K*:

$$\frac{Q}{t} = -K\frac{dT}{dx}.$$ 2.6.1

Here the minus sign is required if K is to be positive, since the heat flow is from high to low temperature, that is in the direction of negative temperature gradient.

To interpret this from the point of view of kinetic theory we take the temperature gradient dT/dx to be in the direction shown in *fig.* 2.3*b*. Say the temperature is T at plane P. It will then be $T-\Lambda(dT/dx)$, which is greater than T, since $dT/dx<0$ at plane P' and $T+\Lambda(dT/dx)$ ($<T$) at plane P''. Further if C_V' is the specific heat per molecule– that is the molar heat at constant volume divided by Avogadro's number–then each molecule coming from P' towards P will on the average have energy $C_V'(T-\Lambda dT/dx)$ while those coming from the right, that is from P'', will have average energy $C_V'(T+\Lambda dT/dx)$. Since the number crossing unit area in unit time is $\frac{1}{6}n\bar{v}$, the net transport of energy across unit area of P per second is

$$\frac{Q}{t} = \frac{1}{6}n\bar{v}C_V'\left(T-\frac{dT}{dx}\Lambda\right) - \frac{1}{6}n\bar{v}C_V'\left(T+\frac{dT}{dx}\Lambda\right)$$

$$= -\frac{1}{3}nC_V'\bar{v}\frac{dT}{dx}\Lambda,$$

whence using 2.6.1 we obtain a formula for the thermal conductivity:

$$K = \frac{1}{3}nC_V'\bar{v}\Lambda.$$ 2.6.2

An expression for nC_V' has already been obtained in chapter 1. There, equation 1.5.4 gave the result that the amount of heat required to raise the temperature of N_0 monatomic molecules by one degree at constant volume is $\frac{3}{2}N_0k$. The corresponding value for n molecules is $\frac{3}{2}nk$. Using this value together with equation 2.2.4 for Λ gives K for monatomic gases to be

$$K = \frac{1}{2}\frac{k\bar{v}}{\pi d^2}, \qquad\qquad 2.6.3$$

while for gases composed of polyatomic molecules the equation would have the same form but with a different numerical constant corresponding to the different expressions found in § 1.6 and § 1.7 for the specific heats.

Equation 2.6.3 is surprising since it predicts that the thermal conductivity of a gas should be independent of pressure and that this pressure independence arises from the fact that, although at high pressure there are more molecules to carry the heat, each molecule carries it for a shorter distance than at low pressures. In fact, experiment confirms that K, measured to $\pm 1\%$, is independent of pressure provided that the mean free path is at least two orders of magnitude less than the dimensions of the vessel but not so small as to be comparable with atomic dimensions. When the pressure is so low that most of the molecules go direct from the high temperature wall of the container to the low temperature wall without meeting another molecule, the heat transfer is proportional to the number of molecules–that is to the pressure; it is in such conditions that a vacuum flask operates. Problem 2.13.2 discusses the complex events which cause a slow variation of K at intermediate pressures.

The only temperature dependent term in the formula 2.6.3 for K is $\bar{v}$, which, on the same assumptions as in § 2.2, we take to be proportional to $T^{\frac{1}{2}}$. *Fig.* 2.4 shows how well this temperature dependence is obeyed in practice. In general K is found to be proportional to some power of T between $\frac{1}{2}$ and 1. This must mean that the hard sphere model is not entirely successful for, if we allow the molecules to be slightly compressible, it is natural to expect that the more energetic the molecules the closer will their centres approach when they collide. Thus d goes down as T goes up, giving a qualitative explanation of why K varies with T more rapidly than does $\bar{v}$.

Since everything on the right-hand side of equation 2.6.3 is known except d, we can use measured values of K to estimate the sizes of atoms and molecules. In general, as shown in problem 2.13.3, the

4

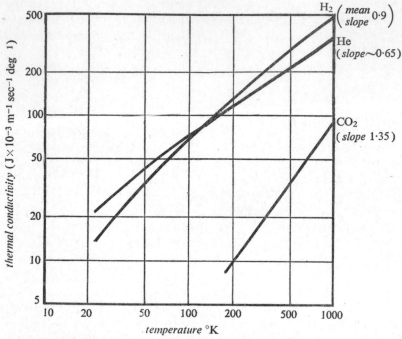

Figure 2.4. Temperature dependence of the thermal conductivity.

values of d thus found are in good qualitative agreement with those found from measurements of interatomic spacings in condensed phases. We should not expect better than qualitative agreement, mainly because of the crudity of our model but partly because of the difficulty of measuring K, since thermal conductivity is only one of the ways by which heat is transported in gaseous media. The others are convection and radiation and these are difficult either to eliminate or to allow for.

§ 2.7 Viscosity

In order to make a gas flow through a tube there must be a pressure difference between the ends. To produce a given flow in a tube of circular cross-section the pressure difference required increases with the fourth power of the radius; in a parallel-sided channel the pressure required increases with the cube of the channel depth.

The kinetic explanation of how gas flows in a tube is that the molecules have a drift velocity in the direction of flow, superposed on their random motions. This drift velocity is greatest at points furthest removed from the (stationary) walls of the tube and is zero for molecules which have just collided with a wall. If the random motions were left out of account one might say that the gas in contact with the walls was at rest and that the drift velocity increased with distance from the wall. The effect of the random velocities is to cause molecules to move from the faster drifting layers to the slower and vice versa. Thus, momentum is transferred from a faster drifting layer to a neighbouring slower one and eventually to the stationary wall. The rate at which momentum is destroyed is, by Newton's laws, a force called the viscous drag.

To put the viscous drag in quantitative terms, suppose we have a gas contained between two horizontal plates, distance l apart, the lower fixed, the upper moving with uniform velocity u_0 (*fig.* 2.5).

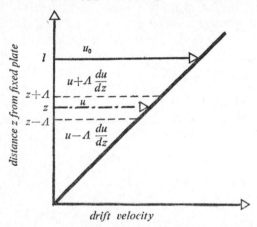

Figure 2.5. *Velocity profile in a viscous fluid; the arrows indicate the stream velocities at various distances from the fixed surface* $z = 0$.

Then the drift velocity of the gas is zero in contact with the lower plate increasing uniformly to u_0 for gas in contact with the upper plate. Momentum may be said to be transferred through the gas from the upper to the lower plate and indeed a force must be applied to the lower plate to hold it steady. This force, the viscous drag, referred to unit area is proportional to the velocity gradient u_0/l:

$$F = \eta \frac{u_0}{l}. \qquad 2.7.1$$

The coefficient of proportionality η is called the *viscosity* and has units of force per unit area per unit velocity gradient. To make 2.7.1 applicable to cases where the velocity gradient is not uniform we may replace u_0/l by a differential coefficient and write

$$F = \eta \frac{du}{dz}, \qquad 2.7.2$$

where $u(z)$ is the drift velocity, varying in the z-direction as shown in *fig.* 2.5. The analogy between 2.6.1 and 2.7.2 will be obvious: 2.6.1 describes the rate of change of energy in terms of a conductivity and a gradient; 2.7.2 similarly describes a rate of change of momentum.

Now in *fig.* 2.5 we apply kinetic ideas as before by considering transport of molecules across an imaginary plane, in this case one parallel to the direction of flow and shown chain-dotted in the figure. Say that the drift velocity of the gas is u on this plane. Molecules crossing this plane in a downward direction will, on the average, have come from a plane a distance Λ above the chain-dotted plane, and will have drift velocity $(u+\Lambda du/dz)$. Molecules crossing the reference plane from below will, on average, have come from a plane Λ below and will have drift velocity $(u-\Lambda du/dz)$.

The number of molecules crossing in each direction per unit area and unit time is, as before, $\frac{1}{6}n\bar{v}$, where $\bar{v}$, the mean speed of random motion, must not be confused with u, the drift velocity. If molecules have mass m, the net rate of transfer of momentum per unit area is then

$$\frac{1}{6}n\bar{v}m\left(u+\frac{du}{dz}\Lambda\right) - \frac{1}{6}n\bar{v}m\left(u-\frac{du}{dz}\Lambda\right)$$

$$= \frac{1}{3}nm\bar{v}\Lambda\frac{du}{dz} \qquad 2.7.3$$

$$= F, \quad \text{the viscous force per unit area}$$

$$= \eta\frac{du}{dz}.$$

Thus $\quad \eta = \frac{1}{3}nm\bar{v}\Lambda$

$$= \frac{1}{3}\rho\bar{v}\Lambda, \qquad 2.7.4$$

where ρ is the density, and substituting for Λ from 2.2.4 we obtain from 2.7.4

$$\eta = \frac{1}{3}\frac{m\bar{v}}{\pi d^2}. \qquad 2.7.5$$

Once again the transport coefficient is independent of pressure and for the same reason and under the same conditions as were discussed for K.

Again the temperature dependence of η is the same as that of $\bar{v}$, so we would expect η to be proportional to $T^{\frac{1}{2}}$. *Fig.* 2.6 shows how well this is realised in practice.

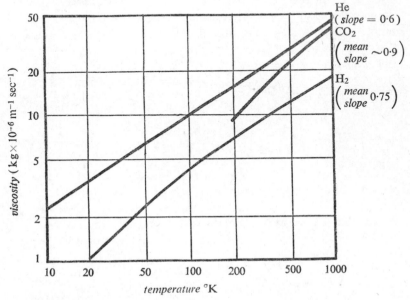

Figure 2.6. *Temperature dependence of viscosity.*

Comparison with *fig.* 2.4 shows that the temperature dependence of K and η is the same for helium, which is a monatomic gas. For gases composed of more complex molecules the temperature dependence of the two coefficients is different. Presumably this is because the mechanism whereby energy is transferred between molecules with internal degrees of freedom varies with temperature, whereas transfer of momentum is the same for simple and complex molecules.

§ 2.8 Diffusivity

In the preceding two sections we have examined the elementary kinetic theory of energy transport and momentum transport. It now seems logical to extend the theory to matter transport.

Suppose we have a mixture of gases A and B. Let there be n_A molecules of type A per unit volume and n_B of type B. In equilibrium these will be uniformly mixed. We now consider, as in the previous sections, a non-equilibrium state where there is a gradient, dn_A/dx, of type A molecules in the x-direction. If the pressure is to be everywhere constant then $n_A + n_B$ is constant, so there must be an equal and opposite gradient $-dn_B/dx$ for the B-type molecules.

Setting up our imaginary plane in the gas we see that more A-type molecules will cross it in one direction than in the other, simply because there are more A-type molecules on one side than the other. Similarly there will be a net flux of B-type molecules in the opposite direction. Each flux Γ is found experimentally to be proportional to the concentration gradient dn/dx. Thus

$$\Gamma_A = -D_A \frac{dn_A}{dx} \qquad\qquad 2.8.1$$

and

$$\Gamma_B = -D_B \frac{dn_B}{dx}. \qquad\qquad 2.8.2$$

The coefficients D_A and D_B are called *diffusion coefficients* or *diffusivities* and the minus signs show that the flux is down the concentration gradient, that is in the direction of negative dn/dx. The analogy between these equations and equations 2.6.1 and 2.7.2 is obvious.

If the density of the mixture is to remain uniform then in the case of a perfect gas

$$n_A + n_B = \text{constant},$$

or

$$\frac{dn_A}{dx} = -\frac{dn_B}{dx},$$

which was what we had above.

Also for uniform density

$$\Gamma_A = \Gamma_B,$$

so

$$D_A = D_B,$$

or the diffusion can be described by a single diffusion coefficient.

Before attempting to deal with a mixture of gases having each a different value of $\bar{v}$ and Λ it is instructive and much more useful to start by assuming that we are dealing with an isotopic mixture so that the molecular diameter is the same for both species, and the mass and mean speed very little different. The resulting D is then the coefficient of self-diffusion.

Since for such a mixture Λ does not vary with concentration, we can say that molecules crossing the reference plane have on the average come from planes a distance Λ on either side. If, on the reference plane, the number of A-type molecules per unit volume is n_A then the corresponding number at a distance $(-\Lambda)$ away on the higher concentration side is $n_A-(dn_A/dx)\Lambda$, with a similar expression at distance $(+\Lambda)$ on the low concentration side. The net flux across the reference plane is then, as before,

$$\Gamma = \tfrac{1}{6}\bar{v}\left(n_A-\frac{dn_A}{dx}\Lambda\right)-\tfrac{1}{6}\bar{v}\left(n_A+\frac{dn_A}{dx}\Lambda\right)$$

$$= -\tfrac{1}{3}\bar{v}\frac{dn_A}{dx}\Lambda, \qquad\qquad 2.8.3$$

so that $D = \tfrac{1}{3}\bar{v}\Lambda$. $\qquad\qquad 2.8.4$

In this case the transport coefficient is not independent of the density of the gas; in fact, combining equations 2.7.4 and 2.8.4 we obtain $D/\eta = 1/\rho$, so that

$$D = \eta/\rho \qquad\qquad 2.8.5$$

–a very useful formula, since viscosity is much easier to measure than diffusivity, particularly self-diffusivity.

The difference between the pressure, or density, dependence of diffusivity and that of the other transport coefficients is only a matter of definition: it would have been possible, though inconvenient, to re-define D and Γ not in terms of n_A but of c, where

$$c_A = \frac{n_A}{n_A+n_B}\equiv\frac{n_A}{n}$$

is the concentration of A-type molecules in the mixture. In this case equation 2.8.1 would become

$$\Gamma_A = -(D_A n)\frac{dc_A}{dx}$$

$$= -D'_A\frac{dc_A}{dx}. \qquad\qquad 2.8.6$$

The new diffusion coefficient D'_A is then, by the argument for isotopic mixtures, given by

$$D'_A = \tfrac{1}{3}n\bar{v}\Lambda, \qquad\qquad 2.8.7$$

which is independent of density, since Λ is inversely proportional to n. It is quite common to find diffusion coefficients tabulated as pD, or ρD where p is the pressure, and ρ the density. These forms avoid the density dependence.

TABLE 3 : self-diffusion coefficients at 300°K and 1 atm. pressure

gas	η (kg×10⁻⁵ m⁻¹ sec⁻¹)	ρ kg m⁻³	η/ρ m²×10⁻⁵ sec⁻¹	D m²×10⁻⁵ sec⁻¹	$D\rho/\eta$
He	2·01	0·16	12·5	—	—
Ne	3·17	0·82	3·9	5·16	1·3
H₂	0·95	0·08	11·9	14·0	1·2
CO₂	1·50	1·80	0·83	1·15	1·4

Table 3 compares measured values of the self-diffusion coefficient for various gases with the corresponding values of η/ρ. If equation 2.8.5 had been exact then

$$D\rho/\eta = 1\cdot0.$$

In fact, $D\rho/\eta \sim 1\cdot3$. The discrepancy can be accounted for if the molecular cross-sections (and hence free paths) for diffusion, viscosity and, for that matter, thermal conduction are not all the same.

§ 2.9 Transport processes in gaseous mixtures

We may extend the idea of molecular free paths to gases composed of molecules which are not all alike. Suppose we have a mixture containing n_A molecules of type A per unit volume and n_B of type B.   Both types may be treated as hard spheres having diameters d_A and d_B respectively.

Consider first the motion of an A-type molecule: the methods of § 2.2 give directly the result that Z_{AA}, the number of collisions which a molecule makes per second with others of the same kind, is

$$Z_{AA} = n_A \bar{v}_{AA} \pi d_A^2, \qquad\qquad 2.9.1$$

where $\bar{v}_{AA}$ is the mean speed of A-type molecules relative to each other. $\bar{v}_{AA}$ is the same as $\bar{v}_r$ used in § 2.2.

Similarly, a simple extension of the argument in § 2.2 gives Z_{AB}, the number of collisions which an A-type molecule makes with a B-type. This is

$$Z_{AB} = n_B \bar{v}_{AB} \pi (\tfrac{1}{2}d_A + \tfrac{1}{2}d_B)^2, \qquad\qquad 2.9.2$$

where here $\bar{v}_{AB}$ is the mean speed of A-type molecules relative to B-type. Of course, $\bar{v}_{AB} = \bar{v}_{BA}$.

The total number of collisions Z_A which an A-type molecule makes per second is then

$$Z_A = Z_{AA} + Z_{AB}, \qquad 2.9.3$$

while the corresponding formula for the number of collisions made by a B-type molecule is

$$Z_B = Z_{BA} + Z_{BB}. \qquad 2.9.4$$

We may now define Λ_A, the mean free path of an A-type molecule in the mixture. The expression for Λ_A is obviously

$$\Lambda_A = \bar{v}_A / Z_A, \qquad 2.9.5$$

with a similar definition and expression for Λ_B.

The expressions for Λ_A (and Λ_B), which have not been written out in full, take specially simple forms in various cases:

(i) if we ignore the difference between $\bar{v}_{AA}$, $\bar{v}_{AB}$ and $\bar{v}_A$, that is, if we consider the A-type molecule to be moving with speed $\bar{v}_A$ in a gas of stationary molecules, then

$$\Lambda_A = 1 / \{ n_A \pi d_A^2 + n_B \pi (\tfrac{1}{2} d_A + \tfrac{1}{2} d_B)^2 \} ; \qquad 2.9.6$$

(ii) if the mixture is very dilute, for example if $n_B \to 0$, then an A-type molecule collides mainly with other A-type molecules and

$$\Lambda_{A(n_B \to 0)} = \frac{\bar{v}_A}{\bar{v}_{AA}} \cdot \frac{1}{n_A \pi d_A^2}, \qquad 2.9.7$$

which is the same as 2.2.3.

Under the same conditions of $n_B \to 0$, a B-type molecule collides mainly with A-types, so

$$\Lambda_{B(n_B \to 0)} = \frac{\bar{v}_B}{\bar{v}_{BA}} \cdot \frac{1}{n \pi (\tfrac{1}{2} d_A + \tfrac{1}{2} d_B)^2}, \qquad 2.9.8$$

where $\qquad n = n_{A(n_B \to 0)}$.

Similarly, if $n_A \to 0$, we have the formula for Λ_A analogous to 2.8.6 This is

$$\Lambda_{A(n_A \to 0)} = \frac{\bar{v}_A}{\bar{v}_{AB}} \cdot \frac{1}{n \pi (\tfrac{1}{2} d_A + \tfrac{1}{2} d_B)^2}, \qquad 2.9.9$$

where $\qquad n = n_{B(n_A \to 0)}$.

In 2.9.8 and 2.9.9 the denominators, which are $Z_{BA(n_B \to 0)}$ and $Z_{AB(n_A \to 0)}$, are equal at a given pressure. We shall use this result in § 2.10.

Using the definitions given above (2.9.5) for Λ_A and Λ_B, we may readily extend the mean-free-path method to give formulae for K and η in two-component mixtures. Thus, since the heat transport in a mixture is simply the sum of the transport by the different types of molecule, we have by the same reasoning as gave equation 2.6.2

$$K = \tfrac{1}{3}n_A C'_A \bar{v}_A \Lambda_A + \tfrac{1}{3}n_B C'_B \bar{v}_B \Lambda_B$$

$$= K_A \frac{\Lambda_A}{\Lambda'_A} + K_B \frac{\Lambda_B}{\Lambda'_B}, \qquad\qquad 2.9.10$$

where Λ'_A and Λ'_B are the free paths which n_A and n_B molecules respectively per unit volume would have if the other type were absent.

The general expressions for Λ_A/Λ'_A and Λ_B/Λ'_B are complex and not very informative. However, using the simplified expression 2.9.6 for Λ_A and the equivalent expression 2.2.4 for Λ'_A we obtain

$$\frac{\Lambda_A}{\Lambda'_A} = \frac{n_A \pi d_A^2}{n_A \pi d_A^2 + n_B \pi (\tfrac{1}{2}d_A + \tfrac{1}{2}d_B)^2}$$

$$= \frac{1}{1 + \alpha_{AB}(n_B/n_A)}, \qquad\qquad 2.9.11$$

where $\quad \alpha_{AB} = \dfrac{(\tfrac{1}{2}d_A + \tfrac{1}{2}d_B)^2}{d_A^2} \qquad\qquad 2.9.12$

is a non-dimensional parameter of order unity and independent of the concentration of the mixture. A similar expression is found for Λ_B/Λ'_B.

In this simplification, equation 2.9.10 then becomes

$$K = \frac{K_A}{1 + (n_B/n_A)\alpha_{AB}} + \frac{K_B}{1 + (n_A/n_B)\alpha_{BA}}. \qquad 2.9.13$$

In the special case of a mixture of gases having approximately the same molecular diameters $\alpha_{AB} \simeq \alpha_{BA} \simeq 1$ and 2.9.13 reduces to

$$K = K_A c + K_B(1-c), \qquad\qquad 2.9.14$$

where $\quad c = \dfrac{n_A}{n_A + n_B}$

is the fraction of A-type molecules. In this case the variation of K is linear with concentration, from K_A for pure A-type gas to K_B for pure B-type. In cases where the molecular diameters are not equal, equation 2.9.13 predicts deviations from the linear law.

Viscosity of gaseous mixtures can be treated in the same way as we used for thermal conductivity, simply replacing K by η throughout. Thus the prediction is that the transport property should everywhere lie between the values for the pure constituents and should have a roughly linear concentration dependence. *Fig.* 2.7 shows the concentration dependence of the thermal conductivities of mixtures of krypton with helium and xenon respectively. The table superposed on this figure shows that the atomic or molecular diameters of krypton and xenon *calculated from conductivity data* are not very different. Thus the thermal conductivities of krypton-xenon mixtures are linearly related to composition, the linearity being more impressive than can be shown on the scale of *fig.* 2.7. The molecular diameter of helium, calculated using the hard sphere model for thermal conductivity, is very different from that of krypton, so the thermal conductivities of helium-krypton mixtures are not related to composition by a simple linear law.

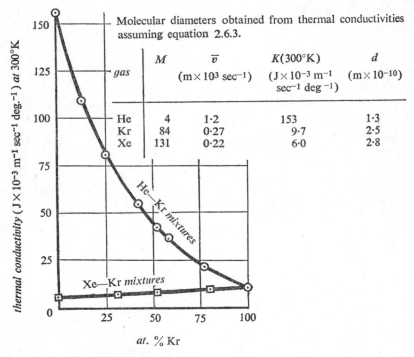

Figure 2.7. *Thermal conductivities of rare gas mixtures.*

§ 2.10   Diffusion in a gaseous mixture

It is instructive to use the mean-free-path method once again, this time to consider the diffusivity of a mixture of different gases. The answer we obtain will be wrong but will serve to illustrate the limitations of the method.

As in § 2.9 we define two mean free paths Λ_A and Λ_B, where Λ_A means the mean free path for A-type molecules in the mixture. Λ_B is similarly defined. Since on our previous assumptions the concentration changes little in distances of the order of Λ, both Λ_A and Λ_B are constant in the region of interest on either side of the reference plane. Further, if $\bar{v}_A$ and $\bar{v}_B$ are the respective mean speeds of the components, we can, by a simple extension of equation 2.8.3, write down formulae for the flux of A- and B-type molecules produced by random molecular motions. We shall call these fluxes Γ'_A and Γ'_B to distinguish them from the fluxes in equations 2.8.1 and 2.8.2. We shall see presently what the difference is. We have

$$\Gamma'_A = -\tfrac{1}{3}\bar{v}_A\Lambda_A\frac{dn_A}{dx} \qquad\qquad 2.10.1$$

and

$$\Gamma'_B = -\tfrac{1}{3}\bar{v}_B\Lambda_B\frac{dn_B}{dx}. \qquad\qquad 2.10.2$$

It is clear from these equations that unless the components are isotopically identical it is only by chance that Γ'_A will be numerically equal to Γ'_B. Thus, if the pressure is to remain constant throughout there must be a mass motion of the gas as a whole through the reference plane. This mass motion is superposed on the random motion we have been considering. If we call the mass velocity v_0 perpendicular to the reference plane, then the number of molecules crossing unit area of this plane per second is nv_0, where

$$n = n_A + n_B.$$

Since there is to be no net flow of gas across the reference plane, we require

$$\Gamma'_A + \Gamma'_B + nv_0 = 0. \qquad\qquad 2.10.3$$

Substituting for Γ'_A and Γ'_B and remembering that

$$\frac{dn_A}{dx} = -\frac{dn_B}{dx},$$

we have that

$$nv_0 = \tfrac{1}{3}\frac{dn_A}{dx}(\bar{v}_A\Lambda_A - \bar{v}_B\Lambda_B)$$

$$= \tfrac{1}{3}\frac{dn_B}{dx}(\bar{v}_B\Lambda_B - \bar{v}_A\Lambda_A). \qquad 2.10.4$$

The total number of A-type molecules crossing unit area of the reference plane is

$$\Gamma_A = \Gamma'_A + n_A v_0 = -\tfrac{1}{3}\frac{dn_A}{dx}\left(\bar{v}_A\Lambda_A - \frac{n_A\bar{v}_A\Lambda_A}{n} + \frac{n_A\bar{v}_B\Lambda_B}{n}\right).$$

Now $\quad 1 - \dfrac{n_A}{n} = \dfrac{n_B}{n}$,

so $\quad \Gamma_A = -\tfrac{1}{3}\dfrac{dn_A}{dx}\left(\dfrac{n_B}{n}\bar{v}_A\Lambda_A + \dfrac{n_A}{n}\bar{v}_B\Lambda_B\right).$ $\qquad 2.10.5$

Similarly

$$\Gamma_B = \Gamma'_B + n_B v_0 = -\tfrac{1}{3}\frac{dn_B}{dx}\left(\frac{n_A}{n}\bar{v}_B\Lambda_B + \frac{n_B}{n}\bar{v}_A\Lambda_A\right). \qquad 2.10.6$$

Comparison of these equations with 2.8.1 and 2.8.2 gives

$$D_A = D_B = D = \tfrac{1}{3}\left(\frac{n_B}{n}\bar{v}_A\Lambda_A + \frac{n_A}{n}\bar{v}_B\Lambda_B\right). \qquad 2.10.7$$

Apart from a slight change in the numerical factor, this is Meyer's formula for diffusion in a gaseous mixture. It predicts that D will vary considerably with concentration though not in the same way as K or η. Since the experimental result is that D does not vary appreciably with concentration, it is not worth working out an explicit expression for the predicted variation, and we content ourselves with showing what would be the limiting values of D if Meyer's formula 2.10.7 were correct.

In the limit when the concentration of A-type molecules is small we have from 2.10.7

$$D_{(n_A \to 0)} = \tfrac{1}{3}\bar{v}_A\Lambda_{A(n_A \to 0)}, \qquad 2.10.8$$

and similarly when the concentration of B-type molecules is small

$$D_{(n_B \to 0)} = \tfrac{1}{3}\bar{v}_B\Lambda_{B(n_B \to 0)}. \qquad 2.10.9$$

Thus the ratio of the diffusivities of the terminal solutions is

$$\frac{D_{(n_A \to 0)}}{D_{(n_B \to 0)}} = \frac{\bar{v}_A}{\bar{v}_B} \cdot \frac{\Lambda_{A(n_A \to 0)}}{\Lambda_{B(n_B \to 0)}}.$$

Using 2.9.8 and 2.9.9 for Λ_A and Λ_B we obtain

$$\frac{D_{(n_A \to 0)}}{D_{(n_B \to 0)}} = \frac{\bar{v}_A}{\bar{v}_B} \cdot \frac{\bar{v}_A}{Z_{AB(n_A \to 0)}} \cdot \frac{Z_{BA(n_B \to 0)}}{\bar{v}_B}$$

$$= \frac{\bar{v}_A^2}{\bar{v}_B^2},$$

since we saw in § 2.9 that

$$Z_{BA(n_B \to 0)} = Z_{AB(n_A \to 0)}.$$

Now from § 1.4, assuming that $\bar{v}^2 \propto \overline{v^2}$, we have

$$\frac{\bar{v}_A^2}{\bar{v}_B^2} = \frac{M_B}{M_A},$$

so that $\quad \dfrac{D_{(n_A \to 0)}}{D_{(n_B \to 0)}} = \dfrac{M_B}{M_A}.$ \hfill 2.10.11

If this result were correct, then the diffusivity of a mixture of two very different gases, for example H_2 and O_2, would vary by a factor of about 16 over the range of concentration. In fact the variation is at most a few per cent – usually less than the accuracy of measurement.

The failure of mean-free-path theory to give a usable formula in the case of inter-diffusion of gases is not due to an ill-advised attempt to apply mean-free-path methods, developed for gases all of one kind, to a mixture of molecules, since we saw that such attempts worked for the thermal conductivity and viscosity of mixtures. The failure for diffusion is rather due to a difference in the nature of the property transported. Thus, in the cases of thermal conductivity and viscosity, the transport is of a dynamic property, energy or momentum respectively; in the case of diffusivity it is of actual material particles. Consider a molecule carrying extra energy or momentum making its last collision before the reference plane. Whether the collision is with a like or an unlike molecule does not affect the chance that the dynamic property is carried across the plane, for it does not matter which type of molecule carries it. However, in material transport, if a type A-molecule is approaching the reference regions, collision with another similar molecule does not affect the transport, but collision with a molecule of type B may result in the 'wrong' molecule going over. Thus, in the case of interdiffusion we have to consider the relative probabilities that the last collision before the reference plane is between like or unlike molecules. If this is done, and in general its application makes the mean-free-path method too complicated, the concentration dependence of D vanishes.

A useful analogy for the difference between transport of material and dynamic properties is to think of a game where points are scored either for transport of a player of type A (material particle) or the ball (a dynamic property) across the goal line. As far as ball-transport goes, a point is scored whether an A-type player forces a B-type by collision to carry the ball over the line or carries it himself. Similarly, in player-transport it does not matter if a player knocks one of his own team over the line rather than crossing himself; it does matter if he knocks a B-type player over.

Practically, the result of these considerations is that the thermal conductivity and viscosity of mixture depend on concentration much as one would expect from the considerations of § 2.9, whereas diffusivity is almost independent of concentration.

§ 2.11 Refinement of elementary transport theory

We can refine transport theory to any degree of mathematical sophistication in a manner similar to that discussed for free-path theory in § 2.3. Thus we can modify our simple formula (originally derived in § 1.15), $\frac{1}{6}n\bar{v}$, for the number of molecules crossing unit area per second by a more rigorous derivation of $|\overline{v_x}|$ in terms of $\bar{v}$. The next most sophisticated result for this formula is obtained in § 4.10 and § 5.10 and is $\frac{1}{4}n\bar{v}$. Again, taking account of oblique transits across the reference plane, we shall find in § 4.10 that the average molecule made its last collision at a distance $\frac{2}{3}\Lambda$ away from the reference plane, so that the calculated flux to this degree of sophistication is the same as in the simple theory. We can further take account of the distribution of molecular speeds and the variation of mean free path with speed and we can develop a theory of free paths in non-uniform gases noting, for example, that a heavy particle will tend to barge through a gas of lighter particles since it requires more than one collision to change its flight appreciably.

As discussed in § 2.3, these refinements are an elegant mathematical theory, but the results are not, for practical purposes, significantly different from those obtained by the simple theory which, as we noted repeatedly, is in good qualitative agreement with experience. Moreover, there seems little point in refining down to the last fraction of a percent, a theory based on the very crude idea of hard spherical molecules. However, if the concept of hard spheres is abandoned, collisions may be treated in terms of assumed laws of force $F(r)$ between molecules approaching to distances r from each other's centres. In this case, the transport parameters turn out to be sensitive tests of $F(r)$. It is on these lines that much modern work is proceeding: the subject is not however relevant to this book.

§ 2.12   The distribution of free paths

There was an interesting early objection to a detail of the application of free-path methods to transport phenomena. It was argued that if the mean free path is Λ then the planes on either side of the reference plane, on which the last collision was supposed to take place, should be not Λ away but $\frac{1}{2}\Lambda$, leaving another $\frac{1}{2}\Lambda$ for the molecule to complete its free path on the other side of the reference plane. We cannot complete the consideration of this objection till we have found how free paths of various lengths are distributed (in chapter 4), but examination of the fallacy of the objection is an instructive preliminary exercise in statistical thinking.

The fallacy lies in assuming that those free paths which intersect a given plane are typical of all free paths: in fact, longer free paths are more likely to intersect a given plane than are short ones. To take a more concrete example, suppose we had a bundle of straws, half of them of length l, the other half of length $3l$. The average length l is thus $2l$. If we threw them high in the air and allowed them to fall on the floor the longer straws would be more likely to intersect a given crack on the floor than would the shorter straws. In fact, the straws of length $3l$ are three times more likely to lie across the crack than are the straws of length l, so that if a large number $4N$ of straws is found lying across the crack, $3N$ will be of length $3l$ and N of length l. The mean length of these straws is then

$$ l = \frac{3N \times 3l + N \times l}{4N} = \tfrac{5}{2}l. $$

We shall see in chapter 4 that the ratio between the mean free paths of molecules intersecting a given plane and of all molecules in the gas is exactly two, that is, just the factor necessary to dispose of the fallacious argument above.

§ 2.13   Problems

1. The monatomic gases, Ne, A, Kr, etc., all crystallise at very low temperatures. If the density of the solid is ρ, calculate the volume occupied by an atom in the solid.

Assuming that an atom of the gas is the same size as an atom of the solid, show that the mean free path Λ at pressure p is given by

$$\Lambda = \frac{kT}{\pi p}\left(\frac{M}{\rho N_0}\right)^{-\frac{2}{3}}.$$

Is Λ really a function of temperature?

ρ for solid Ne is $1\cdot 6$ gm/cm³. Calculate Λ at 1 atmosphere pressure. (*Answer:* about 2×10^{-7} m.)

2. Values of the thermal conductivity K of gases were obtained by measuring the heat input required to maintain a temperature difference of about $50°C$ between flat nickel plates a distance $d = 1\cdot 25$ mm apart in the gas. Results for air and carbon dioxide at various pressures p are given in table 4.

(i) Use these results to show that a variation of K with pressure can be detected at pressures such that the mean free path Λ is of the order of a few per cent of d. This is the quantitative statement of the remark on 'intermediate pressures' in the penultimate paragraph of § 2.6.

The elementary concepts of § 2.6 predicted that K should be independent of pressure except at pressures so low that molecules could make direct transitions from the hot to the cold surface of the container. The explanation of this departure from simple free-path theory is found when conditions in the gas close to solid surfaces are taken into account. In particular, it is observed that gas molecules striking a surface do not attain its full temperature before losing contact; for example, molecules striking the hotter nickel plate in these experiments and coming from cooler regions of the gas, carry away less energy on impact than if they came into full thermal equilibrium with the nickel. The ratio of the actual energy change per collision to the change which would occur if molecules came into equilibrium with the surface is called the *accommodation coefficient* and depends on the nature of both gas and surface. Thus, at a distance of one mean free path Λ from a solid surface at temperature T_s, the mean molecular energy is not that corresponding to $T_s - \Lambda(dT/dx)$, where dT/dx is the temperature gradient in the gas, but rather $T_s - n\Lambda(dT/dx)$ where $n > 1$.

(ii) Assuming $n\Lambda \ll d$, show that the relationship between the conductivity K_∞ at high pressures and the measured conductivity K_p at pressure p is

$$(K_\infty/K_p) - 1 = n\Lambda/d.$$

5

(iii) Analyse the results of table 4 to show that, for nickel surfaces and either CO_2 or air, n is about 3. Similar experiments using hydrogen give $n \sim 18$. Note that a pressure variation of K will be detected even if $n = 1$ or (as in 4.10.17) $n = \frac{2}{3}$, in which cases the accommodation coefficient is unity.

TABLE 4 : conductivity of gases at various pressures

air		CO_2	
pressure mm Hg	K watt cm^{-1} deg^{-1}	pressure mm Hg	K watt cm^{-1} deg^{-1}
7·80	3·17	9·65	2·84
3·80	3·11	5·93	2·83
2·60	3·01	4·14	2·81
1·73	2·92	3·00	2·79
1·40	2·86	1·70	2·75
atmospheric	3·24	atmospheric	2·86

3. Use the transport data in *figs.* 2.4, 2.6, 2.7 and in table 3 to obtain estimates of the sizes of molecules of H_2, CO_2, He, Kr and Xe. Compare these values with others estimated from the densities of condensed phases given in table 5.

TABLE 5 : densities of condensed phases of substances gaseous at normal temperatures

substance	condensed phases	temperature °K	density kg $\times 10^3$ m^{-3}
He	liquid	4·22	0·12
H_2	solid	20	0·07
Kr	solid	127	2·2
Xe	solid	164	3·5
CO_2	solid	194	1·5

Data mainly from Kaye and Laby *Physical and Chemical Constants* Longmans Green, London, 1959.

§ 2.14   Further reading
See § 1.18 for some books on the kinetic theory of gases.

Chapter 3

DISTRIBUTIONS AND PROBABILITY

§ 3.1   Distribution functions

If we rewrite 1.12.5, putting $R = N_0 k$, we obtain

$$n = n_0 \exp\left(-mgz/kT\right).$$

Plotting n/n_0 against z for a given value of T, we obtain a curve
(*fig.* 3.1) which shows the distribution of molecules with height. A
function such as $n(z)$ is therefore called a *distribution function*. Since
$n(z)$ is the number per unit volume, the actual number in a small volume
ΔV at height z is $n(z)\Delta V$. If the volume ΔV is made very small then
there may not be a molecule in it at all because molecules in a gas are
widely separated. However, $n(z)\Delta V$ will still be a measure of the
probability that there is a molecule in volume ΔV. This probability
will be greater when z is small than when z is large.

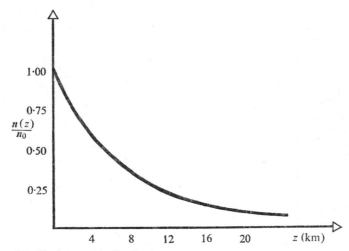

Figure 3.1. *The barometric distribution.*

The distribution shown in *fig.* 3.1 is determined by a balance
between the effects of potential energy (mgz) and thermal energy

(kT). We can see this best by considering what happens when one or other of these competing energies is absent: first suppose we could switch off the thermal energy; this is equivalent to letting T tend to zero. When this occurs, the exponential also tends to zero, giving a new distribution where the density of molecules at any height above $z = 0$ is zero, and there is no probability of finding a molecule except on the ground. The distribution function of *fig.* 3.1 becomes a thin dense strip along the *n* axis.

If, on the other hand we could switch off gravity, this is equivalent to making g tend to zero so that the potential energy of a particle is zero at any height. Under these circumstances the atmosphere would disperse throughout space as has happened in the case of bodies such as the moon, where the gravitational field is too weak to retain an atmosphere. We can, however, obtain a more instructive distribution by arranging, before altering gravity, to retain the atmosphere in a vessel so large that variation of density with height can be observed – we saw in § 1.12 that a vessel 10 km high would be satisfactory for this purpose. If gravity is now switched off there is no gravitational field acting on the molecules so there is no reason why the density of molecules should be greater at the bottom of the vessel than at great heights; that is, $n(z)$ would be a constant, or the probability of

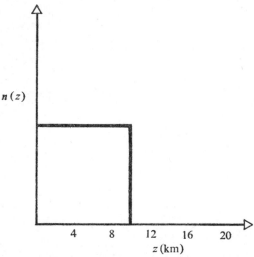

Figure 3.2. *The barometric distribution in a container* 10 *km high with gravity switched off.*

finding a molecule in a given small volume would be the same any-where in the vessel. The new distribution function $n(z)$ is shown in *fig.* 3.2.

The uniform distribution of *fig.* 3.2 is changed to that of *fig.* 3.1 by the factor exp $(-mgz/kT)$, that is, by a factor involving a comparison of gravitational and thermal energies. We shall meet other cases where a similar balance of energy determines the distribution function.

The distribution shown in *fig.* 3.1 is the first for which we have an explicit expression; it is not the first distribution we have met, since in § 1.2 we implied that there might be a distribution of speeds amongst the molecules of our model gas and we calculated a mean speed. We can now use results on the constant temperature atmos-phere to show that it is impossible for all molecules in our gas to have the same speed.

Suppose that the atmosphere is composed of non-interacting particles as in the model we were using in chapter 1. Further suppose that molecules striking the Earth's surface all acquire a vertical component of velocity v_z given by

$$\tfrac{1}{2}mv_z^2 = \tfrac{1}{2}kT,$$

where T is the temperature of the surface and v_z is the same for all. There is thus no bar over the v_z and no need for one. Since the particles do not collide or otherwise interact they will rise to a height z_{max} given by

$$mgz_{max} = \tfrac{1}{2}mv_z^2,$$

that is $\quad z_{max} = v_z^2/2g = kT/2mg = RT/2Mg.$

Taking $T = 300°K$ and $M = 30$ we obtain

$$z_{max} \simeq 4\cdot 1 \text{ km}.$$

Above this height there can be no molecules so that the atmosphere would simply stop, which is contrary to experience. Moreover, as the molecules gain height they exchange kinetic energy for potential energy and so move more slowly. Thus the temperature of the atmosphere would fall by about $75°C/km$ reaching $0°K$ at $4\cdot1$ km. This is contrary to our assumption of a constant temperature atmos-phere and also contrary to experience.

We cannot escape from this paradoxical situation except by postulating that there is a spread or distribution of velocities of gas molecules, so that the faster molecules then rise higher than the slower molecules. Presumably the distribution of velocities is such that there are many less fast molecules than slow ones since the density of the atmosphere falls rapidly with height. If the temperature of the atmosphere is taken as constant, which is not far from the truth on the absolute scale, then the distribution must be such that the survivors at any height have the same mean-square velocity. These clues are in fact enough to enable us to calculate a distribution function for velocities of molecules in the atmosphere, though we shall not do so until we have some further knowledge about distribution in general. Finding the velocity distribution in the way suggested above is set as problem 5.15.1.

It is worth saying here, however, that the above conclusions are not affected by the fact that we know that real molecules, unlike the model particles, do collide with each other, since the only effect of a collision is to exchange momentum between particles. As will be shown later, the velocity distribution is not changed. Neither is the conclusion affected by introduction of velocity components v_x and v_y parallel to the earth's surface since we have already assumed, and will see later, that the components are independent.

It appears, therefore, that we may be able to calculate the distribution of molecular velocities. We shall first digress to acquire techniques for dealing with distributions of large numbers of entities.

§ 3.2 Probability theory

It is convenient to approach the concept of distribution functions and averages from the ideas of probability theory.

Definition of probability. If as a result of a very large number N of trials (e.g. tosses of a coin) a certain event (e.g. coming down heads) occurs n times, then the probability p of the event is n/N, or more strictly

$$p = \lim_{N \to \infty} (n/N); \qquad 3.2.1$$

p is thus the fraction of successful trials and

$$0 \leqslant p \leqslant 1 .$$

We can also define probability by symmetry considerations: for example, the probability of obtaining heads in a single toss of a coin is $p = \frac{1}{2}$; of throwing a 'one' with a die is $p = \frac{1}{6}$; of drawing a face card from a pack is $p = 12/52 = 3/13$. We call these *a priori* probabilities and we generally assume that they are the same as the empirical probabilities defined first. Such an assumption implies that the coin, for example, is symmetrical and that it is *equally likely* that it will come down heads or tails. A real coin might not have this property and so our probability theory is based on an ideal assessment of what events, such as heads or tails, are equally probable. If we correctly identify the equally probable events then our physical predictions on the basis of the theory of probability will be correct; but if the events we assume to be equally likely are not so, then we shall obtain the wrong answer. For example, in § 2.12 we might easily have wrongly assumed that free paths of all lengths are equally likely to intersect a given plane. Problem 3.12.1 gives classical examples of errors introduced by failure to identify correctly the equally probable events.

The important words in the empirical definition are 'very large number'. It is clear that if we toss the ideal coin only twice we may not obtain just one head but that if we toss it a thousand times our yield of heads is not likely to be far from 500. We shall not of course find that the deviations from the expected number n can be ignored.

If then p is the probability that an event happens, the probability that the event will *not* happen is

$$(N-n)/n = 1-p,$$

which shows that the probability of an event which can never happen is $p = 0$.

If two events are *independent* and have probabilities p_1 and p_2 then the probability that both will happen is obtained by multiplying the probabilities of the separate events. For example, whether a coin came down heads or tails in one toss has no influence on how it comes down at a subsequent toss, so the probability of two heads in successive tosses is $\frac{1}{2} \times \frac{1}{2} = \frac{1}{4}$ and of a succession of N heads in N tosses is $(\frac{1}{2})^N$. Here the important word is 'independent', as we can illustrate by some simple, but physically significant, calculations of the relative probabilities that balls are distributed in various ways over boxes. We shall later use such calculations to predict, for example, how molecules, represented by the balls, are distributed in space, represented by the boxes.

Suppose we have two boxes into which N balls are successively put by some random method; for example, a coin might be tossed to decide which box is to receive each ball. Then by symmetry considerations we find that the probability that a given ball goes into box [1] is $\frac{1}{2}$. If the presence or absence of a ball in a box has no influence on the probability that subsequent balls can enter the same box, the probability that the second ball also goes into box [1] is again $\frac{1}{2}$; the events are independent and the probability of finding two balls in a given box is $\frac{1}{2} \times \frac{1}{2} = \frac{1}{4}$. Similarly the probability that we shall find all N balls in a given box is $(\frac{1}{2})^N$. If however the events are not independent, if, for example, one ball already in a box makes it less likely that another can enter, the probability of finding two balls in the given box is less than $\frac{1}{4}$; and conversely if the balls attract each other the same probability is greater than $\frac{1}{4}$. In the extreme case where a box can contain either one ball or no ball the probability of two in a box is, of course, zero.

If two events are *mutually exclusive*, so that if event [1] happens event [2] cannot happen and vice-versa, then the probability that *either* of the events will happen is the sum of the probabilities of the separate events. For example, the probability that we obtain either a head or a tail on tossing a coin is $\frac{1}{2} + \frac{1}{2} = 1$, that is a certainty. The probability of either a 'one' or a 'two' in a throw of a die is $\frac{1}{6} + \frac{1}{6} = \frac{1}{3}$. We have already tacitly used the idea of mutually exclusive events when we saw that the probability p of an event happening or $(1-p)$ of it not happening was $p + (1-p) = 1$.

Confusion over whether events are dependent or independent is the most common cause of fallacies in elementary probability, as we can illustrate by using our boxes and balls introduced above and asking the question 'what is the probability that *either* the first *or* the second ball goes into box [1]?' Here we must not be misled by the 'either/or' into thinking that we add the probabilities, each $\frac{1}{2}$, obtaining the obviously false result that there will certainly be a ball in box [1] after two trials. We assume that the events are independent and hence obtain the correct answer in two ways:

(*a*) the probability that the first ball will *not* go into box [1] is $\frac{1}{2}$ and the probability that the second will *not* go in box [1] is also $\frac{1}{2}$. These events are independent; so the probability of no ball in the box after two trials is $\frac{1}{4}$ giving the probability of at least one ball in box [1] as $1 - \frac{1}{4} = \frac{3}{4}$;

(*b*) we may use a combination of dependent and independent events as follows: the probability that there will be a ball in box [1] after two trials = (the probability that the first ball goes in box [1]) + (the probability that the second ball in goes in box [1] *when we already know* that the first ball has not gone into box [1]). The two probabilities in each of the two brackets are now mutually exclusive and the addition is valid. The events described in the second bracket are independent and the combined probability is the product. So we have that the required probability $= \frac{1}{2}+(\frac{1}{2}\times\frac{1}{2}) = \frac{3}{4}$, the same result as before.

A slightly simpler calculation tells us that, since the probability that all N balls fall in a given one of the two boxes is $(\frac{1}{2})^N$ and since the presence of all balls in one box excludes the possibility of them being in the other, the probability that all the balls will fall in either one of the two boxes is $2(\frac{1}{2})^N$.

The above is all we need to know about probability and we are now in a position to apply it to the problem of how a large number of entities may be expected to behave. We shall start with small numbers and work up, first asking the question: if a coin is tossed twice, what are the probabilities of getting no heads, one head, two heads? We can proceed in various ways:

(i) Write out the various possibilities denoting head by H and tail by T. These are

TT, TH, HT, HH,

that is, four possible events, each one of which excludes all the others. Of the four, one includes no heads so, by our definition of probability, the probability of no heads is $\frac{1}{4}$. Similarly the probability of two heads is $\frac{1}{4}$. For one head and one tail there are two possibilities out of four so the required probability of one head is $\frac{1}{2}$. It is instructive to compare this correct conclusion with an incorrect eighteenth-century result described in problem 3.12.1.

(ii) Alternatively we may argue that the probability of two successive heads can be obtained by the rule for independent events and is

$$p_H \times p_H = \frac{1}{4}.$$

This is also the probability of two successive tails. The probability of one head and one tail is

$$(p_H \times p_T)+(p_T \times p_H) = (\frac{1}{2}\times\frac{1}{2})+(\frac{1}{2}\times\frac{1}{2}) = 2\times\frac{1}{4}.$$

The events within each pair of brackets are independent since the event in the first pair of brackets excludes the event in the second pair. Thus the probability of a mixed event is $\frac{1}{4}$ multiplied by the number of ways in which the mixed event can be obtained, that is two.

Similarly if we toss a coin three times

the probabilities of 0, 1, 2, 3 heads

can be written $(\frac{1}{2})^3\{1, 3, 3, 1\}$ respectively,   3.2.2

where the 3's are simply the number of ways of arranging 3 things two of one kind and one of another or $^3C_2$ where

$$^NC_n = \frac{N!}{n!(N-n)!}$$ 3.2.3

is the number of permutations of N things of which n and $N-n$ are identical.

It is instructive to write out the ways in which the various combinations of heads and tails can be obtained.

§ 3.3   Pascal's triangle

In the same way we can write down the probabilities of $0, 1, 2, \ldots, N$ heads in N tosses of a coin. It is customary to express the results in the following way:

Number of tosses N	$(\frac{1}{2})^N$	Coefficients ^NC_n
0	1	0
1	$\frac{1}{2}$	1 1
2	$\frac{1}{4}$	1 2 1
3	$\frac{1}{8}$	1 3 3 1
4	$\frac{1}{16}$	1 4 6 4 1
5	$\frac{1}{32}$	1 5 10 10 5 1
6	$\frac{1}{64}$	1 6 15 20 15 6 1
7	$\frac{1}{128}$	1 7 21 35 35 21 7 1
8	$\frac{1}{256}$	1 8 28 56 70 56 28 8 1

This is called *Pascal's triangle* and it is to be read in exactly the same way as expression 3.2.2 above, that is, for example, that

the probabilities of   0, 1, 2, 3, 4, 5 heads

in 5 tosses of a coin are $\frac{1}{32}\{1, 5, 10, 10, 5, 1\}$ respectively.   3.3.1

Such a set of probabilities is a distribution, in this case of a variable which can take only a limited range of discrete values. Each coefficient of $(\frac{1}{2})^N$ is ^NC_n, which means that the probability of obtaining n heads and $(N-n)$ tails in N tosses is $(\frac{1}{2})^N \, ^NC_n$. This is of course the same as the probability of obtaining $(N-n)$ heads and n tails and this symmetry is reflected in the symmetry of Pascal's triangle. Again the arrangement of the triangle with the gap below each entry shows that each entry is obtained by adding those to left and right immediately above it. The reason for this is that

$$^{N}C_{n} + {}^{N}C_{n+1} = {}^{N+1}C_{n+1}.$$ 3.3.2

Finally the terms in Pascal's triangle are the binomial coefficients, and the probabilities of the various numbers of heads and tails, for example those in expressions 3.2.2 and 3.3.1, are obtained by expanding $(\frac{1}{2}+\frac{1}{2})^{N}$ by the binomial theorem. The sum of the probabilities across any row is unity, as it must be, since one or other of the $N+1$ events must occur. Consequently in Pascal's triangle, the sum of the binomial coefficients across any row must equal 2^{N}, that is

$$\sum_{n=0}^{n=N} {}^{N}C_{n} = 2^{N}.$$ 3.3.3

To agree with what we do in § 5.2 we shall call each of the 2^{N} events a *complexion* so that HHT and HTH and THH are different complexions of the distribution of heads and tails amongst three tosses of a coin. The set of complexions which have the same numbers of heads and tails will be called a *configuration*. Our statement about certain events being favoured statistically then becomes: all complexions are equally likely and the most probable configurations are those which include the greatest number of complexions.

§ 3.4 The binomial distribution

In greater generality, the rule is that if a certain event has probability p, and the probability of the excluded event is q ($\equiv 1-p$), then if the trial is repeated N times the probabilities of 0, 1, 2, 3, . . . events are the terms in the expansion of $(p+q)^{N}$, where

$$(p+q)^{N} = \sum_{n=0}^{n=N} p^{N-n}q^{n}\,{}^{N}C_{n}.$$ 3.4.1

Using the rules above there should be no difficulty in proving this. Since $p+q = 1$, the sum of all these probabilities is unity; that is, one or other of the $N+1$ sets of events must occur.

Simple though the above consideration of coin-tossing and its generalisation is, we can derive important conclusions from it: first, even for such small numbers–small, that is, in comparison with the numbers of physical entities–it is clear that certain configurations are favoured statistically. Thus, when $p = q = \frac{1}{2}$, Pascal's triangle line

8 shows that the probability of obtaining 3, 4 or 5 heads in 8 tosses of a coin is

$$\frac{56+70+56}{256} \sim \frac{3}{4};$$

so these three configurations include three times as many complexions as all the other six and are thus three times as likely to be observed.

The second conclusion is that if, instead of tossing a single coin N times, we had tossed a set of N coins 2^N times and counted the number of heads in each tossing, then the number of times we observe any given complexion should be close to the corresponding entry in the Pascal triangle. For example, if a set of eight coins had been tossed 256 times we would expect to get the configuration with 5 heads and 3 tails about 56 times and that with eight heads only once. We shall not of course get exactly the expected numbers. Similarly, if we had 256 sets of 8 coins and tossed all the sets at once, we would expect to find that in about 56 of the sets there were 5 heads and 3 tails. If we actually did such an experiment, or the one where the same set of 8 coins was tossed 256 times, we might exhibit our results by

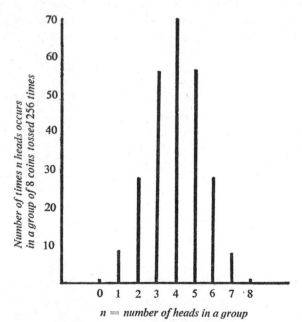

$n = $ number of heads in a group

Figure 3.3. Histogram of 256 trials each involving tossing 8 coins.

means of a histogram, that is a plot of the number of heads in each set against the number of times this number of heads was found. This histogram could then be compared with that of the distribution calculated using symmetry considerations. The calculated histogram is shown in *fig.* 3.3.

The histogram is the graph of a distribution function, in this case a function of a variable which can take only a limited range of discrete values. The distribution we have been studying, where the numbers involved are the terms in the expansion of $\{p+(1-p)\}^N$, is called the *binomial distribution*.

§ 3.5 The multinomial distribution

If the probabilities of r *mutually exclusive* events are $p_1, p_2, p_3, \ldots, p_r$ such that

$$\sum_{i=1}^{i=r} p_i = 1,$$

then the probability that event i occurs n times in N trials is given by the sum of the terms in p_i^n in the expansion of

$$\{p_1 + p_2 + \ldots + p_r\}^N.$$

This is the *multinomial distribution*. From it we see that the probabilities of various combinations of faces in N throws of a die are given by the appropriate terms in the expansion of

$$\{\tfrac{1}{6} + \tfrac{1}{6} + \tfrac{1}{6} + \tfrac{1}{6} + \tfrac{1}{6} + \tfrac{1}{6}\}^N.$$

For example, the probability of throwing N sixes in N throws of a die is simply $(\tfrac{1}{6})^N$, while the probability of throwing exactly $N-1$ sixes is $5N(\tfrac{1}{6})^N$. The latter figure may also be obtained by calculating the probabilities of $N-1$ sixes together with any one of the other five faces; each of these events excludes all the others, so the probabilities may be added. We then multiply the sum by N, since the non-six can be obtained at any one of the N trials.

In the case of an ideal die where all faces are equally likely to turn up, the distribution giving the probabilities of $0, 1, 2, \ldots, N$ of any face is the same as for any other face. In such a simple case it would be easier to say the probability of throwing a six is $\tfrac{1}{6}$, and the probability of *not* throwing a six is $\tfrac{5}{6}$; so the required probabilities are the terms in the expansion of

$$\{\tfrac{1}{6} + \tfrac{5}{6}\}^N,$$

which is the binomial distribution again.

§ 3.6   Averages : discrete distributions

We have used the word 'average' from the beginning of this book, because its meaning is well known. In words, the average of a set of quantities is obtained by adding them all up and dividing by the number of quantities, that is, if $x_1, x_2, x_3, \ldots, x_N$ are N quantities their average is

$$\bar{x} = \frac{1}{N} \sum_{i=1}^{i=N} x_i ,$$ 3.6.1

where, of course,

$$\sum_{i=1}^{i=N} x_i = x_1 + x_2 + \ldots + x_N.$$ 3.6.2

In this way the average of the squares of the velocities of N gas molecules was introduced in § 1.2 and was

$$\overline{v^2} = \frac{1}{N} \sum_{i=1}^{N} v_i^2 ;$$ 3.6.3

the average speed was introduced in § 1.15 as

$$\bar{v} = \frac{1}{N} \sum_{i=1}^{N} |v_i| ,$$ 3.6.4

where $|v_i|$ is the speed (i.e. the velocity without regard to direction) of the ith molecule. The average *velocity* would be

$$\text{average velocity} = \frac{1}{N} \sum_{i=1}^{N} v_i$$
$$= 0 ,$$

since the assumption of random motion may be taken to mean that for every v_i in one direction there will be an equal one in the opposite direction. We shall qualify and prove this later. A symbol for average velocity has not been introduced since it is not of much use, and $\bar{v}$ has already been used for average speed.

Now if the quantities x_i are arranged in groups so that there are

v_1 observations each x_1,

v_2 „   „ x_2,

· · · · · · ·

v_i „   „ x_i,

and so on, we have

$$\bar{x} = \frac{\sum_i v_i x_i}{\sum_i v_i} = \frac{1}{N} \sum_i v_i x_i ,$$ 3.6.5

where in each case the sum is over all i until all the quantities have been accounted for. Applying this to the ideal distributions described by Pascal's triangle, we now take x_i as the number of heads in a set of 8 coins, and v_i as the number of times x_i is observed in the 256 tosses of the set. Then the average number of heads $\bar{x}$ for the distribution shown in *fig.* 3.3 is

$$\bar{x} = \frac{\sum\limits_{i=0}^{8} v_i x_i}{\sum\limits_{i=0}^{8} v_i} \qquad\qquad 3.6.6$$

$$= \frac{(0 \times 1) + (1 \times 8) + (2 \times 28) + (3 \times 56) + (4 \times 70) + \ldots + (8 \times 1)}{1 + 8 + 28 + 56 + 70 + \ldots + 1}$$

$$= 4,$$

as we would have expected. In this simple case it would have sufficed to take i as the number of heads, obtaining the mean number as

$$\bar{\imath} = \frac{\sum\limits_{i=0}^{8} i v_i}{\sum v_i}. \qquad\qquad 3.6.7$$

§ 3.7 Averages : continuous distributions

In 3.6.6 we were calculating the average value of a distribution of discrete quantities. Indeed, the x_i had to be positive integers or zero.

If the variable can take any of a continuous range of values we can still construct a histogram by dividing up the continuous variable into discrete intervals. For example, if we wished to find the average speed of traffic past a certain point we might count the numbers of vehicles with speeds between 0 and 2 m/s, 2 and 4 m/s, and so on. Labelling the numbers v_i in each group by the mean speed of the group i m/s, we have

$$v_1 \text{ vehicles with speeds } 0\text{–}2 \text{ m/s}$$
$$v_3 \qquad\qquad\qquad\qquad\quad 2\text{–}4 \text{ m/s}$$

and so on.

The resulting histogram might then look like *fig.* 3.4a and the average speed would be

$$\bar{v} = \frac{1.v_1 + 3.v_3 + 5.v_5 + \ldots}{v_1 + v_3 + \ldots}$$

$$= \frac{\sum\limits_{i=1,3,5,\ldots} v_i v_i}{\sum\limits_{i=1,3,5,\ldots} v_i}. \qquad\qquad 3.7.1$$

v_i here means 'the average speed of vehicles whose average speed is i', and so, like the x_i in equation 3.6.6, could be eliminated. We shall, however, need it shortly and so we retain it.

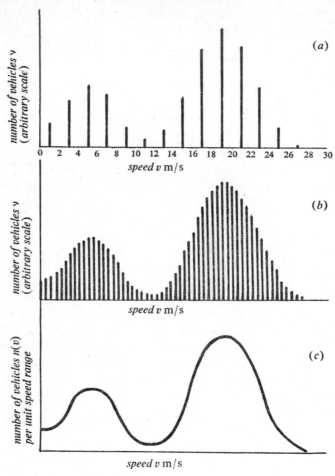

Figure 3.4. *Statistics of vehicle speeds.*

The number of vehicles in each group will depend on the mean speed of the group. For example, if the measuring point is on a motorway there are likely to be more vehicles travelling at 30–32 m/s than at 10–12 m/s. The number in a group will also depend on the size of the speed interval defining the group. If the number of vehicles is large we can reduce the size of the speed intervals while still retaining a reasonable number of vehicles in each group. Thus in *fig.* 3.4*b* the same distribution as in *fig.* 3.4*a* is shown but with the total number of vehicles increased by a factor of four and the speed intervals reduced by the same factor.

If the intervals are still further reduced to width Δv_i, say, the ordinate $v(v_i)$ will differ little from $v(v_i + \Delta v_i)$ so the number of vehicles in the speed interval v_i to $v_i + \Delta v_i$ will actually be proportional to the width of the interval, that is, to Δv_i.

We now introduce, instead of v, a new variable n, the number of vehicles per unit speed range. n, like v, is a function of v and can be written $n(v)$. The actual number of vehicles in the speed range v_i to $v_i + \Delta v_i$ is then $n(v_i)\Delta v_i$. The spread of speeds amongst the group is, by hypothesis, small so all may be taken to have the same speed v_i. The mean speed over the whole distribution is then

$$\bar{v} = \frac{\sum_i v_i n(v_i)\Delta v_i}{\sum_i n(v_i)\Delta v_i}.$$

3.7.2

In the limit when all $\Delta v_i \to 0$ the distribution curve of *fig.* 3.4*b* becomes a smooth curve like that in *fig.* 3.4*c* and the sums in 3.7.2 can be replaced by integrals. Thus

$$\bar{v} = \frac{\int v n(v)dv}{\int n(v)dv}.$$

3.7.3

This is the same formula as 3.7.2 but expressed in terms of a continuous variable. The denominator is the area under a smooth histogram such as *fig.* 3.4*c* and simply represents the total number of vehicles which we have assumed to be large. The limits of integration are such as to include all vehicles with speeds from zero to the highest observed but, since there will be no vehicles with very high speeds, the upper limit could be taken as ∞ if it seemed desirable.

If we knew the distribution function $n(v)$ for gas molecules we could readily calculate

$$\overline{v^2} = \frac{\int_0^\infty v^2 n(v)dv}{\int_0^\infty n(v)dv}$$

3.7.4

6

$$\text{and} \qquad \bar{v} = \dfrac{\displaystyle\int_0^\infty vn(v)dv}{\displaystyle\int_0^\infty n(v)dv}. \qquad\qquad 3.7.5$$

These formulae are not essentially different from 3.6.3 and 3.6.4. They are however more physically realistic since we now need know only the form of the distribution whereas formerly we were tacitly assuming that we could measure the velocity of every molecule in the gas to any required accuracy.

We shall shortly set out to discover the function $n(v)$, showing that it can be derived assuming only the laws of probability and the conservation of gas molecules. Apart from the latter there are no physical assumptions whatever. We expect, since the number of gas molecules is so large, that $n(v)$ will be a smooth curve. However, we shall find it convenient occasionally to consider groups of molecules in the same way as we did for vehicles and to assume that in each group all the molecules have a discrete energy or velocity. The results so obtained will be useful in chapter 9, when we deal with the less material entities mentioned in the introduction, where the energies may be really discrete.

§ 3.8   Normalisation

We shall frequently find it convenient to use not the actual numbers of entities with some specified property but the fraction of the total number which have this property.

In the discrete distribution of § 3.6 the fraction ϕ_i of quantities which have magnitude x_i is

$$\phi_i = \frac{v_i}{N} = \frac{v_i}{\sum_i v_i}. \qquad\qquad 3.8.1$$

In the continuous distribution of § 3.7 we may write similarly that the fraction ϕ_i of entities (vehicles in § 3.7) which have the property v (speed) between v and $v+dv$ is $f(v)dv$ given by

$$f(v)dv = \frac{n(v)dv}{\int n(v)dv}, \qquad\qquad 3.8.2$$

the limits of integration being taken as before so as to include all the entities in the distribution.

Now by our definition of probability (3.2.1), ϕ in 3.8.1 or $f\,dv$ in 3.8.2 is the probability that a given entity chosen at random from the total number will have the given property. Thus the probability that one of the vehicles selected by chance from those discussed above has speed between v and $v+dv$ is given by 3.8.2.

From 3.8.1 we have

$$\sum_i \phi_i = 1,$$ 3.8.3

while from 3.8.2 we have

$$\int_{\text{all } v} f(v)dv = 1.$$ 3.8.4

Equations 3.8.3–4 express the fact that it is a certainty that each entity belonging to the distribution has some property or other.

It frequently happens that an expression for f first appears in the form

$$f = AF,$$

where A is an undetermined constant. Equations 3.8.3–4 give us an immediate process for finding A. This process is called *normalisation*. It is often convenient, however, *not* to evaluate A but to use f un-normalised. In this case the means of the discrete (3.6.5) and continuous (3.7.5) distributions would be

$$\bar{x} = \frac{\sum_i \phi_i x_i}{\sum_i \phi_i}$$ 3.8.5

and $$\bar{v} = \frac{\int v f(v)dv}{\int f(v)dv}.$$ 3.8.6

If ϕ or f had been normalised the denominators would be unity in each case.

§ 3.9 Expectation values

Writing equations 3.8.5–6 with normalised ϕ or f gives

$$\bar{x} = \sum_i \phi_i x_i$$ 3.9.1

and $$\bar{v} = \int v f(v)dv.$$ 3.9.2

Written this way, the expressions on the right-hand sides of these equations are sums of products of probabilities and effects. Such sums are often called *expectations*, defined as follows: if the probabilities of certain mutually exclusive events are $p_1, p_2, \ldots, p_i, \ldots$ and if event i produces effect (for example, some prize) P_i, then the expectation value is

$$\langle E \rangle = \sum_i P_i p_i. \qquad\qquad 3.9.3$$

For example, if a gambler agrees to pay the value in shillings of the spots on the face of a die the expectation value of his pay-out is

$$\langle E \rangle = \sum_{r=1}^{6} P_r p_r.$$

All $p_i = \frac{1}{6}$ since the probability of throwing any face of a die is $\frac{1}{6}$ and the payment P_i is $1, 2, \ldots, 6$ shillings, depending on which face is uppermost; so

$$\langle E \rangle = \tfrac{1}{6}(1+2+3+4+5+6)$$
$$= \tfrac{21}{6} \text{ shillings,}$$

and this sum would be the minimum he would charge his opponent for the privilege of playing with him.

Expectations of the results of gambling provide excellent practice in the theory of probability. Some examples are included among the problems at the end of this chapter. Amongst them is the very famous St Petersburg paradox (problem 3.12.2).

§ 3.10   The barometric distribution

We began this chapter with a discussion of the distribution of gas molecules at various heights in the atmosphere, that is of the formula

$$n(z) = n_0 \, e^{-mgz/kT}, \qquad\qquad 3.10.1$$

where $n(z)$ was the number of molecules of mass m in unit volume at height z.

The quantity $n(z)dz$ is then the number of molecules in a small volume having unit area parallel to the Earth's surface and extending from height z to height $z+dz$ and

$$n(z)dz = n_0 \, e^{-mgz/kT} \, dz.$$

If now we think of a column of unit cross-sectional area extending from the Earth's surface upwards without limit then the fraction of molecules in this column which are in the layer between z and $z+dz$ is

$$f(z)dz = A \, e^{-mgz/kT} \, dz, \qquad\qquad 3.10.2$$

where A is a constant which can be obtained by normalisation. Thus

$$\int_0^\infty f(z)dz = \int_0^\infty A\, e^{-mgz/kT}\, dz = 1.$$ \hfill 3.10.3

The limits have been taken so as to be sure of including all molecules. In fact the function $f(z)$ goes rapidly to zero as z increases. Integrating 3.10.3 gives

$$A = mg/kT,$$

and the normalised function $f(z)$ is

$$f(z)dz = (mg/kT)\, e^{-mgz/kT}\, dz,$$

which gives the normalised probability that a given molecule is at a height between z and $z+dz$; f is also the fraction of the total number of molecules in the column which are within these limits. The mean or expectation value of the potential energy of a molecule in an isothermal (constant temperature) atmosphere is then

$$\overline{mgz} \text{ or } \langle mgz \rangle = \int_0^\infty mgz f(z)dz$$

$$= \frac{(mg)^2}{kT} \int_0^\infty z\, e^{-mgz/kT}\, dz.$$

The integral can be evaluated by parts and gives

$$\overline{mgz} = \langle mgz \rangle = kT.$$ \hfill 3.10.4

The value kT for a term occurring as the first power of a co-ordinate in the expression for the energy may be contrasted with the equipartition (§ 1.3) value $\tfrac{1}{2}kT$ for each term occurring as a *square* of a co-ordinate. We shall leave the discussion of this point till § 5.10.

§ 3.11 Average velocities and average speeds in kinetic theory

In chapter 5 we shall obtain the velocity distribution function $f_x(v_x)dv_x$, which gives the fraction of molecules having x-components of velocity between v_x and v_x+dv_x, or the probability that a given molecule has velocity within this range. We shall also obtain the speed distribution function $f(v)dv$ which gives the fraction of molecules which have speeds between v and $v+dv$ and has the corresponding probability interpretation.

While we do not yet have explicit formulae for $f_x(v_x)dv_x$ and $f(v)dv$, we can immediately write down expressions for some averages already used. Thus, remembering that by definition of these functions,

$$\int_{-\infty}^{\infty} f_x(v_x)dv_x = 1,$$

3.11.1

with similar results for $f_y(v_y)dv_y$ and $f_z(v_z)dv_z$

and

$$\int_0^{\infty} f(v)dv = 1,$$

3.11.2

we have

$$\overline{v_x^2} \quad (1.2.1)$$

$$= \int_{-\infty}^{\infty} v_x^2 f_x(v_x)dv_x,$$

3.11.3

with similar expressions for $\overline{v_y^2}$ and $\overline{v_z^2}$;

$$\overline{v^2} \quad (1.2.5)$$

$$= \int_0^{\infty} v^2 f(v)dv;$$

3.11.4

$$\overline{|v_x|} \quad (1.15.1)$$

$$= \int_{-\infty}^{\infty} |v_x| f_x(v_x)dv_x,$$

3.11.5

while

$$\overline{v_x} \quad (1.15.4)$$

$$= \int_{-\infty}^{\infty} v_x f_x(v_x)dv_x = 0$$

3.11.6

and

$$\overline{|v|} = \bar{v} \quad (1.15.6)$$

$$= \int_0^{\infty} v f(v)dv.$$

3.11.7

The quantity we called $\overline{|v_x|}$ (1.15.1 and 3.11.5) is obtained by noting that if a fraction $f_x(v_x)dv_x$ of molecules have velocities between v_x and v_x+dv_x, then an equal fraction have velocities in the same range of absolute magnitude but opposite direction, that is between $-v_x$ and $-(v_x+dv_x)$. Thus

$$\overline{|v_x|} \quad (1.15.1)$$

$$= 2\int_0^{\infty} v_x f_x(v_x)dv_x,$$

3.11.8

so that the number of impacts with unit area of the wall in unit time is

Γ   (1.15.3)

$$= n\int_0^\infty v_x f_x(v_x)dv_x,$$ 3.11.9

while the number of impacts per unit area and time by molecules which have velocity components between v_x and $v_x + dv_x$ is

$$\Gamma(v_x)dv_x = nv_x f(v_x)dv_x.$$ 3.11.10

§ 3.12   Problems

1. In the application of statistics to physics (and gambling) the important thing is to identify what events are equally likely. Discuss the following paradoxes:

(i) In two tosses of a single coin, what is the probability that heads will appear at least once? § 3.2 gave the answer $\frac{3}{4}$, but d'Alembert, a distinguished French mathematician of the eighteenth century, argued as follows: 'There are only 3 possible events: heads on the first throw; heads on the second throw; heads not at all. Now 2 of these 3 events – the first two – are favourable. Therefore the required probability is $\frac{2}{3}$.'

(ii) Three coins are tossed at once. What is the probability that all three come down alike – that is to say, that all three are either heads or tails? It could be argued that two of the coins must come down alike so that it is only necessary to consider the third; this can come down either head or tail and in either case the probability is $\frac{1}{2}$. The required probability is thus 1 (certainty) $\times \frac{1}{2} = \frac{1}{2}$. Alternatively, an argument based on § 3.2 might be that the probability of 3 heads is $(\frac{1}{2})^3$ and of 3 tails is $(\frac{1}{2})^3$, and since these events are mutually exclusive the required probability is $\frac{1}{8} + \frac{1}{8} = \frac{1}{4}$.

2. Reference was made in § 3.9 to the St Petersburg paradox (1713). Here Peter and Paul play a game with the following rules: a coin is tossed; if it comes down heads Peter gives Paul one shilling; if it comes down tails the coin is tossed again; if it now comes down heads Peter gives Paul two shillings. If the coin comes down tails a second time it is tossed a third time and if it comes down heads Paul receives 4 shillings. This continues indefinitely, the reward being doubled after every tail and the game ending when a head is thrown. The problem is to calculate Paul's expectation, or in other words to

calculate how much Peter would require Paul to pay him in order to have the privilege of playing.

Defining expectation as in § 3.9 gives

$$\langle E \rangle = \sum_{r=1}^{\infty} P_r p_r$$

$$= \sum_{r=1}^{\infty} 2^{r-1} (\tfrac{1}{2})^r$$

$$= \tfrac{1}{2} + \tfrac{1}{2} + \tfrac{1}{2} + \ldots (\text{to } \infty)$$

$$= \infty .$$

This answer is obviously fallacious though mathematicians are not agreed as to what the fallacy is. Northrop (reference below) suggests that the solution assumes that $P_r \rightarrow \infty$ as $r \rightarrow \infty$, so that there is no limit to the prize which banker Peter can pay if the run of tails is long enough. Since no bank can pay out an unlimited sum, we can correct the fallacious answer by setting an upper limit to Peter's liability say; 2^{20} shillings ($\simeq$ £50,000).

With this limit, show that Paul's expectation is now

$$\langle E \rangle = \sum_{r=1}^{21} 2^{r-1} (\tfrac{1}{2})^r + \tfrac{1}{2} \sum_{r=0}^{\infty} (\tfrac{1}{2})^r$$

$$= 11 \text{ shillings},$$

which is probably a reasonable sum to pay to play.

3. Six dice are shaken up together in a cup and thrown. Show that the probabilities of getting 0, 1, 2, 3, 4 sixes are in the ratios $5/6 : 1 : 1/2 : 2/15 : 1/50$.

Extend this to include the probabilities of 5 and 6 sixes and show the complete distribution as a histogram.

4. In the game of Crown and Anchor, the banker presides over a board marked with six symbols: spade, heart, diamond, club, crown and anchor, and gamblers are invited to bet on any symbol. Three dice are then thrown, each marked with one of these symbols on each face. For each symbol which lands uppermost, the investor on that symbol receives winnings equal to his stake; for example, if crowns land uppermost on two of the dice and an anchor on the third then stakes on the crown symbol are paid twice over, while those on the anchor symbol are paid once, in each case, of course, with stake money returned.

(i) Show that the banker must win.

(ii) Under current British gambling law the banker is not allowed to have any advantage. Show that the game could be made legal by simple changes in the odds.

(iii) Show that in the game as played at present, the banker stands to gain $17/216$ for each unit of stake money.

5. In the example discussed in § 2.12 a bundle of straws of varying lengths were tossed high in the air and allowed to fall across a crack in the floor. Show that when the straws have lengths distributed equally between 0 and l the ratio of the average lengths of those lying across the crack to the average length of all the straws is $4/3$.

6. In an imaginary gas all molecular speeds v from zero to V are equally probable. Find the mean speed and mean-square speed in terms of V and show that:

$$\bar{v}/(\overline{v^2})^{\frac{1}{2}} = 3^{\frac{1}{2}}/2 \simeq 0{\cdot}87 .$$

If this imaginary gas were allowed to escape from its container through a small hole, show that the mean energy of the molecules escaping is 50% larger than the mean energy of those remaining. (Use § 1.15.)

7. The mean of a large number of observations is $\bar{x}$. Show that

(i) $\overline{x^2} = \overline{x(x-1)}+\bar{x}$;

(ii) $\overline{\Delta x^2} \equiv \overline{(x-\bar{x})^2}$
$\qquad = \overline{x^2}-(\bar{x})^2.$

§ 3.13 Further reading

B. V. Gnedenko and A. Ya. Khinchin *An Elementary Introduction to the Theory of Probability* Dover Publications, New York, 1962.

Problems 3.12.1–2 together with many other paradoxes in probability are discussed in

E. P. Northrop *Riddles in Mathematics* Penguin Books, London, 1961.

Chapter 4

EXAMPLES OF DISTRIBUTIONS

We have already met the mean free path Λ in chapter 2 and have seen that, by use of such a simple concept, we can formulate explanations for the various transport phenomena in gases. The fact that there must be a distribution of free paths did not appear to affect the physical arguments although, as we saw in § 2.12, a presumed distribution might alter numerical factors.

Consider, however, a different type of transport process: one where a beam of particles is being attenuated by collisions with material lying in its path. For example, in a cathode ray tube, electrons passing from cathode to fluorescent screen may be deflected by collisions with residual gas molecules in the nominally evacuated tube; here we do not want to know the mean distance an electron goes without a collision but rather the condition whereby a high proportion of electrons may travel the length of the tube undeflected. At the other extreme, if we are shielding the surroundings of a nuclear reactor from its radiations we want to know how thick the shielding material must be in order to stop as many of the neutrons as possible.

We shall now obtain the distribution function for free paths, that is the function $f(s)ds$ which gives the fraction of free paths ending in distances between s and $s+ds$, first obtaining $f(s)$ by a physical argument based on our model of a gas of molecules which collide with each other. We shall later re-derive $f(s)$ by use of a purely mathematical model which gives less physical idea of what is happening but which, being more general, can be applied to other physical problems.

§ 4.1 Statistics of free paths

Consider n_0 molecules which have just suffered a collision, and let us find how the number of those which do not suffer a further collision is depleted with distance gone or with time.

First, the number of molecules dn which make a collision in distance ds is obviously proportional to the distance, the longer the distance the less survivors there will be at the end, that is

$$dn \propto (-ds),$$

where the minus sign indicates that the number of survivors goes down as distance increases.

Secondly, the number of molecules dn which make their first collision in the distance between s and $s+ds$ is proportional to the number which have survived to go distance s, that is

$$dn \propto n.$$

Combining these two proportions, we have

$$dn = -\alpha n\, ds, \qquad\qquad 4.1.1$$

where α is a positive constant. α obviously depends on the size of the molecules and their density in space.

We can rewrite equation 4.1.1 in probability terms by noting that the probability that a given molecule has *not* suffered a collision in distance s is, by our definition of probability, $n(s)/n_0$. Dividing both sides of 4.1.1 by n_0 gives

$$\frac{dn}{n_0} = -\alpha \frac{n}{n_0}\, ds, \qquad\qquad 4.1.2$$

which means that the probability that one of the original group of molecules makes a collision in distance s to $s+ds$ is equal to the product of the independent probabilities:

(i) that it has survived to distance s without a collision. This is $n(s)/n_0$.

(ii) that it collides in the distance s to $s+ds$. This is $(-\alpha\, ds)$.

Integrating 4.1.1 we have

$$n = \text{constant} \times e^{-\alpha s}.$$

Since at $s = 0$, $n = n_0$, the integration constant is clearly n_0, so the number of survivors after distance s is

$$n(s) = n_0\, e^{-\alpha s}, \qquad\qquad 4.1.3$$

and the probability of survival to distance s from the start of the free path is consequently

$$n(s)/n_0 = e^{-\alpha s}.$$

Now the fraction of free paths ending in s to $s+ds$ may be written

$f(s)ds$ and is measured by the difference between the fraction of survivors at distances s and $s+ds$. Thus

$$f(s)ds = \frac{n(s)}{n_0} - \frac{n(s+ds)}{n_0},$$

where $n(s+ds)$ can be expanded by Taylor's theorem * to give

$$n(s+ds) = n(s) + \frac{dn}{ds} ds,$$

whence by use of 4.1.3 we obtain

$$f(s)ds = \alpha \, e^{-\alpha s} \, ds. \qquad 4.1.4$$

As in the distribution function we met in § 3.10, there is no limit to the variable s. Thus, very long free paths are possible, though the exponential dependence makes long free paths very rare. We can check that f is already normalised by noting that it is certain that all free paths will be somewhere between zero and infinite length, that is

$$\int_0^\infty f(s)ds = \int_0^\infty \alpha \, e^{-\alpha s} \, ds = 1. \qquad 4.1.5$$

The mean free path s is given by

$$\bar{s} = \int_0^\infty \alpha s \, e^{-\alpha s} \, ds. \qquad 4.1.6$$

This integral can be evaluated by parts (§ 12.1) or by the methods of § 12.2, whence we obtain

$$\bar{s} = 1/\alpha.$$

Now $\bar{s}$ is the quantity we called Λ in chapter 2 so the fraction of free paths ending in s to $s+ds$ or the probability that a free path will end in s to $s+ds$ is given by the normalised distribution function

$$f(s)ds = \frac{1}{\Lambda} e^{-s/\Lambda} \, ds. \qquad 4.1.7$$

The function $f(s)$ is shown in *fig.* 4.1.

It is sometimes convenient to use an unnormalised function such as $n(s)$ from which we calculate the mean free path as

$$\bar{s} = \frac{\displaystyle\int_0^\infty n_0 s \, e^{-\alpha s} \, ds}{\displaystyle\int_0^\infty n_0 \, e^{-\alpha s} \, ds}. \qquad 4.1.8$$

---

* *Alternatively* we remember that
$$\frac{dn}{ds} = \frac{n(s+ds)-n(s)}{ds}.$$

There are special techniques for dealing with quotients of integrals having this form. These are given in § 12.3. Using these or elementary methods we obtain

$$\bar{s} = 1/\alpha = \Lambda,$$

which is the same result as before.

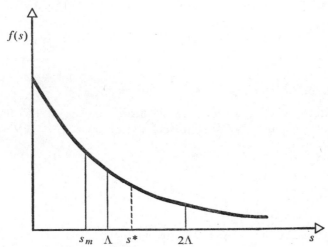

Figure 4.1. The distribution of free paths: the most probable free path is $s = 0$; the ordinates corresponding to $s = s_m$, $s = \Lambda$, and $s = 2\Lambda$ (§ 4.2) are shown. s^* is an arbitrary distance used in § 4.2.

It is easy to see that if we had considered the number of collisions as a function of time rather than distance, then we would have found that the fraction of flights ending in t to $t + dt$ is

$$f(t)dt = \frac{1}{\tau} e^{-t/\tau} dt,$$

where τ is the mean time of free flight.

The above statistical reasoning takes no account of the possibility that Λ might be different for free paths performed at different speeds. If so, there would be a different function f, with the same form as that in equation 4.1.7, for each speed. Now, we saw in § 2.3 that, for a gas of billiard-ball-type molecules, the effect of variation of Λ with v was to make a small and largely academic correction to the mean free path averaged over all molecules and free paths. With other entities where the hard-sphere model is not even roughly valid the dependence of Λ on v may be more spectacular and the variation of 4.1.7 with v more important. For example, fast neutrons are much more likely than slow ones to have long free paths, while for the slow neutrons the variation of free path with speed is not regular.

§ 4.2   Consideration of the distribution function for free paths

We can now consider the distribution function for free paths in more detail–more detail, indeed, than it merits except as an introduction to more important but mathematically intractable functions.

We find that

(i) the *most probable* free path is zero. The preponderance of short free paths is compensated for by the few long ones.

(ii) the *median* free path s_m, i.e. the distance such that half the free paths are longer and half shorter, is given by

$$\int_0^{s_m} e^{-s/\Lambda}\,ds = \int_{s_m}^{\infty} e^{-s/\Lambda}\,ds; \qquad 4.2.1$$

carrying out the integrations gives

$$s_m = \Lambda \ln 2 \simeq 0\cdot7\,\Lambda,$$

which again shows that free paths shorter than the mean are more probable. Alternatively the median s_m is the distance in which our original n_0 molecules have been reduced to half, that is

$$n_0\,e^{-s_m/\Lambda} = \tfrac{1}{2}n_0,$$

giving the same value for s_m as before. s_m is indicated in *fig.* 4.1.

(iii) the fraction of free paths which are some multiple of Λ, say $r\Lambda$, or longer is

$$\Lambda^{-1}\int_{r\Lambda}^{\infty} e^{-s/\Lambda}\,ds = e^{-r}, \qquad 4.2.2$$

from which we might calculate that e^{-1} or 37 % of free paths are greater than Λ, and e^{-5} or less than 1 % are greater than five times Λ.

(iv) the probability that a given molecule will make a collision in the next element of distance ds is unchanged however far it has gone. As a statistical statement this is the same as saying that the probability that an ideal coin will come down heads is still $\tfrac{1}{2}$ after it has come down heads many times running.

We can illustrate the apparent paradox in (iv) by calculating the mean free path $\bar{s}$ for molecules which have already gone the distance s^* (*fig.* 4.1). For these molecules:

$$\bar{s} = \frac{\displaystyle\int_{s^*}^{\infty} sn_0\, e^{-s/\Lambda}\, ds}{\displaystyle\int_{s^*}^{\infty} n_0\, e^{-s/\Lambda}\, ds}. \tag{4.2.3}$$

Note that we are here using an unnormalised function $n(s)$, since the normalisation of $f(s)$ carried out in equation 4.1.5 is not valid for the fraction of the original set in which we are now interested.

The integrals in 4.2.3 can each be evaluated by elementary means. It is however very convenient to use logarithmic differentiation (§ 12.3). Using this method we obtain (cancelling constant factors):

$$\bar{s} = -\frac{\partial}{\partial(1/\Lambda)} \ln \int_{s^*}^{\infty} e^{-s/\Lambda}\, ds$$

$$= -\frac{\partial}{\partial(1/\Lambda)} \ln (\Lambda\, e^{-s^*/\Lambda})$$

$$= s^* + \Lambda, \tag{4.2.4}$$

that is, the *selected group*, which has gone any distance s^*, has still Λ to go.

Similarly, if we could enquire of passing molecules how far they had come since the last collision the average answer would be Λ. And if they could subsequently inform us how far they got before the next collision the average distance would be Λ. We might thus conclude that the mean free path was 2Λ but, if we did so add mean free paths, we would be making the same fallacious argument as was discussed in § 2.12 in assuming that free paths which cross a given plane are typical of free paths as a whole. In § 2.12 this was illustrated by calculating the average length of straws which fell across a given line: we noted that the longer straws had a greater probability of falling across the reference line and that indeed the probability of so falling was proportional to the length. The result was that the average length of the selected straws was greater than that of straws in general.

In the distribution derived for free paths we may write that the probability that a path of length s intersects a given plane is Cs where

C is a constant. The average length of all paths which intersect the plane is then

$$\bar{s} = \frac{\displaystyle\int_0^\infty Cs^2 n(s)\,ds}{\displaystyle\int_0^\infty Csn(s)\,ds} \qquad\qquad 4.2.5$$

$$= 2\Lambda \qquad \text{when } n(s) = n_0\, e^{-s/\Lambda}.$$

In 4.2.5 as in 4.2.3 we have used the unnormalised form of the distribution function since the normalisation in 4.1.5 is not valid for this special group of free paths.

We may thus conclude that we obtain the same value of Λ by measuring distances between collisions (as we did in § 4.1) or by measuring the distances molecules go from the time they cross some arbitrary plane until they make their next collision.

§ 4.3 Exponential distribution with cut-off

Suppose that we have a distribution of lengths s given by

$$n(s)\,ds = n_0\, e^{-\alpha s}\,ds,$$

that is, the same as for free paths. Suppose, however, that the lengths are limited so that none can exceed s_0. This is in fact usually the case with gases, since the free path is limited by the dimensions of the vessel.

The mean limited free path is now

$$\bar{s} = \frac{\displaystyle\int_0^{s_0} s\, e^{-\alpha s}\,ds}{\displaystyle\int_0^{s_0} e^{-\alpha s}\,ds}$$

$$= \frac{1}{\alpha} - \frac{s_0}{e^{\alpha s_0} - 1}.$$

If $s_0 \to \infty$ then $\bar{s} \to 1/\alpha$, the same as obtained from 4.1.6.

If $s_0 \gg 1/\alpha$ the expression for $\bar{s}$ reduces to

$$\bar{s} = 1/\alpha - s_0\, e^{-\alpha s_0},$$

where the second term represents the reduction in mean free path produced by the absence of very long free paths. For example, if $s_0 = 5\Lambda \simeq 5/\alpha$, the reduction is $5e^{-5} \sim 1/30$, which is quite unnoticeable.

This is a useful general result, which shows that the mean of an exponential distribution is not affected by the presence or absence of the tail of the exponential. This means that provided the maximum of the distribution is not less than a few times the mean it is safe to replace the maximum and the upper limit of integration by ∞. The simplification of algebra is frequently considerable.

§ 4.4 Sequences of events

The discussion of the distribution of free paths in § 4.1 involved consideration of the probability that a molecule would fail to suffer a collision for a certain interval of time or distance and would then collide in the next short interval. The use of the word 'collision' tends to obscure the fact that the form of the distribution function is governed purely by the laws of probability and not by any assumptions about the mechanism of collision. The assumptions have to be brought in only when the constant Λ or τ has to be evaluated. We shall therefore attempt to derive a formula for the distribution of random events using a purely statistical model.

The essential fact about free paths is that they have equal probability of ending in any equal short interval of time. Say that the probability of ending in an interval t_0, where $t_0 \ll \tau$, is $p(t_0)$. We wish to calculate the probability that n intervals each t_0 will pass before the end of the free path.

The problem of the probable length of a sequence of events is of importance, not only in free-path statistics but in other branches of human activity. For example, in science: a nuclear particle counter records events at random intervals, what is the probability that a given time will elapse between counts? Or what is the probability that two independent counts will take place within the resolving time of the counter? In technology we have the telephone problem: calls arrive at an exchange at random intervals and last for random durations. What is the probability that a call will be lost because all available equipment is in use? In business we have insurance problems: a car may have an accident at any time; what is its expectation of accident-free life?

§ 4.5 Sequences of discrete events

Suppose that a specified event has just taken place as the result of a certain trial; for example, a coin has come down heads. We now ask

7

what is the probability that n trials will occur before the same event recurs?

If the probability of the event is p, then the probability it will not happen is $1-p$ and the required probability of a sequence of exactly n non-happenings is

$$P(n) = (1-p)^n p, \qquad \qquad 4.5.1$$

that is, the required probability is equal to the product of n independent events with probability $(1-p)$ followed by another independent event with probability p which terminates the sequence. For example, the probability that we shall make n throws of a die before a six is thrown is

$$\left(\tfrac{5}{6}\right)^n \cdot \tfrac{1}{6}.$$

The probability that the number of non-happenings is between 0 and ∞ is the sum of the probabilities of events each of which excludes all the others:

$$\sum_{n=0}^{\infty} P(n) = \sum_{n=0}^{\infty} (1-p)^n p$$

$$= p \sum_{n=0}^{\infty} (1-p)^n. \qquad \qquad 4.5.2$$

The sum in 4.5.2 is a simple geometric series, which converges since the ratio of successive terms, $1-p < 1$. The value of the sum is $1/p$. Thus

$$\sum_{n=0}^{\infty} P(n) = 1,$$

or a certainty, as it must be.

Similarly, the probability that there will be n trials between successive events is

$$P'(n) = (1-p)^{n-1} p. \qquad \qquad 4.5.3$$

P' is the probability of $n-1$ non-events followed by an event. Once again

$$\sum_{n=1}^{\infty} P'(n) = 1. \qquad \qquad 4.5.4$$

The mean number of trials between successive events with probability p is

$$\bar{n} = \sum_{n=1}^{\infty} n P'(n) = p \sum_{n=1}^{\infty} n(1-p)^{n-1}, \qquad \qquad 4.5.5$$

that is, the sum of the quantities whose mean we require, each multiplied by its probability of occurrence. The denominator in 4.5.5, which is the sum of these probabilities, is unity because of 4.5.4. The sum in 4.5.5 is easily evaluated by writing $1-p = q$, which gives

$$\sum_{n=1}^{\infty} n(1-p)^{n-1} = \sum_{n=1}^{\infty} nq^{n-1} = \frac{d}{dq} \sum_{n=0}^{\infty} q^n, \qquad 4.5.6$$

assuming that the infinite series can be differentiated term-by-term. Now

$$\frac{d}{dq} \sum_{n=0}^{\infty} q^n = \frac{d}{dq} \cdot \frac{1}{1-q} = \frac{1}{(1-q)^2} = \frac{1}{p^2}; \qquad 4.5.7$$

So $\qquad \bar{n} = 1/p,$ $\qquad\qquad\qquad\qquad\qquad$ 4.5.8

which is what we would have expected since by our definition of probability (3.2.1) p is the fraction of trials which yield events.

§ 4.6 Continuous sequences

We can now generalise the results of § 4.5 to a continuous distribution: suppose we have a very large number N of balls in a bag of which Np are red and $N(1-p) \gg Np$ are white. Then if we select balls at random (replacing the ball each time) the probability of a run of n white balls is

$$P(n) = (1-p)^n p. \qquad 4.6.1$$

The probability of a run of between n and $n+dn$ white balls will be the added probabilities of $n, n+1, n+2, \ldots, n+dn$. If, as we supposed, $p \ll 1$, then $P(n) \simeq P(n+1) \simeq P(n+2) \simeq \ldots \simeq P(n+dn)$, so the required probability is

$$P(n)dn = (1-p)^n p \, dn. \qquad 4.6.2$$

To obtain a more useful expression for $P(n)$ we write

$$P(n) = p(1-p)^{\bar{n}(n/\bar{n})}.$$

Substituting for p from 4.5.8 gives

$$P(n) = \frac{1}{\bar{n}} \left(1 - \frac{1}{\bar{n}} \right)^{\bar{n}(n/\bar{n})}. \qquad 4.6.3$$

Our hypothesis was that the probability p of drawing a red ball was very small. Thus the mean number of white balls drawn between successive reds is large, that is $\bar{n} \gg 1$. Now it is proved in § 12.4 that

$$\lim_{\bar{n} \to \infty} \left(1 - \frac{1}{\bar{n}} \right)^{\bar{n}} = e^{-1}. \qquad 4.6.4$$

So, provided $\bar{n}$ is large, we may tentatively write

$$P(n) = \frac{1}{\bar{n}} e^{-n/\bar{n}}, \qquad 4.6.5$$

and assuming that we can treat n as a continuous variable we may combine 4.6.2 and 4.6.5, giving

$$P(n)dn = \frac{1}{\bar{n}} e^{-n/\bar{n}} dn. \qquad 4.6.6$$

It is easy to see that $P(n)$ is still normalised, since

$$\int_0^\infty P(n)dn = 1,$$

and that $\bar{n}$ is the mean number of white balls in the sequence, that is

$$\int_0^\infty nP(n)dn = \bar{n}.$$

An alternative method of obtaining expression 4.6.5 for $P(n)$ will be useful later (§ 5.5). We write from 4.6.1

$$P(n+1) = (1-p)^{n+1}p,$$

so that

$$\frac{P(n+1)}{P(n)} = 1 - p. \qquad 4.6.7$$

Now, expanding $P(n+1)$ by Taylor's theorem we have

$$P(n+1) = P(n) + \frac{dP(n)}{dn}1 + \ldots. \qquad 4.6.8$$

We shall justify terminating* the series at the first term as soon as we have the form of $P(n)$. So

$$\frac{P(n+1)}{P(n)} = 1 + \frac{1}{P(n)} \frac{dP(n)}{dn}, \qquad 4.6.9$$

whence we obtain from 4.6.7

$$\frac{1}{P} \frac{dP}{dn} = -p,$$

which integrates to give

$$P(n) = P_0 e^{-np}, \qquad 4.6.10$$

* 4.6.8 is equivalent to writing $\frac{P(n+1)-P(n)}{(n+1)-n}$ as an approximation for dP/dn.

where P_0 is an integration constant and represents the value of $P(n)$ when $n = 0$.

Again having obtained the form of $P(n)$ we may note that

$$\frac{dP}{dn} = -P_0 p \, e^{-np},$$

$$\frac{d^2 P}{dn^2} = P_0 p^2 \, e^{-np},$$

and so on. So, since it is assumed that $p \ll 1$,

$$\left| \frac{d^2 P}{dn^2} \right| \ll \left| \frac{dP}{dn} \right|,$$

which justifies cutting off the Taylor series 4.6.8 at the first term.

Combining 4.6.10 and 4.6.2 now gives

$$P(n)dn = P_0 \, e^{-np} \, dn. \qquad\qquad 4.6.11$$

If we assume that we can treat n as a continuous variable and integrate with respect to n we can normalise this by writing

$$\int_0^\infty P(n)dn = 1,$$

or
$$P_0 \int_0^\infty e^{-np} \, dn = 1,$$

from which by elementary integration we obtain

$$P_0 = p,$$

as the definition of P_0 requires.

The mean number of white balls in a sequence is then

$$\bar{n} = p \int_0^\infty n \, e^{-np} \, dn$$

$$= 1/p,$$

which is the same result as we obtained in 4.5.3 for a sequence of discrete events.

Thus we finally obtain

$$P(n)dn = \frac{1}{\bar{n}} e^{-n/\bar{n}} \, dn, \qquad\qquad 4.6.12$$

the same result as 4.6.6.

§ 4.7 Application of sequence theory to free paths

To apply 4.6.6 to a physical problem, suppose that events occur at random intervals of n units of time or distance and that the mean number of units between events is $\bar{n}$. Then the probability that the time between successive events lies between t and $t+dt$ (or nt_0 and $nt_0 + t_0\, dn$, where t_0 is the unit of time) is

$$P(t)dt = \frac{1}{\tau} e^{-t/\tau}\, dt, \qquad\qquad 4.7.1$$

where $\tau(=\bar{n}t_0)$ is the mean time between events.

Similarly the probability that the distance between successive events is between s and $s+ds$ is

$$P(s)ds = \frac{1}{\Lambda} e^{-s/\Lambda}\, ds, \qquad\qquad 4.7.2$$

where Λ is the mean distance between successive events.

4.7.1 and 4.7.2 are the same formulae as we obtained for the statistics of free paths by a more physical argument. The fact that we have now obtained them by purely statistical reasoning shows that the 'collisions' are governed solely by the laws of chance. The only assumption is that the probability of collision of a gas molecule like that of selection of a red ball is the same at any instant and is unaffected by anything which happened at any other time.

§ 4.8 Application of sequence theory to nuclear physics and technology

Another physical problem to which we can apply our sequence formula is that of the intervals between the successive emissions from a radioactive source. Suppose, for example, we found that the mean interval between successive counts is τ, obtained by counting many radioactive events over a time many times τ. We can picture the process as one where we count the ticks of a clock at intervals t_0. At any given tick a radioactive event may not occur (nature has drawn a white ball) or an event may occur (a red ball is drawn). The probability of a red ball is always the same.

The results of sequence theory are clearly applicable to this model of radioactive emission, so the probability that time between t and $t+dt$ elapses between successive events is

$$P(t)dt = \frac{1}{\tau} e^{-t/\tau}\, dt. \qquad\qquad 4.8.1$$

Integrating this we find that the probability that the interval between successive counts will fall between t_1 and t_2 is

$$\int_{t_1}^{t_2} P(t)dt = \frac{1}{\tau}\int_{t_1}^{t_2} e^{-t/\tau}\, dt = e^{-t_1/\tau} - e^{-t_2/\tau}. \qquad 4.8.2$$

In particular the probability that two successive counts will occur in a time less than t_r is

$$\int_0^{t_r} P(t)dt = 1 - e^{-t_r/\tau}. \qquad 4.8.3$$

Formula 4.8.3 might be used to determine if the resolving time of the counting apparatus is adequate to record a given proportion of counts without losses due to recording rapid sequences of events as a single event. Formula 4.8.2 might be used to test if a sequence of events were really random.

Such a test appears to have been first carried out by Marsden and Barratt (1911), who analysed the distribution of intervals between the arrival of successive α-particles from a radioactive source. In all, 7563 particles were observed by watching scintillations on a fluorescent screen: the mean time between particles was $\tau = 1\cdot930$ sec. From 4.8.2, the expected number of particles arriving within 1 second of the preceding one is

$$n(0-1) = 7563\{\exp(0) - \exp(-1/1\cdot930)\} = 3059,$$

whereas the measured number was 3106. Similarly, if the assumption that particles arrive at random intervals is correct, the number arriving between 1 and 2 seconds after their predecessor is

$$n(1-2) = 7563\{\exp(-1/1\cdot930) - \exp(-2/1\cdot930)\}$$
$$= 1822.$$

The actual numbers of scintillations within these time limits was 1763.

Continuing thus, a table was constructed comparing the expected number in each time interval with the measured number. In each case agreement within the estimated experimental error (§ 11.6) was obtained, showing that the emission of α-particles occurs at random times: the emission of one particle has no influence on the emission or non-emission of another. The complete table of observations is given in problem 4.11.5.

More recently, similar methods have been used to investigate whether photons are emitted randomly from light sources. One might, for example, imagine that the emission of one photon triggers off an avalanche, or alternatively marks the beginning of a dead time during which emission is less probable. Results, using sources of low intensity, suggest that emission is random.

An example from another branch of science concerns fatigue life of structural components. When a solid is subjected to stresses of alternating sign it is found to fracture under a stress which, at maximum, is much less than that required to break it in a static test. The fatigue life, or the number of cycles of stress which the component can stand before it fractures, depends on the stress amplitude, and the normal process of fatigue testing requires measurement of mean fatigue life as a function of stress. However, if large numbers of apparently identical components are tested under the same stress and other conditions there is a wide scatter of measured fatigue lives about the mean, so it has been suggested that fatigue is a random process, that is, that the component has an equal chance of failure at each cycle. Enough evidence has perhaps not been collected to give full support to the suggestion. If correct it leaves us with the shattering thought that there is a finite probability that an aircraft structure subject to fatigue stresses might break up in the first few cycles instead of after some large fraction of the mean life.

§ 4.9   Angular distribution functions

An important type of distribution describes the probability that a certain direction lies within given angular limits. To take a definite example, consider a rod thrown down at random on a plane ruled with parallel straight lines: what is the probability $P_2(\theta)d\theta$ that the rod lies at an angle between θ and $\theta + d\theta$ to the rulings? Here the answer is easy, for, if the throwing is truly random, no angle is preferred and

$$P_2(\theta)d\theta = C\,d\theta,$$

where C is a constant which may readily be obtained by normalisation. Thus it is certain that the rod lies at some angle between 0 and π radians to the rulings and so

$$\int_0^\pi P_2(\theta)d\theta = \int_0^\pi C\,d\theta = C\pi = 1,$$

giving, for the normalised function,

$$P_2(\theta)d\theta = \frac{1}{\pi}\,d\theta, \qquad\qquad 4.9.1$$

the subscript 2 indicating two dimensions. If there had been a distinction between the two directions along the rod as, for example, if the rod were an arrow, the normalising factor would have been $1/2\pi$.

In three dimensions the corresponding probability is not quite so simple. Consider the probability that the direction of motion of a molecule is between θ and $\theta+d\theta$ to some given direction in space: suppose the molecule has velocity v and construct a sphere with radius numerically equal to v in any convenient units.

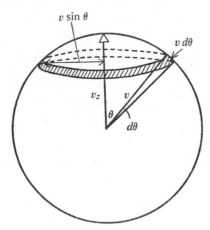

Figure 4.2. *Vector diagram used to obtain p(θ).*

Then, from *fig.* 4.2, the probability that the direction of the velocity vector v lies between θ and $\theta+d\theta$ to a given direction, say that of the north-polar vector v_z, is the same as the probability that the vector v intersects the sphere in the narrow band centred on v_z and shown shaded in the figure. The required probability is thus the ratio of the area of the band to the total area of the sphere, that is

$$P(\theta)d\theta = \frac{(2\pi v \sin \theta)(v\,d\theta)}{4\pi v^2}$$

$$= \tfrac{1}{2} \sin \theta \, d\theta. \qquad 4.9.2$$

Here $2\pi v \sin \theta$ is the circumference of the circle of latitude with radius $v \sin \theta$ and hence the length of the band. The width of the band is $v\,d\theta$, the element of arc between θ and $\theta+d\theta$.

The method of derivation of equation 4.9.2 shows that $P(\theta)$ is already normalised, but this may be confirmed by noting that

$$\int_0^\pi P(\theta)d\theta = \tfrac{1}{2}\int_0^\pi \sin \theta \, d\theta = 1,$$

where the integration is over all angles from the north pole ($\theta = 0$) to the south pole ($\theta = \pi$).

We now apply formulae 4.9.1–2 to specific problems. First suppose a rod of length l is thrown down at random on a plane ruled with an infinite set of parallel lines equally spaced a distance l apart. We use the two-dimensional distribution 4.9.1 to calculate the probability that the rod will intersect a line.

Assume first we know that the rod AB in *fig*. 4.3 lies at an angle θ to the lines, that is somewhere along the direction indicated by CD. The probability that it does *not* intersect a line is then the probability that the end A lies between C and a point $CD-l$ further along the rod; otherwise B will reach as far as D and the rod will intersect the line through D. This probability is then

$$\frac{CD-l}{CD} = \frac{l/\sin\theta - l}{l/\sin\theta} = 1 - \sin\theta,$$

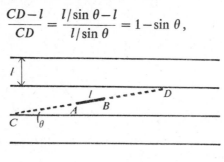

Figure 4.3. *Calculation of the probability that a rod of length l will intersect one of a system of parallel rulings.*

and the probability that, when the rod lies at angle θ to the lines, it does intersect one of them is consequently $\sin\theta$. This probability is independent of $P_2(\theta)d\theta$, the probability that the line lies within the angles θ and $\theta+d\theta$, so the probability of intersecting a line is

$$\frac{1}{\pi}\int_0^\pi \sin\theta \, d\theta = \frac{2}{\pi} \sim 0.64.$$

Similarly the probability that the rod does not intersect a line is

$$1 - \frac{2}{\pi} \simeq 0.36.$$

If a second set of parallel lines is drawn so as to divide the plane up into squares, the probability that the rod at angle θ to the first set will *not* intersect it is still $(1 - \sin\theta)$. The probability that the same

rod does not intersect the second, perpendicular set is similarly
$(1 - \cos \theta)$, but here a little care is required since $\cos \theta$ becomes
negative for values of θ between $\frac{1}{2}\pi$ and π. We can take care of this
and avoid the absurdity of probabilities greater than unity by writing
this probability as $(1 + \cos \theta)$ in the range $\frac{1}{2}\pi \leqslant \theta \leqslant \pi$. The probability
of missing both sets of lines is thus

$$\frac{1}{\pi}\int_0^{\pi/2} (1 - \sin \theta)(1 - \cos \theta)d\theta + \frac{1}{\pi}\int_{\pi/2}^{\pi} (1 - \sin \theta)(1 + \cos \theta)d\theta$$

$$= \frac{1}{\pi}\int_0^{\pi} (1 - \sin \theta)d\theta - \frac{2}{\pi}\int_0^{\pi/2} (1 - \sin \theta) \cos \theta \, d\theta$$

$$= 1 - \frac{2}{\pi} - \frac{2}{\pi} + \frac{1}{\pi}$$

$$= 1 - \frac{3}{\pi}$$

$$\simeq 0.05. \qquad\qquad 4.9.3$$

The interesting thing about this result is that the probability of missing
both sets of lines is not the multiplied probabilities of missing each of
the two sets. This would be

$$\left(1 - \frac{2}{\pi}\right)^2 = 1 - \frac{2}{\pi} - \frac{2}{\pi} + \frac{4}{\pi^2} = 0.13, \qquad\qquad 4.9.4$$

and the difference is that here the two probabilities are not independent. In particular, for values of θ around 0 and $\frac{1}{2}\pi$, where the rod is
least likely to intersect one set, it is most likely to intersect the other.
Writing out the two possible values for the combined probability in
the forms of sums of four terms, as in 4.9.4, serves to show where the
difference lies.

§ 4.10 Applications of angular distributions to kinetic theory

We now apply equation 4.9.2 to the solution of some problems left
over from chapters 1 and 2. First consider the number of molecules
colliding with unit area of a surface in unit time: this was (equation
1.15.3)

$$\Gamma = \tfrac{1}{2}n \, |\overline{v_x}|, \qquad\qquad 4.10.1$$

and we left the problem of relating $|\overline{v_x}|$ to $\bar{v}$ undone. Now any given
v_x is related to v by

$$v_x = v \cos \theta, \qquad\qquad 4.10.2$$

where θ is the angle between the x-direction and the direction of motion (*fig.* 4.4).

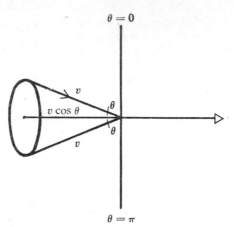

$$\theta = 0$$

$$\theta = \pi$$

Figure 4.4. *Directions of motion of molecules crossing a given plane. Note that* $0 \leqslant \theta \leqslant \pi/2$ *covers all space on the left of the plane.*

Now $|\overline{v_x}|$ was defined by (1.15.1)

$$|\overline{v_x}| = \frac{1}{N}\{|v_{1x}|+|v_{2x}|+ \ldots +|v_{Nx}|\} \qquad 4.10.3$$

$$= \frac{1}{N}\{v_1 \cos \theta_1 + v_2 \cos \theta_2 + \ldots + v_N \cos \theta_N\}, \qquad 4.10.4$$

every term in this series being taken positive and every molecule being represented by a separate term.

We are now to average over two variables v and θ, and may proceed as follows: first take all v positive, that is deal with speeds not velocities, and pick out those terms in the series where the speed is between v and $v+dv$. There will be $Nf(v)dv$ such terms. Of these a fraction,

$$P(\theta)d\theta = \tfrac{1}{2}\sin \theta d\theta,$$

belong to molecules with trajectories at angles between θ and $\theta+d\theta$ to the x-direction and consequently appear in 4.10.4 as $v \cos \theta$. The mean x-component of speed for the group considered is thus

$$v\left\{\int_0^{\pi/2} \cos \theta \, P(\theta)d\theta - \int_{\pi/2}^{\pi} \cos \theta \, P(\theta)d\theta\right\},$$

where both terms in the bracket have been made positive as required, by the same device as in 4.9.3. The mean is then

$$2 \times \tfrac{1}{2}v \int_0^{\pi/2} \cos \theta \sin \theta \, d\theta = \tfrac{1}{2}v,$$ 4.10.5

and the sum in 4.10.4 becomes

$$|\overline{v_x}| = \frac{1}{N} \times N \int_0^\infty \tfrac{1}{2}vf(v)dv$$
$$= \tfrac{1}{2}\bar{v}$$

and

$$\Gamma = \tfrac{1}{4}n\bar{v},$$ 4.10.6

the factor $\tfrac{1}{4}$ replacing the $\tfrac{1}{6}$ provisionally adopted in § 1.15. Another derivation of the factor $\tfrac{1}{4}$ is given in § 5.10.

The averaging over the two variables θ and v involves a double integration, which in this case can simply be split into two separate integrals since the terms in θ are entirely independent of those in v (this is implied by our assumption of molecular chaos).

This rather laboured derivation can be formally simplified by noting that what is really wanted is the quantity called $\vec{v}_x$ in 1.15.5, that is the sum of the x-components of velocity of those molecules which approach the plane at angles to its normal between 0 and $\pi/2$, divided by the *total* number of molecules. Thus

$$\Gamma = \tfrac{1}{2}n|\overline{v_x}| = n\vec{v}_x$$
$$= n \frac{\int_{v=0}^{v=\infty} \int_{\theta=0}^{\theta=\pi/2} vf(v) \cos \theta \, P(\theta)d\theta dv}{\int_{v=0}^{v=\infty} \int_{\theta=0}^{\theta=\pi} f(v)P(\theta)d\theta dv},$$ 4.10.7

where the different limits on the integrals in numerator and denominator stress the observation made in § 1.15 that $\vec{v}_x$ is not a true average. Inserting

$$P(\theta) = \tfrac{1}{2} \sin \theta$$ 4.10.8

and separating the integrations gives

$$\Gamma = n \frac{\left[\int_0^\infty vf(v)dv\right]\left[\int_0^{\pi/2} \tfrac{1}{2} \cos \theta \sin \theta \, d\theta\right]}{\left[\int_0^\infty f(v)dv\right]\left[\int_0^\pi \tfrac{1}{2} \sin \theta \, d\theta\right]}.$$

Both integrals in the denominator are unity if the functions f and $P(\theta)$ are assumed to be normalised, whence evaluating the integrals in the numerator gives

$$\Gamma = \tfrac{1}{4}n\bar{v}.$$

If we keep in mind that integrations giving the numbers of molecules crossing a plane are to be such as to take account of molecules coming from one side only, although the functions used are normalised over the whole sphere, we may write the number crossing unit area in unit time at angles to the normal between θ and $\theta + d\theta$, and with speeds between v and $v + dv$, as

$$\Gamma(v, \theta)dvd\theta = \tfrac{1}{2}nvf(v) \cos \theta \sin \theta \, d\theta dv. \qquad 4.10.9$$

The number crossing with given speed v and in the same angular range is

$$\Gamma(\theta)d\theta = \tfrac{1}{2}nv \cos \theta \sin \theta \, d\theta. \qquad 4.10.10$$

Now, when the x-component of momentum of a molecule is reversed on reflection from a wall, the change of momentum is

$$2mv_x = 2mv \cos \theta, \qquad 4.10.11$$

so that the change of momentum per unit area and unit time, that is the pressure, is (inserting 4.10.11 in 4.10.9 and integrating):

$$p = \tfrac{1}{2} \times 2mn \int_{v=0}^{v=\infty} \int_{\theta=0}^{\theta=\pi/2} v^2 f(v) \cos^2 \theta \sin \theta \, d\theta \, dv,$$

the integration with respect to θ being over the range 0 to $\tfrac{1}{2}\pi$ for the same reasons as before. Separating the integrations gives

$$p = mn \left[\int_0^\infty v^2 f(v)dv \right] \left[\int_0^{\pi/2} \cos^2 \theta \sin \theta \, d\theta \right]$$

$$= \tfrac{1}{3}mn\bar{v^2} \qquad 4.10.12$$

$$= \tfrac{1}{3}\rho\bar{v^2},$$

the same result as 1.2.7 or 1.2.13.

Next consider the quantity v_r, defined in § 2.2 as the mean speed of molecules relative to each other and treated in an elementary way in § 2.3. As in § 2.3, suppose we have two molecules moving with the same speed v but in directions an angle θ apart. Their relative velocity is shown in *fig.* 4.5 to be the vector difference of the velocities of the molecules.

The magnitude of this vector is the relative speed v_r and is

$$v_r = 2v \sin \tfrac{1}{2}\theta. \qquad\qquad 4.10.13$$

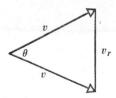

Figure 4.5. Vector diagram for molecular velocities.

The mean relative speed is obtained by using the function $P(\theta)d\theta$ (4.9.2) to average over all directions of relative motion. Thus

$$\bar{v}_r = 2v \int_0^{\pi} \sin \tfrac{1}{2}\theta \, P(\theta)d\theta \,,$$

the integration here going from 0 to π as in the normalisation of $P(\theta)$. Inserting the value of $P(\theta)$ gives

$$\bar{v}_r = v \int_0^{\pi} \sin \tfrac{1}{2}\theta \sin \theta \, d\theta$$

$$= 2v \int_0^{\pi} \sin^2 \tfrac{1}{2}\theta \cos \tfrac{1}{2}\theta \, d\theta$$

$$= 4v \int_0^{\pi} \sin^2 \tfrac{1}{2}\theta \, d(\sin \tfrac{1}{2}\theta)$$

$$= \tfrac{4}{3}v, \qquad\qquad 4.10.14$$

the result quoted as equation 2.3.1.

In § 2.3 we saw why the distribution of speeds of two colliding molecules could not be allowed for by simply writing $\bar{v}$ for v in equation 4.10.14. We shall not pursue this refinement, which would involve averaging of the functions $f(v)dv$ for two separate molecules, and simply requote the result (2.3.2) that when this averaging is done the result is to replace the $\tfrac{4}{3}$ in equation 4.10.14 by $\sqrt{2}$, that is,

$$\bar{v}_r = \sqrt{2}\,\bar{v},$$

the correction being purely academic.

Finally let us reconsider the elementary derivation of the transport parameters introduced in § 2.5. Here we assumed that a molecule transported some property across a reference plane, the property being that corresponding to a plane one mean free path Λ away from the reference plane. Now, as mentioned in § 2.11, molecules will be crossing the reference plane at angles other than right angles so, even taking no account of the distribution of free paths, most of them will be transporting the properties of planes nearer than Λ away.

Consider, for definiteness, the calculation of the viscosity given in § 2.7. Our derivation of equation 2.7.3 gave the net rate of momentum transfer per unit area as

$$F = 2 \times \tfrac{1}{6}nm\bar{v}\frac{du}{dz}\Lambda, \qquad\qquad 4.10.15$$

where $m(du/dz)$ is the gradient of momentum. Gradients of thermal energy or composition would be treated in exactly the same way. We now know (4.10.7) that the factor $\tfrac{1}{6}$ should be replaced by $\tfrac{1}{4}$ and we wish to replace Λ by some other mean distance $\bar{s}$ which takes account of oblique transits of the reference plane. Equation 4.10.15 has thus become

$$F = 2 \times \tfrac{1}{4}nm\bar{v}\frac{du}{dz}\bar{s}.$$

To obtain $\bar{s}$ we recall from equation 4.10.10 that the number of molecules with speed v crossing unit area at angles between θ and $\theta + d\theta$ to the normal is

$$\Gamma(\theta)d\theta = \tfrac{1}{2}nv \cos \theta \sin \theta \, d\theta.$$

If we assume that all molecules have the same free path Λ then all of these have come from a distance Λ away in the direction at angle θ to the normal. They will thus be transporting the momentum corresponding to the plane at distance $s = \Lambda \cos \theta$ to the reference plane, so

$$\bar{s} = \frac{\displaystyle\int_0^{\pi/2} \tfrac{1}{2}nv(\Lambda \cos \theta) \cos \theta \sin \theta \, d\theta}{\displaystyle\int_0^{\pi/2} \tfrac{1}{2}nv \cos \theta \sin \theta \, d\theta}, \qquad\qquad 4.10.16$$

where the denominator is required since the function Γ is not a normalised function. We further note that $\bar{s}$ is a true average, so the limits of integration are the same in numerator and denominator. Simple integrations give

$$\bar{s} = \tfrac{2}{3}\Lambda, \qquad\qquad 4.10.17$$

so that the formula, replacing 2.7.3, for the viscous force F per unit area is

$$F = 2 \times \tfrac{1}{4} nmv(\tfrac{2}{3}\Lambda)\frac{du}{dz}$$

$$= \tfrac{1}{3} nm\bar{v}\Lambda\frac{du}{dz}, \qquad\qquad 4.10.18$$

or the same formula as before. The formula for the coefficient of viscosity is likewise unchanged. Result 4.10.18 is in fact correct, though a more rigorous derivation would have taken account of the distributions of free paths and molecular speeds. The elementary formulae for the other transport parameters are likewise unchanged by the considerations of this section.

§ 4.11 Problems

1. Show that 63 % of all free flights of gas molecules last for less than the mean time of free flight.

2. In a certain apparatus (like a cathode ray tube) electrons are emitted from one end and it is required that a fraction $1 - x$ of them should reach the other end, a distance l away, without suffering a collision with a gas molecule.

   (i) Show that the necessary mean free path of the electrons in the gas can be written

   $\Lambda \simeq l/x$ if $x \ll 1$.

   (ii) Find a formula, akin to 2.2.3 giving Λ for electrons in a gas. Remember that electrons are much smaller than atoms and, in apparatus of this type, have energies of the order of thousands of electron volts.

   (iii) If $x = 1 \%$ and $l = 1$ metre, estimate the pressure required in microns $(1\ \mu\mathrm{m} = 10^{-3}\ \mathrm{mm})$ of mercury.

   (iv) Insert the value of Λ in the relation obtained in (i) and show that, under the conditions specified, x is simply the ratio of the cross sectional area of all the gas molecules to the cross sectional area of the container.

3. Assuming that our atmosphere is at a constant temperature throughout, find the height at which the pressure is $1/100$ of that at sea level. (*Answer*: about 46 km.)

   At that height, what will be the relative concentrations of nitrogen and oxygen?

8

4. In a model designed to account for electrical conductivity, particles with charge q and mass m move at random making collisions at mean intervals τ where τ is derived from distribution 4.7.1. In a gas or a liquid electrolyte, these charge-carrying particles would be ions colliding with other ions or with uncharged molecules; in a metal, the charge carriers are assumed to be electrons colliding with the ions of the metallic lattice.

When a field of strength E is applied, the charge carriers experience a force qE in the direction of the field (or against it if q is negative) and hence experience an acceleration $a = qE/m$ for a time t until their next collision. Thus in time t, they drift a distance $\frac{1}{2} at^2$. Show that the mean drift velocity is

$$\bar{u} = \frac{\frac{1}{2}a\overline{t^2}}{\bar{t}} = a\tau \qquad\qquad 4.11.1$$

so that the mobility μ, defined as the drift velocity per unit force is

$$\mu = \tau/m. \qquad\qquad 4.11.2$$

In conductivity theory, it is more usual to define the mobility as the drift velocity per unit field, in which case it is given by

$$\mu_{\text{field}} = q\tau/m. \qquad\qquad 4.11.3$$

The former definition is more general and is the one used in the discussion of the Einstein relation in problem 6.11.2.

In the early days of the electron theory of metals and in modern popular expositions of it, the distribution of free flights is often ignored giving, instead of 4.11.1,

$$\bar{u} = \frac{1}{2}a\tau,$$

the intrusive factor $\frac{1}{2}$ appearing in the formula for electrical conductivity.

5. Rutherford and Geiger placed a disc coated with polonium inside an evacuated tube closed at one end by a zinc sulphide screen. Scintillations, produced when α-particles from the polonium struck the screen, were observed and recorded by marking a chronograph tape. The times between the arrival of successive particles, measured from the tape, were analysed by Marsden and Barratt (*Proc. Phys. Soc. London,* **23,** 367 (1911)) by the method described in § 4.8.

Complete table 6 which gives these results and show that the assumption of random emission is justified. A further discussion of Rutherford and Geiger's results appears in § 11.6 and in problem 11.7.3.

TABLE 6 : nuclear counting data

Total number of intervals = 7,564
Total time = 14,598 sec
Average interval = 1·930 sec

duration of interval between successive scintillations, sec	number of intervals	
	experimental	calculated
0·0 to 1·0	3,106	3,059
1·0 to 2·0	1,763	1,822
2·0 to 3·0	1,115	
3·0 to 4·0	658	
4·0 to 5·0	389	
5·0 to 6·0	206	
6·0 to 7·0	130	
7·0 to 8·0	86	
8·0 to 9·0	42	
9·0 to infinity	68	

6. A rod of length $2l$ is thrown at random on to a plane ruled with an infinite system of parallel lines uniformly spaced a distance l apart. What is the probability that it will intersect a line? Uncritical use of the argument in § 4.9 would give the answer $2 \times 2/\pi = 1·27$, which is obviously wrong, since a probability cannot be greater than 1. Moreover, no matter how long the rod may be, there is always a finite probability that it will fall between adjacent lines without intersecting either of them. The correct answer $[\frac{2}{3}+(4-2\sqrt{3})/\pi \simeq 0·84]$ is obtained by noting that, while the angle of the rod to the lines is governed by the expression $P_2(\theta)$, a rod of length ml will certainly intersect a line if the angle θ is such that $\sin \theta > 1/m$. For such angles the probability of intersection is simply the probability that the rod falls at that angle. A rod of length $2l$ may intersect more than one line and the mean number of intersections is in fact 1·27.

§ 4.12 Further reading

P. D. Present *The Kinetic Theory of Gases* McGraw-Hill, New York and London, 1958.

Chapter 5

THE MAXWELL–BOLTZMANN DISTRIBUTION

§ 5.1 The scope of statistical physics

The last chapter introduced the idea that purely statistical methods could give the answers to physical problems. Thus, if we assumed that events such as radioactive disintegrations or the passage of cosmic rays occurred at times governed purely by the laws of probability we could calculate the chances of significant deviations from the average time between successive events. Conversely if we measured how the times between events were distributed, we could satisfy ourselves that the events were truly random. We now apply the same methods to other typical problems in physics. In general these problems will involve very large numbers of entities so that it will not be possible to count them one-by-one to test our hypotheses as we could with nuclear radiations. We shall however be able to devise indirect experimental tests of our results.

Typical problems in statistical physics are:

(i) What is the most probable distribution of gas molecules within their container? Here we may expect the answer to be that a uniform distribution, such that the number of particles per unit volume is the same everywhere, is the most probable.

(ii) What are the chances of observing a non-uniform distribution? We realise that since we are dealing with individual particles, equal small volumes may not always contain the same numbers of particles; in particular, since the particles of a gas themselves occupy only a small fraction of the volume there will be volumes with no particles at all. On the other hand we shall expect that it is extremely unlikely that all the molecules in a container should crowd into one half.

(iii) What is the most probable distribution of the energies or velocities of gas molecules?

(iv) What is the most probable distribution of impurity atoms in a crystal?

(v) What is the most probable distance from its starting point, of a particle moving in Brownian motion or diffusing in a solid? All these problems and many others can be answered using only statistical methods together with conservation laws. No other assumptions are required other than the assumption that we can apply statistical methods. The test of this asumption is, as always, in the success of our predictions.

In each case, all the probability theory we require is summed up in the problem: given N boxes and n balls, what are the relative probabilities of the various ways in which the balls can be distributed over the boxes? Thus in problems (i) and (ii) described above, we may imagine the space in the container divided up into N boxes and the problem is reduced to enumerating the possible configurations. We shall find, as we found in our coin-tossing investigations, that some configurations are much more likely than others. In (iii) the balls will again be molecules but the boxes will represent different energies and the problem will be to distribute the molecules over the energies subject to the total energy being constant. In (iv) the boxes will be sites in the crystal lattice and the balls will be of two kinds – ordinary atoms and impurity atoms. An additional factor will arise here since now each box can contain one ball only. Finally in (v) we may picture the possible positions of the randomly-moving particle to be arranged like the compartments in an egg-crate, the ball or particle making random jumps from one compartment to any neighbouring compartment.

We may note that the method used in § 4.5 in discussion of the probability of a sequence of events is another example of the statistical use of balls and boxes. Here we had only two boxes and one kind of ball, one box had probability p of receiving a ball, the other had probability $1 - p$.

§ 5.2 Distribution of gas molecules in space

We begin by considering how the molecules of a gas are distributed in their containing vessel. We divide the vessel into two equal parts by an imaginary partition and adopt the hypothesis that the presence or absence of a given molecule in one half of the container is governed by pure chance and is the same no matter how many molecules are already there. This is true for a perfect gas at any pressure and for any gas at not too high pressure. Thus the probability that the given molecule is in a given half is $\frac{1}{2}$. To satisfy conservation of molecules we require that the probability that it is in one half or the other is $\frac{1}{2}+\frac{1}{2} = 1$. We may remark in passing that if the compartments had not been equal then the probability p that a given molecule goes into the compartment with volume v is

$$p = v/V,$$

where V is the volume of the whole vessel. Our choice of v, which makes $p = \frac{1}{2}$, serves to simplify the algebra and leave the physical arguments more obvious. The algebra required for $p \neq \frac{1}{2}$ is given in § 11.2. We may now transfer the problem to one where balls are put into one or other of two boxes according to whether a coin comes down heads or tails. We wish to find the most probable distribution and, as in the case of the coin tosses discussed in § 3.4, we can adopt one of two methods. In the first we might make up a large number of copies of the model; that is, we would have a large number of pairs of equal boxes and the same number of sets of balls, and we would put the balls of each set into one or other of each pair of boxes by our random method. For example we might toss a coin to decide the fate of each ball. We would then find the average number of balls in the left hand box, say, by counting the number in all such boxes and dividing by the number of copies. This average is then an average over the large number of copies. By dividing the large number of copies into smaller groups and finding how much the average varies from group to group we would obtain a measure of the size of the fluctuations to be expected from the average.

The other method we might adopt is to use only two boxes, put in the balls by the same random method and record the results. We then take the balls out, or alternatively take out a number of balls determined by chance, replace them by the same method and again record the results. The average number of balls in the left-hand box would then be a time average obtained by averaging over our records. The fluctuations would be measured by averages taken from time to time. This second method is nearer to what happens in a real gas where we can picture the molecules moving at random within each compartment and from compartment to compartment so that, in time, the system will run through all possible complexions. In the case of the balls, we may reasonably assume that the statistical data obtained by averaging over the copies will be the same as those obtained by the time averages. In the same way, we assumed in chapter 3 that we should obtain the same average number of heads by tossing and retossing a small batch of coins as by a single toss of a large batch.

In general it is more convenient to take our averages by the former method, that is by writing down all the possible configurations and seeing which occur most frequently. This is exactly what we did in the discussions of coin tossing in chapter 3.

Thus if we have N balls and put them in one of two boxes accord-ing to the spin of a coin–heads for the left-hand box, tails for the right-hand–then the probability that all the balls go in the left-hand box is the same as the probability of getting all heads from N tosses of a coin, that is $(\frac{1}{2})^N$. This is very much less than the probability of a mixture of n heads and $N-n$ tails, which we saw (equation 3.2.3) was

$$(\tfrac{1}{2})^N \, {}^N C_n = (\tfrac{1}{2})^N \frac{N!}{n!(N-n)!} \equiv (\tfrac{1}{2})^N w_n; \qquad 5.2.1$$

–how much less, we have already seen in § 3.3 for quite small values of N and n. Equation 5.2.1 defines w_n as the number of *distinguishable* ways of distributing the balls between the boxes, where exchanging two balls between boxes is distinguishable; exchanging two balls within the same box is not. With only two boxes

$$w_n = {}^N C_n. \qquad 5.2.2$$

In accord with § 3.3 we call each of the $w_n \equiv \dfrac{N!}{n!(N-n)!}$ arrange-ments of n balls in one box and $N-n$ in the other a *complexion* and the set of all these w_n complexions a *configuration*. Since w_n can range from unity when $N = n$ (all balls in one box) to huge numbers when $n \simeq \frac{1}{2}N$ we shall expect that some configurations are much more probable than others even though the probability of finding any given ball in a given box is still $\frac{1}{2}$ and the probability of all complexions is the same. This gives the obvious result that we are unlikely to find that we have put all the balls into one box. Applying this result to a gas and making the assumption that the gas spends equal time in each complexion we infer that we are unlikely to find that all the molecules have spontaneously moved to one half of the container.

In the context of the last paragraph 'unlikely' means that 'while not impossible it will never happen'. Thus as we shall see in § 5.3, with only 20 balls the ratio of the probability of the most probable, ten-a-side configuration, to that of the least probable (20–0) exceeds 10^5, while with 100 balls the corresponding ratio exceeds 10^{29}. Applying the latter figure to molecules, we remember from § 2.2 that each molecule in a gas at N.T.P. makes $\sim 10^9$ free paths per second, so we may tentatively take 10^{-9} seconds as the lifetime of each complexion. Thus only once in 10^{20} seconds would the 100-0 configuration arise: the age of the Earth (10^{10} years) is less than 10^{18} seconds. When the numbers of molecules approach those which are found in real volumes of real gases ($10^{19}/cm^3$ at N.T.P.) the corresponding ratio of probabilities is inconceivably small.

But suppose now we deliberately start out from an improbable configuration, for example one in which all the balls are in the left-hand box. We now take balls out one at a time and toss a coin to decide whether each goes back in the left-hand box or moves to the right. We would expect that only about half would have to be replaced in the left-hand box and that in consequence balls will appear in the right-hand box. If we continue to take balls at random and decide their fate by chance, some of the right-hand balls will have the opportunity of returning to the left hand but there will be a net movement from left to right simply because there are more balls on the left than on the right and they have a correspondingly larger chance of being able to change boxes. Eventually the distribution between the boxes will tend to equality, after which equal numbers will go in each direction. It is important to realise that the tendency to fill up the empty box is entirely due to there being a greater number of left-hand balls available to make random movements. It is not that nature abhors an empty box.

Referring the above discussion to the case of a gas we see that we have a model which can explain effusion of gas through a hole from a vessel into an empty space. Phenomenologically we might introduce a concept such as pressure to give the direction of flow and measure the rate of flow, but pressure is simply a measure of the number of molecules on either side of the partition, that is of the relative probability of passing through it. Similarly, if there were no pressure difference but there were different molecules on either side, say type L on the left and type R on the right, then there will be a net flow of L to the right simply because there are more L-type molecules on the left available to move to the right than there are L-type molecules on the right with the possibility of moving left. The net flow of R-type molecules is in opposite sense until eventually the concentrations become the same on both sides. This is the phenomenon of inter-diffusion considered from a free-path point of view in § 2.8 and § 2.10, and from a random walk point of view in § 6.4.

The same model can be used to explain evaporation or sublimation. Here our model is that one box is full and represents the condensed (solid or liquid) phase, the other starts out empty. Once again we remove molecules from the full box and apply a method based on chance to decide whether they go back to the original box or into the other box. The difference is that the probabilities are no longer equal – there is a greater probability that the balls go into the 'condensed phase' box than into the 'gas' box, the relative probability being measured by the strength of the binding between molecules in the condensed phase. By this simple model we shall calculate the vapour pressure in § 10.4.

In each case the principle is the same: we enumerate all the possible configurations; we then apply our model to gas molecules by assuming that the gas will in time pass through all the complexions. Some configurations will occur so much more frequently than others that we can expect that they and they alone will represent the observable state of the gas.

If we start from an improbable configuration then the laws of probability tell us that it will tend to one of greatest probability, which is the state of equilibrium. Since equilibrium is produced by chance changes, we shall expect that there will be fluctuations from the most probable configuration: for example, the number of molecules in the two halves of our container will seldom be quite equal. This means that the pressure in each half will fluctuate about an average. With sensitive apparatus we may be able to detect these fluctuations but normally pressure-measuring devices are sluggish and provide only an average value, the average of the instantaneous pressures taken over relatively long periods of time. It is such a time average that we are seeking to calculate by our statistical methods. We assume that this time average can be found by the easier method of averaging over a large number of copies of the system.

§ 5.3 Small numbers of molecules

It is instructive to begin by actually listing the possibilities for a simple system in full, for example the number of ways in which four balls can be distributed over two boxes. If we take each ball in turn and decide by tossing a coin which box it is to go into, then we have already enumerated the possibilities in line 4 of Pascal's triangle (§ 3.3).

The probability of four heads—all balls in the left-hand box—is $(\frac{1}{2})^4 = \frac{1}{16}$; that of three heads and one tail is $(\frac{1}{2})^4 \frac{4!}{3!\,1!} = (\frac{1}{2})^4 \times 4$— and so on. All the various possibilities are drawn out in *fig.* 5.1, where it will be noted that HHHT is a separate complexion from HHTH and so on, for we are assuming that we can distinguish which of the four balls is in the right-hand box. On the other hand we do not count permutations of the same balls within the same box as separate complexions. Then we note that all the 2^4 complexions are accounted for and that all possibilities have been listed since the number of complexions in each configuration, that is 1, 4, 6, 4, 1, respectively, are the coefficients of $(\frac{1}{2})^4$ in the expansion of $(\frac{1}{2}+\frac{1}{2})^4$.

coins	box L	box R	number of complexions in each configuration
HHHH	①②③④		1
HHHT	①②③	④	
HHTH	①② ④	③	
HTHH	① ③④	②	4
THHH	②③④	①	
HHTT	①②	③④	
HTHT	① ③	② ④	
HTTH	① ④	②③	
THHT	②③	① ④	6
THTH	② ④	① ③	
TTHH	③④	①②	
HTTT	①	②③④	
THTT	②	① ③④	
TTHT	③	①② ④	4
TTTH	④	①②③	
TTTT		①②③④	1

totals over all 16 copies	32	32	
average number per box	2	2	

Figure 5.1. *The* 16 *complexions of four balls in two boxes.*

We can then regard *fig.* 5.1 as being 16 copies of our system of 2 boxes and 4 balls. Averaging over the 16 copies we find that the average number of balls in a box is 2, as of course it must be, since we listed the possibilities by using *a priori* probabilities. We may also conclude that there are 14 chances of a more-or-less uniform configuration (1–3 balls in a box) against only 2 for the improbable configurations at top and bottom. All this we saw before when discussing the distributions of heads and tails which occur when coins are tossed; we also noted that the relative probability of the uniform configurations increased rapidly with increasing numbers of coins.

It is instructive to extend the considerations embodied in *fig.* 5.1 to numbers of balls greater than 4 but still many orders of magnitude less than the numbers of molecules in any imaginable volume of gas. Some calculations are shown in table 7.

TABLE 7 : number of ways of distributing N balls in two boxes

no. of balls N	*no. of complexions* $w_n = {}^N C_n$			*logarithms*	
	even distribution $n = \frac{1}{2}N$	*even* ± 1 *ball* $n = \frac{1}{2}N \pm 1$	*all complexions* $2^N = \Sigma w_n$	$\ln w_{\frac{1}{2}N}$	$\ln (\Sigma w_n)$
4	6	2×4	16	1·8	2·8
10	252	2×210	1,024	5·5	6·9
20	184,756	$2 \times 167,960$	1,048,576	12·1	13·8
100	$1·01 \times 10^{29}$	$0·99 \times 10^{29}$	$1·27 \times 10^{30}$	66·8	69·3

There are three conclusions to be drawn from this table:

(i) the two configurations in which all the balls are in one or other of the boxes have each only one complexion whatever the number of balls. It is thus clear that when the numbers become large, the probabilities of the even configuration are so much greater than the probabilities of very unsymmetrical configurations that we may assume, as we did in § 5.2, that the latter never occur.

(ii) the ratio of the probability of the even distribution to the probability of either of the (even ± 1) distributions decreases as N increases. In fact

$$\frac{p(\text{even})}{p(\text{even} \pm 1)} = \frac{w_{\frac{1}{2}N}}{w_{\frac{1}{2}N \pm 1}} = \frac{\dfrac{N!}{(\frac{1}{2}N)!(\frac{1}{2}N)!}}{\dfrac{N!}{(\frac{1}{2}N+1)!(\frac{1}{2}N-1)!}} = \frac{\frac{1}{2}N+1}{\frac{1}{2}N} = 1 + \frac{2}{N}.$$

As N becomes large this ratio becomes closer and closer to unity. This is as we should expect since we have already concluded that the even distribution has maximum probability and we know that when we say that a function of a variable has a maximum at a certain value of the variable it means that small changes in the variable near the maximum make little change in the function. We use this result in § 5.4.

(iii) comparison of columns 2 and 4 shows that as the number of entities N increases, the fraction $(w_{\frac{1}{2}N}/\Sigma w_n)$ of all complexions which belong to the most probable configuration decreases. On the other hand comparison of columns 5 and 6 shows that $\ln(\Sigma w_n) - \ln w_{\frac{1}{2}N}$ decreases relative to $\ln w_{\frac{1}{2}N}$ as N increases. Now we shall see in chapter 8 that the natural logarithm of the number of complexions is an important physical quantity: this result shows that for large N it is immaterial whether we use the logarithm of the total number of complexions or of the number of complexions in the most probable configuration.

§ 5.4   Large numbers of molecules

We shall now drop the pretence that we are interested in the arrangement of balls in boxes and proceed to calculate the most probable distribution of gas molecules in space. We suppose that we have a container divided into two equal parts by an imaginary division and the problem is to distribute N molecules at random between two halves, each molecule having equal chance of entering either half. Then the probability that there will be n molecules in one half and $N-n$ in the other is:

$$p(n) = (\tfrac{1}{2})^N \frac{N!}{n!(N-n)!}.$$

We may first check that this covers all possibilities. This requires

$$\sum_{n=0}^{N} p(n) = 1,$$

which means that the sum of the mutually exclusive probabilities of finding some number between 0 and N molecules in one half is a certainty. We have

$$\sum_{n=0}^{N} p(n) = \sum_{n=0}^{N} (\tfrac{1}{2})^N \frac{N!}{n!(N-n)!} = \sum_{n=0}^{N} \frac{N!}{n!(N-n)!} (\tfrac{1}{2})^n (\tfrac{1}{2})^{N-n}.$$

The terms in this series are the terms in the expansion of $(\tfrac{1}{2}+\tfrac{1}{2})^N$.

Thus

$$\sum_{n=0}^{N} p(n) = 1.$$ 5.4.1

The probability $p(n)$ is a maximum when
$n = N-n$, that is $n = \frac{1}{2}N$.

This result is really obvious but it is instructive, and will be useful in § 5.7, to prove it by investigating the effect on $p(n)$ of moving a molecule from one half-container to the other. Suppose for definiteness that we have a distribution such that
$n > N-n$, i.e. $n > \frac{1}{2}N$.

If the maximum probability corresponds to $n = \frac{1}{2}N$, then movement of a molecule from the volume containing n to the other should increase $p(n)$, and $p(n)$ should continue to increase with every molecule moved out of the half containing the greater number until the maximum is reached. At this point, by the properties of a maximum, movement of a molecule from one side to the other should leave p unchanged. When $n < \frac{1}{2}N$, movement of molecules out of the volume containing n will reduce $p(n)$. All this can be clearly seen on our small scale model in *fig.* 5.1.

We had

$$p(n) = (\tfrac{1}{2})^N \frac{N!}{n!(N-n)!}.$$ 5.4.2

Shifting one molecule from the side containing n to the side containing $N-n$ changes $p(n)$ to $p(n-1)$, where

$$p(n-1) = (\tfrac{1}{2})^N \frac{N!}{(n-1)!(N-n+1)!}.$$

So $$\frac{p(n-1)}{p(n)} = \frac{n!(N-n)!}{(n-1)!(N-n+1)!}$$

$$= \frac{n}{N-n+1}$$

$$> 1 \text{ if } n > N-n+1,$$

that is, the probability has increased as a result of moving a molecule from the fuller half-container to the less full. At maximum

$$\frac{p(n-1)}{p(n)} = 1,$$

or $$\frac{n}{N-n+1} = 1.$$

Now N is a large number and, near to maximum, so also are n and $N-n$, so, at maximum, $n = N-n$, or

$$n = \tfrac{1}{2}N. \qquad 5.4.3$$

We should also check mathematically the obvious fact that the mean number of molecules in either half is

$$\bar{n} = \tfrac{1}{2}N.$$

By the definition of a mean we have

$$\bar{n} = \frac{\displaystyle\sum_{n=0}^{N} np(n)}{\displaystyle\sum_{n=0}^{N} p(n)} \qquad 5.4.4$$

$$= \sum_{n=1}^{N} np(n),$$

since equation 5.4.1 shows us that the $p(n)$ are normalised, and the first term in the numerator was zero. Introducing the values of $p(n)$, we obtain

$$\bar{n} = \frac{1}{2^N} \sum_{n=1}^{N} \frac{nN!}{n!(N-n)!}$$

$$= \frac{N}{2} \cdot \frac{1}{2^{N-1}} \sum_{n=1}^{N} \frac{(N-1)!}{(n-1)!\{(N-1)-(n-1)\}!}$$

$$= \frac{N}{2} \cdot \frac{1}{2^{N'}} \sum_{n'=0}^{N'} \frac{N'!}{n'!(N'-n')!}, \qquad 5.4.5$$

where $N' = N-1$ and $n' = n-1$.

Using 5.4.1 and 5.4.2 we obtain

$$\bar{n} = \tfrac{1}{2}N. \qquad 5.4.6$$

§ 5.5 Deviations from the mean

It is possible to use a technique similar to that of equations 5.4.4–6 to calculate the probable deviation from the mean. It is easier, however, to use the method of equations 4.6.7–9 to obtain an analytic expression for the probability of such deviations. The results we obtain in this section will be restricted to the case where $\bar{n} = \tfrac{1}{2}N$ and will not necessarily be applicable to more general cases. These are discussed in §§ 11.2–3.

Writing $P(q)$ to mean the probability of a distribution such that q molecules have been transferred from one box of an equal distribution to the other, that is

$$q = n - \bar{n} \quad \text{where} \quad \bar{n} = \tfrac{1}{2}N,$$

we have

$$P(q) = (\tfrac{1}{2})^N \frac{N!}{(\bar{n}+q)!(\bar{n}-q)!}.$$ 5.5.1

Transferring one more molecule gives

$$P(q+1) = (\tfrac{1}{2})^N \frac{N!}{(\bar{n}+q+1)!(\bar{n}-q-1)!}$$

and

$$\frac{P(q+1)}{P(q)} = \frac{\bar{n}-q}{\bar{n}+q+1}.$$ 5.5.2

Now if there is an analytic function for $P(q)$ we can expand it in a Taylor series:

$$P(q+1) = P(q) + \frac{dP}{dq} \cdot 1 + \dots.$$

Alternatively we can look on this step as one of writing

$$\frac{dP}{dq} = \frac{P(q+1)-P(q)}{(q+1)-q}.$$

In either case

$$\frac{P(q+1)}{P(q)} = 1 + \frac{1}{P} \cdot \frac{dP}{dq}.$$ 5.5.3

From 5.5.2–3 we have

$$\frac{1}{P}\frac{dP}{dq} = \frac{-2q-1}{\bar{n}+q+1} \simeq \frac{-2q}{\bar{n}},$$ 5.5.4

since $\bar{n} \gg q$ and $q \gg 1$.

Integrating 5.5.4 gives

$$P(q) = P_0 \, e^{-q^2/\bar{n}},$$ 5.5.5

where P_0 is the value of P at maximum, i.e. when $q = 0$.

The probabilities of finding $q, q+1, q+2, \dots, q+dq$, extra molecules in one half of the vessel are written $P(q)$, $P(q+1)$, $P(q+2)$, ..., $P(q+dq)$ respectively. Since $\bar{n} \gg q \gg 1$, all these probabilities are nearly equal; each also excludes the others, so repeating the argument as in § 4.6, we find that the probability of finding between q and $q+dq$ extra molecules in one half and an equal deficiency from the mean in the other is

$$P(q)dq = P_0\, e^{-q^2/\bar{n}}\, dq\,.\qquad\qquad 5.5.6$$

Strictly, of course, molecules are not continuous variables but provided $\bar{n}$ and q are large, we are justified in treating them as if they were. Assuming this, we must have

$$\int_{-\bar{n}}^{\bar{n}} P(q)dq = 1\,,$$

since it is certain that the deviation from the mean in one box must be between $-\bar{n}$ and $\bar{n}$, that is

$$P_0 \int_{-\bar{n}}^{\bar{n}} e^{-q^2/\bar{n}}\, dq = 1\,.$$

In this form the integral cannot be evaluated but, remembering that $\bar{n}$ is a very large number, we might tentatively replace the limits by $\pm\infty$. The correctness of this step can be confirmed numerically. Thus

$$P_0 \int_{-\infty}^{\infty} e^{-q^2/\bar{n}}\, dq = 1\,.$$

This definite integral is one of the special type discussed in § 12.6. Its value is $(\bar{n}\pi)^{\frac{1}{2}}$, so

$$P_0 = (\bar{n}\pi)^{-\frac{1}{2}}\,,$$

and the normalised probability $P(q)$ is

$$P(q)dq = (\bar{n}\pi)^{-\frac{1}{2}}\, e^{-q^2/\bar{n}}\, dq\,,\qquad\qquad 5.5.7$$

or in terms of n

$$P(n)dn = (\bar{n}\pi)^{-\frac{1}{2}}\, e^{-(n-\bar{n})^2/\bar{n}}\, dn\,.\qquad\qquad 5.5.8$$

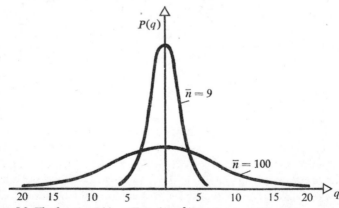

Figure 5.2. The function $P(q) = (\bar{n}\pi)^{-\frac{1}{2}} e^{-q^2/\bar{n}}$ for $\bar{n} = 9$ and $\bar{n} = 100$.

The function $P(q)$ is shown for two values of $\bar{n}$ in *fig.* 5.2.
The mean value of q, given by

$$\bar{q} = (\bar{n}\pi)^{-\frac{1}{2}} \int_{-\infty}^{\infty} q \, e^{-q^2/\bar{n}} \, dq, \qquad\qquad 5.5.9$$

is of course zero. The mean value of q^2 is

$$\overline{q^2} = (\bar{n}\pi)^{-\frac{1}{2}} \int_{-\infty}^{\infty} q^2 \, e^{-q^2/\bar{n}} \, dq. \qquad\qquad 5.5.10$$

Once again the integral can be evaluated by the methods of § 12.6, whence

$$\overline{q^2} = (\bar{n}\pi)^{-\frac{1}{2}} \tfrac{1}{2} \pi^{\frac{1}{2}} \bar{n}^{\frac{3}{2}}$$

$$= \tfrac{1}{2}\bar{n}. \qquad\qquad 5.5.11$$

The relative fluctuation from the mean can be defined as

$$\delta = q/\bar{n}, \qquad\qquad 5.5.12$$

and its root-mean-square value is

$$\overline{\delta^2} = \overline{q^2}/(\bar{n})^2 = 1/2\bar{n}, \qquad\qquad 5.5.13$$

which shows that the relative fluctuation decreases as $\bar{n}$ increases. This result is true in the more general case where the most probable distribution is not one of two equal divisions; but then, as shown in § 11.2, the numerical constant is different. In any case the square root of the mean-square fluctuation is

$$(\overline{\delta^2})^{\frac{1}{2}} \propto \bar{n}^{-\frac{1}{2}} \propto N^{-\frac{1}{2}}.$$

The root-mean-square deviation from the mean is called the *standard deviation*.

§ 5.6 Stirling's formula

It is instructive to derive formula 5.5.5 in another way. Both methods will be useful in later work.

Starting from equation 5.5.1,

$$P(q) = (\tfrac{1}{2})^N \frac{N!}{(\bar{n}+q)!(\bar{n}-q)!},$$

we take logarithms and obtain

$$\ln P = C_1 - \ln\{(\bar{n}+q)!\} - \ln\{(\bar{n}-q)!\}, \qquad\qquad 5.6.1$$

where C_1, and later C_2 and C_3, are constants incorporating all terms which do not involve q.

9

Now, by Stirling's formula (§ 12.5.1), we may approximate to $\ln N!$ by

$$\ln N! \simeq N \ln N - N, \qquad 5.6.2$$

provided $N \gg 1$.

Thus, 5.6.1 becomes

$$\ln P = C_2 - (\bar{n}+q) \ln (\bar{n}+q) - (\bar{n}-q) \ln (\bar{n}-q)$$
$$= C_2 - \bar{n} \ln \bar{n}(1+q/\bar{n}) - \bar{n} \ln \bar{n}(1-q/\bar{n}) -$$
$$-q \ln \bar{n}(1+q/\bar{n}) + q \ln \bar{n}(1-q/\bar{n}).$$

We now expand the logarithms and obtain, remembering that $q/n \ll 1$,

$$\ln P = C_3 - \bar{n}\left(\frac{q}{\bar{n}} - \frac{q^2}{2\bar{n}^2} + \ldots\right) - \bar{n}\left(-\frac{q}{\bar{n}} - \frac{q^2}{2\bar{n}^2} - \ldots\right) - \frac{q^2}{\bar{n}} - \frac{q^2}{\bar{n}}$$

$$= C_3 - \frac{q^2}{\bar{n}}, \qquad 5.6.3$$

which, writing $\ln P_0$ for C_3, is the same result as equation 5.5.5.

§ 5.7 Distribution of gas molecules in one-dimensional momentum space

We now apply the same techniques as in § 5.5 to the problem of finding the most probable distribution of kinetic energy or speed amongst the molecules of a gas; that is, we wish to find the fraction of molecules which have energies in some narrow range between E and $E+dE$ or speeds between v and $v+dv$. This we shall do by a model in which we place the molecules by a random method in boxes each representing a small range of energy or velocity and pick out the most probable distribution as we did before. If, however, it were simply a matter of putting a constant number of molecules in energy boxes according to pure chance we would get the same result as before, namely that boxes of equal size were equally populated. The difference is that we have to take account of conservation of energy and this will rule out certain distributions: for example, a distribution is not allowed in which all the molecules fall in boxes each marked with an energy greater than the mean.

There are difficulties in applying statistical methods to a gas moving in three dimensions – difficulties connected with the fact that a given energy $\frac{1}{2}mv^2$ can be made up by many combinations of v_x, v_y and v_z. This complicates the estimate of the number of ways of arranging molecules of a given speed (also a combination of v_x, v_y and v_z) over boxes of different energies. We shall therefore illustrate the method by the example of a one-dimensional system without for the moment enquiring what sort of system it is, but perhaps picturing it as a large collection of beads sliding without friction on a string, colliding with each other and exchanging energy. We should not take the applicability of the result to a gas too literally though we shall find later that the one-dimensional model is not entirely useless. We shall further simplify the introductory discussion by measuring the energies of the particles of our one-dimensional system in integral multiples of some small unit. There is nothing unphysical about this, for we can make the unit as small as we like; alternatively we can say we are grouping the particles in such a way that each group has so nearly the same energy that we can treat them as if they had.

We may now begin with a small-scale example similar to that we used in § 5.3. We still have four particles and two boxes but the boxes are now labelled, one 'zero energy' and the other 'one unit of energy'. Further, to remind us that the boxes are not in real space but represent different energies, we shall rename them 'cells'. The problem is to find the most probable distribution of the particles between the cells subject now to the condition that the total energy available to distribute, is one unit. The four possibilities are all drawn

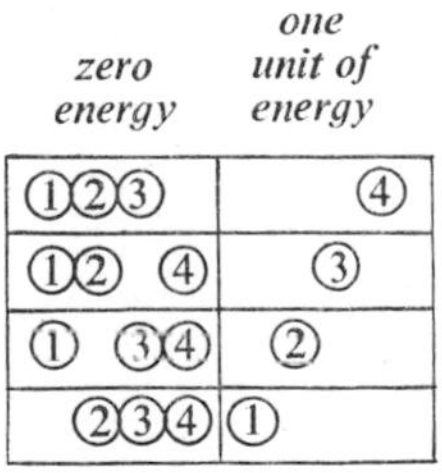

Figure 5.3. Distribution of particles in energy cells: four particles; one unit of energy; four complexions.

out in *fig.* 5.3. Comparison with *fig.* 5.1 shows that 12 of the 16 possibilities have been eliminated by the new conservation condition.

We now double the number of cells and allow the four particles to share three units of energy. All the possible copies of this system are then shown in *fig.* 5.4, where it is clear that there is a tendency for the particles to be preferentially in the cells corresponding to lower energy and that the average number in each energy cell falls off rapidly as the energy increases. These averages are given in *fig.* 5.4 and may be compared with the corresponding averages in *fig.* 5.1, where the only quantity to be conserved was the number of particles.

units of energy →

0	1	2	3	
①②③			④	⎫
①② ④			③	⎬ 4
① ③④			②	⎪
②③④			①	⎭
①②	③	④		⎫
①②		④	③	⎪
① ③	②	④		⎪
① ③		④	②	⎪
① ④	②	③		⎪
① ④	③	②		⎬ 12
②③	①	④		⎪
②③	④①			⎪
② ④	①	③		⎪
② ④	③	①		⎪
③④	①	②		⎪
③④	②	①		⎭
①	②③④			⎫
②	① ③④			⎬ 4
③	①② ④			⎪
④	①②③			⎭

	0	1	2	3
totals over all complexions	40	24	12	4
average number per cell	2	1·2	0·6	0·2

Figure 5.4. *Distribution of particles in energy cells:* 4 *particles;* 3 *units of energy;* 20 *complexions.*

We can now extend these results to more particles and more energy. Let the total energy be E, the unit of energy ε_0 and the numbers in the various energy cells $0, 1, 2, \ldots$ be n_0, n_1, n_2, and so on. Then conservation of particles gives

$$N = n_0 + n_1 + n_2 + \ldots$$
$$= \sum_i n_i, \tag{5.7.1}$$

while conservation of energy gives

$$E = n_0 0 + n_1 \varepsilon_0 + n_2 (2\varepsilon_0) + \ldots$$

$$= \sum_i i n_i \varepsilon_0, \qquad 5.7.2$$

where, in each case, the sum extends from $i = 0$ to i such that all the N particles have been accounted for.

As before we shall assume that the configuration which occurs in the greatest number of ways is the most probable; we are already predisposed to expect that such a configuration is likely to be one where the population of the cells falls rapidly as the energy increases. Now the number of ways of arranging N particles in cells containing $n_1, n_2, \ldots$, is

$$w = \frac{N!}{n_0! \, n_1! \ldots n_i! \ldots}, \qquad 5.7.3$$

where w is the number of complexions in the configuration and is a generalisation of the w defined by equation 5.2.1. To obtain the *probability* of the configuration, w would have to be multiplied by the *a priori* probability of one complexion and, while we could calculate this, the calculation would be much more difficult than in the simpler case where there was no restriction on the number in any box. It is not, however, very profitable to calculate the probability factor since, as we have seen previously, it is the ratios of probabilities which we require, the factor cancelling out. If later we want an actual probability the missing factor can be obtained by normalisation.

It is instructive to use 5.7.3 as we did (table 7, p. 113) to compare the relative probabilities of an improbable and a probable configuration. Say that we have 20 particles and 20 units of energy. We know that a population which decreases towards the higher energies is likely to be more probable, so let us arbitrarily suppose that we have:

8 particles each with 0 units of energy, totalling 0 units of energy,
6   1   6
4   2   8
2   3   6
in all, 20 particles   of all energies   totalling 20 units of energy.

w for this configuration is

$$w = \frac{20!}{8! \, 6! \, 4! \, 2!} \simeq 2 \times 10^8,$$

whereas w for the configuration where all 20 particles have one unit of energy each is

$$w = \frac{20!}{20!} = 1.$$

Once again, even for small numbers of particles, the ratios of probability between probable and improbable configurations are very large numbers.

To find w_{max} we note, as in § 5.4, that, at maximum, small changes in the distribution will leave w unchanged. We cannot now simply transfer a particle from one cell to another since, because all the cells represent different energies, such a transfer violates conservation of energy. We can, however, arrange for energy to be conserved by removing *two* particles from cell i which has energy $i\varepsilon_0$, putting one in cell $(i-1)$ with energy $(i-1)\varepsilon_0$, the other in cell $(i+1)$ with energy $(i+1)\varepsilon_0$. The new configuration includes w^* complexions given by

$$w^* = \frac{N!}{n_0!n_1!\dots(n_{i-1}+1)!(n_i-2)!(n_{i+1}+1)!\dots}. \qquad 5.7.4$$

Now, at maximum,

$$\frac{w^*}{w} = 1 = \frac{n_i(n_i-1)}{(n_{i-1}+1)(n_{i+1}+1)}$$

$$\simeq \frac{n_i^2}{n_{i-1}n_{i+1}} \quad \text{since all } n_i \gg 1. \qquad 5.7.5$$

Thus, we have the relation between the populations of successive energy cells:

$$\frac{n_{i-1}}{n_i} = \frac{n_i}{n_{i+1}}. \qquad 5.7.6$$

This relation is true for any value of i, so we have the result that

$$\frac{n_0}{n_1} = \frac{n_1}{n_2} = \dots = \frac{n_i}{n_{i+1}} = \dots = \text{constant}, \qquad 5.7.7$$

that is, the populations of cells with successively increasing energy fall in geometrical progression.

To find an explicit expression for n_i we remember that n_i is a function of energy $\varepsilon_i(=i\varepsilon_0)$ and it is then easy to see that a satisfactory expression is

$$n_i = n_0\,e^{-\beta\varepsilon_i}, \qquad 5.7.8$$

where β is a positive constant having the dimensions of the reciprocal of energy; for then

$$\frac{n_i}{n_{i+1}} = \frac{e^{-\beta i \varepsilon_0}}{e^{-\beta(i+1)}\varepsilon_0} = e^{\beta \varepsilon_0} = \text{constant},$$

which is what equation 5.7.7 required. The minus sign in the exponential in 5.7.8 shows that n_i falls as i increases.

We have obtained this result for our fictitious one-dimensional system where the energies of the particles are integral multiples of some unit of energy ε_0. The result is, however, more general: there is no need for the energy differences to be constant, and we can write

$$\frac{n(\varepsilon_1)}{n(\varepsilon_2)} = e^{-\beta(\varepsilon_1 - \varepsilon_2)}. \qquad 5.7.9$$

This is left as problem 5.15.2. We shall not digress at the moment to find a physical meaning for β, for to do so would require too close identification of our model with a real physical system.

§ 5.8 Distribution of gas molecules in three-dimensional velocity space

The statistical methods just developed can now be applied to the problem of the distribution of velocities amongst molecules in a three-dimensional gas. We want $f(v)dv$, the fraction of molecules with speeds between v and $v+dv$ or $f(v_x, v_y, v_z)\,dv_x dv_y dv_z$, the fraction of molecules with x-component of velocity between v_x and v_x+dv_x, y-component between v_y and v_y+dv_y and z-component between v_z and v_z+dv_z. We shall consider $f(v_x, v_y, v_z)$ first.

We begin by considering a monatomic gas where the only energy is the kinetic energy of the molecules due to their translational motion. We then construct a velocity space – or phase space – marked out by three mutually perpendicular axes on which we measure the components of velocity v_x, v_y, v_z. To simplify the model as much as possible we now arrange to measure the velocities in multiples of some small unit velocity $\delta v_x = \delta v_y = \delta v_z$ and mark out the axes in multiples of this unit. We then construct planes perpendicular to each of the three axes through each of the marked points.

The result of these operations is to give a three-dimensional array of small cubical cells each of volume $\delta v_x \delta v_y \delta v_z = (\delta v_x)^3 = (\delta v_y)^3 = (\delta v_z)^3$, which between them fill all space rather as in an egg-box. We may call the centre of each cell the point (v_x, v_y, v_z), or we may give one of the corners this label; for if the size of a side is small enough it does not matter. Since we know that the mean velocity of a gas molecule at ordinary temperatures is $\sim 10^3$ m sec^{-1}, a suitable value for δv_x might be 1 m sec^{-1}; but it could be much smaller, the only condition being that it must not be so small that when a number of the order of 10^{20} molecules is distributed amongst the cells there are any which do not contain a reasonably large number.

Strictly, we cannot distribute molecules in velocity space as we did in ordinary space, so we should speak of distributing 'representative points' amongst the cells, each representative point standing in for a molecule and giving values for its three components of velocity. The number of representative points falling in the cell centred on (v_x, v_y, v_z) will then give the number of molecules which have components of velocity in the range v_x to $v_x + \delta v_x$, v_y to $v_y + \delta v_y$ and v_z to $v_z + \delta v_z$. The energy of all molecules represented by points in a single cell is taken to be the same.

Since we have a finite unit of velocity δv_x we have also a finite unit of energy $\frac{1}{2}m(\delta v_x)^2 = \frac{1}{2}m(\delta v_y)^2 = \frac{1}{2}m(\delta v_z)^2$. We shall call this unit of energy ε_0 and the energies of all molecules will then be integral multiples of ε_0.

Degeneracy. It is at once obvious that not all the cells have different energies: the energy corresponding to a cell

$$E = \frac{1}{2}mv_x^2 + \frac{1}{2}mv_y^2 + \frac{1}{2}mv_z^2$$

can be made up by many different combinations of v_x, v_y and v_z. For example, the cells

$$v_x = 0, \quad v_y = 0, \quad v_z = V;$$

$$v_x = 0, \quad v_y = V, \quad v_z = 0;$$

$$v_x = V, \quad v_y = 0, \quad v_z = 0,$$

all have the same energy. It is also clear that the larger the energy $\frac{1}{2}mv^2$, the more ways it can be made up by different combinations of v_x, v_y and v_z. Cells which have the same energy but belong to different combinations of v_x, v_y and v_z are said to be *degenerate* and the number of such cells is called *the degree of degeneracy* for that energy. In the one-dimensional case, all cells are thus doubly degenerate, since $\frac{1}{2}mv_x^2$ is the energy of a particle with velocity v_x or $-v_x$. This constant degeneracy allowed us to use the simplification of § 5.7.

We now number the cells by using two sets of integer suffixes i and j, such that n_{ij} means the number of representative points in the

jth cell with energy $i\varepsilon_0$. For the cell with energy 0 there is only one combination of v_x, v_y and v_z which gives zero kinetic energy, namely $v_x = v_y = v_z = 0$. Similarly there are six cells with energy one unit given by $v_x = \pm\delta v_x$, $v_y = v_z = 0$ and two similar expressions obtained by permuting v_x, v_y and v_z. As the energy corresponding to a cell increases, the degree of degeneracy increases rapidly. There is no need to calculate the actual degree; we need only indicate the existence of degeneracy by the suffixes.

We can now write down the number of ways w of arranging the N representative points amongst the cells in such a way that:

the cell of zero energy contains n_0 points;

the cells of energy 1 unit contain $n_{11}, n_{12}, \ldots, n_{1j}$ points, the suffix
j reminding us that there are several cells of the same energy
which may contain different numbers of representative points;

· · · · · · · · · ·

the cells of energy i units contain $n_{i1}, n_{i2}, \ldots, n_{ij}, \ldots$ representative
points and so on.

The expression for w is

$$w = \frac{N!}{n_0!\,n_{11}!\,n_{12}!\ldots n_{ij}!\ldots},$$ 5.8.1

where $\sum_i \sum_j n_{ij} = N$.

This expression is the same as 5.7.3 except that account has now been taken of degeneracy.

To find $w_{\max}$ we start by transferring a representative point from cell (i,j) to cell $(i,j+1)$, both cells being of equal energy. If w is a maximum then the result of making such a small change is to give a new expression w^* which is equal to w. Thus

$$\frac{w^*}{w} = \frac{n_{ij}!\,n_{i,j+1}!}{(n_{ij}-1)!\,(n_{i,j+1}+1)!},$$ 5.8.2

all other factors cancelling, so

$$\frac{w^*}{w} = \frac{n_{ij}}{n_{i,j+1}+1} \simeq \frac{n_{ij}}{n_{i,j+1}},$$ 5.8.3

since all $n_{ij} \gg 1$. Thus

$$n_{ij} = n_{i,j+1}.$$

This gives the obvious result that the most probable configuration is one in which all cells representing equal energy are equally populated, the actual population being proportional to the size of the cell, that is to $\delta v_x \delta v_y \delta v_z$. An alternative way of saying the same thing is that cells of arbitrary size, containing representative points all of the same energy, are populated in proportion to their size.

To interchange representative points between cells of different energy while still conserving energy, we proceed, almost as in § 5.7, to remove two points from two different cells with energy $i\varepsilon_0$ one to a cell with energy $(i-1)\varepsilon_0$, the other to a cell with energy $(i+1)\varepsilon_0$. This apparently rather artifical procedure is easier to justify physically in three dimensions than in one, since in three dimensions a collision of two molecules leads to a rearrangement of their components of velocity, that is to a movement of their representative points from one cell to another. Our special case is thus one where two molecules with the same energy but different directions of motion collide in such a way that one gains a little energy which the other loses.

Once again these small changes in distribution give a new w^* which at maximum is the same as w:

$$\frac{w^*}{w} = \frac{n_{i+1}!\, n_i!\, n_i!\, n_{i-1}!}{(n_{i+1}+1)!\,(n_i-1)!\,(n_i-1)!\,(n_{i-1}+1)!}, \qquad 5.8.4$$

where all other factors have cancelled and we have omitted the suffixes j because we now know that all cells with energy $i\varepsilon_0$ are equally populated. Cancelling further gives

$$\frac{w^*}{w} = \frac{n_i^2}{(n_{i+1}+1)(n_{i-1}+1)} \qquad 5.8.5$$

$$\simeq \frac{n_i^2}{n_{i+1}n_{i-1}} \text{ (since all } n_i \gg 1)$$

$$= 1 \text{ at maximum},$$

or $$\frac{n_{i+1}}{n_i} = \frac{n_i}{n_{i-1}}, \qquad 5.8.6$$

the same relation as in one dimension. The solution is the same, namely

$$n_i = n_0\, e^{-\beta\varepsilon_i}, \qquad 5.8.7$$

where $\varepsilon_i = i\varepsilon_0$ and n_0 and β are constants still to be determined.

In terms of velocity, this result means that the number of representative points in the cell centred on (v_x, v_y, v_z) is proportional to

$$\exp\left\{-\tfrac{1}{2}m\beta(v_x^2 + v_y^2 + v_z^2)\right\}. \qquad 5.8.8$$

We already have the result that the number in the same cell is proportional to the volume of the cell, so writing $n(v_x,v_y,v_z)\delta v_x \delta v_y \delta v_z$ for the number of representative points, that is of molecules with velocities between v_x and $v_x+\delta v_x$, v_y and $v_y+\delta v_y$, v_z and $v_z+\delta v_z$, we have

$$n(v_x,v_y,v_z)\delta v_x \delta v_y \delta v_z = A\, e^{-\frac{1}{2}m\beta(v_x^2+v_y^2+v_z^2)}\, \delta v_x \delta v_y \delta v_z, \qquad 5.8.9$$

where A is a constant, proportional to the total number of molecules. We now assume that we can replace the constants δv_x, δv_y, δv_z by differentials dv_x, dv_y, dv_z, giving

$$n(v_x,v_y,v_z)dv_x dv_y dv_z = A\, e^{-\frac{1}{2}m\beta(v_x^2+v_y^2+v_z^2)}\, dv_x dv_y dv_z. \qquad 5.8.10$$

We now express n as a fraction f of the total number of molecules N, that is

$$n(v_x,v_y,v_z)dv_x dv_y dv_z = N f(v_x,v_y,v_z)dv_x dv_y dv_z, \qquad 5.8.11$$

where f is, by the definition of probability, also the probability that a given molecule has components of velocity within the ranges

$$v_x \text{ to } v_x+dv_x, \quad \text{and} \quad v_y \text{ to } v_y+dv_y, \quad \text{and} \quad v_z \text{ to } v_z+dv_z.$$

The probability that a molecule has x-component of velocity within a given range is entirely independent of the values of its other components; in fact, we assumed this when we put the representative points at random into the cells. Thus we can write

$$f(v_x,v_y,v_z)dv_x dv_y dv_z = f(v_x)dv_x \cdot f(v_y)dv_y \cdot f(v_z)dv_z, \quad 5.8.12$$

that is, we express our probability f as the product of three independent probabilities. Then from 5.8.10–12 we have

$$f(v_x)dv_x \cdot f(v_y)dv_y \cdot f(v_z)dv_z$$
$$= A'(e^{-\frac{1}{2}mv_x^2\beta}\, dv_x) \cdot (e^{-\frac{1}{2}mv_y^2\beta}\, dv_y) \cdot (e^{-\frac{1}{2}mv_z^2}\, dv_z),$$

$$5.8.13$$

A' being another constant. The next step is to note that, since the value of one component of the velocity has no influence on the others, the factor involving v_x on the left must be equal to the corresponding factor on the right with similar conclusions for v_y and v_z. That is we can split equation 5.8.13 into three:

$$f(v_x)dv_x = C\, e^{-\frac{1}{2}mv_x^2\beta}\, dv_x,$$
$$f(v_y)dv_y = C\, e^{-\frac{1}{2}mv_y^2\beta}\, dv_y,$$
$$f(v_z)dv_z = C\, e^{-\frac{1}{2}mv_z^2\beta}\, dv_z, \qquad\qquad 5.8.14$$

where C is a constant, the same in each equation. C is obtained by normalising:

$$\int_{-\infty}^{\infty} f(v_x)dv_x = 1,$$

which means as usual that the x-component of velocity must be between $-\infty$ and $+\infty$; that is

$$C\int_{-\infty}^{\infty} e^{-\frac{1}{2}mv_x^2\beta}\, dv_x = 1.$$

The value of the integral (§ 12.6) is $(2\pi/m\beta)^{\frac{1}{2}}$, so

$$C = (m\beta/2\pi)^{\frac{1}{2}}. \tag{5.8.15}$$

β is obtained from the law of equipartition of energy:

$$\tfrac{1}{2}m\overline{v_x^2} = \tfrac{1}{2}kT. \tag{5.8.16}$$

Now

$$\overline{v_x^2} = \frac{\displaystyle\int_{-\infty}^{\infty} Cv_x^2\, e^{-\frac{1}{2}mv_x^2\beta}\, dv_x}{\displaystyle\int_{-\infty}^{\infty} C\, e^{-\frac{1}{2}mv_x^2\beta}\, dv_x}. \tag{5.8.17}$$

Writing $\tfrac{1}{2}m\beta = h$ and treating these integrals as in § 12.3 gives

$$\overline{v_x^2} = -\frac{\partial}{\partial h} \ln \int_{-\infty}^{\infty} e^{-hv_x^2}\, dv_x$$

$$= -\frac{\partial}{\partial h} \ln \sqrt{\frac{\pi}{h}} = \frac{1}{2h} = (m\beta)^{-1}. \tag{5.8.18}$$

Alternatively we can use the value of C from 5.8.15 to give $\overline{v_x^2}$ directly:

$$\overline{v_x^2} = \left(\frac{m\beta}{2\pi}\right)^{\frac{1}{2}} \int_{-\infty}^{\infty} v_x^2\, e^{-\frac{1}{2}mv_x^2\beta}\, dv_x$$

$$= (m\beta)^{-1}.$$

In either case, using 5.8.16 gives

$$\beta = 1/kT, \tag{5.8.19}$$

so we have the complete expression for the probability that a molecule has x-component of velocity in the range v_x to v_x+dv_x,

$$f(v_x)dv_x = \left(\frac{m}{2\pi kT}\right)^{\frac{1}{2}} e^{-mv_x^2/2kT}\, dv_x, \tag{5.8.20}$$

with similar expressions for v_y and v_z.

The function $f(v_x)$ is shown in *fig.* 5.5 for various values of the temperature T.

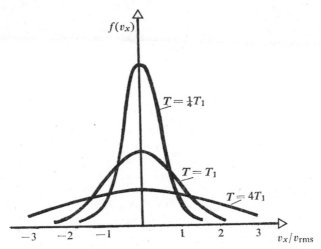

Figure 5.5. The function $f(v_x)$ plotted for 3 values of T. The units of v_x and v_{rms} are such that $\frac{1}{2}mv_{rms}^2 = \frac{1}{2}kT$.

The mean x-component of velocity is

$$\bar{v}_x = \left(\frac{m}{2\pi kT}\right)^{\frac{1}{2}} \int_{-\infty}^{\infty} v_x \, e^{-mv_x^2/2kT} \, dv_x \qquad 5.8.21$$
$$= 0.$$

It is obvious from the shape of the curve of $f(v_x)$ as well as from our basic assumptions that $\bar{v}_x = 0$, since it is equally likely that a molecule has velocity $+v_x$ or $-v_x$.

If, however, we define $|\,\bar{v}_x\,|$ as the mean *speed* in the x-direction we have

$$|\bar{v}_x| = 2\int_0^{\infty} v_x f(v_x) dv_x, \qquad 5.8.22$$

the factor 2 occurring because we are now taking both v_x and $-v_x$ as positive. We did the same thing in § 1.15 except that there we did not know $f(v_x)$ but simply assumed we could find the velocity of every molecule. Inserting the formula for $f(v_x)$ we obtain

$$|\bar{v}_x| = 2\left(\frac{m}{2\pi kT}\right)^{\frac{1}{2}} \int_0^{\infty} v_x \, e^{-mv_x^2/2kT} \, dv_x$$
$$= 2\left(\frac{kT}{2\pi m}\right)^{\frac{1}{2}}. \qquad 5.8.23$$

$|\,\overline{v_x}\,|$ is obviously the mean speed in any single direction. It is the quantity required in the expression (1.15.3),

$$\Gamma = \tfrac{1}{2}n\,|\,\overline{v_x}\,|,$$

which we derived to represent the number of collisions of molecules with unit area of a wall in unit time,* so that for this we have

$$\Gamma = n\left(\frac{kT}{2\pi m}\right)^{\frac{1}{2}}.\qquad\qquad 5.8.24$$

The relationship of $|\,\overline{v_x}\,|$ to $\bar{v}$, the mean speed of molecules in any direction, is derived as equation 5.10.5.

Before proceeding to consider the three-dimensional case, it is instructive to apply the one-dimensional formula to a practical problem.

§ 5.9   Evaporation from the surface of a liquid

In a liquid, unlike a perfect gas, there are forces holding the molecules together. However, at a temperature near to the boiling point we can imagine that the molecules will move about with a velocity distribution the same as we have found for a gas.

If we take the x-direction to be normal to the surface, then a molecule will be able to escape if its x-component of velocity is so large that the attractive forces of the other molecules are not enough to prevent it; that is, a molecule will leave the surface if

$$\tfrac{1}{2}mv_x^2 > U_0,\qquad\qquad 5.9.1$$

where U_0 is the work to remove a superficial molecule from the liquid to infinity. U_0 is the latent heat of evaporation referred to a single molecule.

---

* A word of warning is needed here. Some books write the formula for $|\,\overline{v_x}\,|$ without the factor 2, so that, in terms of the unnormalised $f(v_x)$,

$$|\,\overline{v_x}\,| = \frac{\displaystyle\int_0^\infty v_x f(v_x)\,dv_x}{\displaystyle\int_{-\infty}^\infty f(v_x)\,dv_x}.$$

This is an odd kind of average being really the quantity we called $\vec{v}_x$ in 1.15.5. If, however, one accepts it, formula 1.15.3 would have to be written

$$\Gamma = n\,|\,\overline{v_x}\,|.$$

The matter is further discussed in § 4.10.

Now, if we have n molecules per unit volume, the number of these which have x-components of velocity between v_x and $v_x + dv_x$ is $nf(v_x)dv_x$. All of these have approximately the same speed v_x, so from § 1.15 the number of impacts they make on unit area of the surface per second is

$$\Gamma = \tfrac{1}{2} n v_x f(v_x) dv_x,$$ 5.9.2

and the number Γ' leaving unit area of the surface per second is

$$\Gamma' = 2 \times \tfrac{1}{2} n \int_{v_x = (2U_0/m)^{\frac{1}{2}}}^{v_x = \infty} v_x f(v_x) dv_x,$$ 5.9.3

the factor 2 arising, as in equation 5.8.22, because molecules with speeds corresponding to *both* high positive and high negative values of v_x are involved. These molecules are found in both right-hand and left-hand tails of the curves in *fig. 5.5*.

Inserting the expression for $f(v_x)$ in equation 5.9.3 gives

$$\Gamma' = n \left(\frac{m}{2\pi kT} \right)^{\frac{1}{2}} \int_{v_x = (2U_0/m)^{\frac{1}{2}}}^{v_x = \infty} v_x\, e^{-mv_x^2/2kT} dv_x.$$

The integral can be evaluated by elementary methods (§ 12.1). Its value is $(kT/m) \exp(-U_0/kT)$, so the rate of evaporation from unit area is

$$\Gamma' = n \left(\frac{kT}{2\pi m} \right)^{\frac{1}{2}} e^{-U_0/kT}.$$ 5.9.4

The number Γ'' returning to the liquid surface from the vapour in unit time is clearly proportional to the vapour pressure. In equilibrium $\Gamma'' = \Gamma'$, so that Γ' is proportional to the equilibrium vapour pressure p. Thus

$$p \propto T^{\frac{1}{2}} e^{-U_0/kT},$$ 5.9.5

or $\ln p = \text{const.} + \tfrac{1}{2} \ln T - U_0/kT.$ 5.9.6

Verification of formula 5.9.6 consists in measuring the vapour pressure as a function of temperature and plotting $\ln p$ against $1/T$. Experimentally, in general, over a not-too-large temperature range, a straight line is obtained showing that

$$\ln p = \text{const.} - U_0/kT$$
$$= \text{const.} - L/RT,$$

where $L = N_0 U_0$ is the latent heat per kg-mole and $R = N_0 k$ is the gas constant. The deviation from a straight line which would show the influence of the $\ln T$ term is usually too small to measure.

Some figures obtained for the vapour pressure of water at various temperatures near the boiling point are given in problem 10.11.1. We shall be reconsidering the problem of evaporation, treating it as a thermally activated process, in § 10.4.

§ 5.10   The Maxwell distribution

We now return to the problem of finding $n(v)dv$, the number of molecules with speed between v and $v+dv$. The most direct method is to use our result, obtained in § 5.8, that the number of molecules in a given energy range is proportional to the volume of velocity space required to represent the range of velocities and also proportional to $\exp(-\beta \times \text{energy})$. We use the same axes as before but define our cells by concentric spheres of radius v, whereupon the volume between spheres of radius v and $v+dv$ is $4\pi v^2\, dv$.

All representative points falling within such a spherical shell have almost the same energy $\frac{1}{2}mv^2$. So

$$n(v)dv = B'v^2\, e^{-\frac{1}{2}mv^2\beta}\, dv$$

and $$f(v)dv = Bv^2\, e^{-\frac{1}{2}mv^2\beta}\, dv,$$

where B' and B are constants. Alternatively, if we wish to keep cells all of the same volume in our velocity space, we start from equation 5.8.9 and calculate how many cells of volume $\delta v_x \delta v_y \delta v_z$ there are in the region of constant energy $\frac{1}{2}mv^2$ between spheres of radii v and $v+\delta v$. This is a measure of the degeneracy of the energy $\frac{1}{2}mv^2$. We have

$$\text{no. of cells} = \frac{\text{volume of spherical shell}}{\text{volume of a single cell}}$$

$$= \frac{4\pi v^2\, \delta v}{\delta v_x \delta v_y \delta v_z}.$$

The number of representative points in this volume of velocity space is obtained by multiplying the number of cells by the number of points in each cell. Since the energy is constant in each, this number is the same for each. Thus

$$n(v)dv = 4\pi v^2 \frac{\delta v}{\delta v_x \delta v_y \delta v_z} n_0\, e^{-\frac{1}{2}mv^2\beta}\, \delta v_x \delta v_y \delta v_z$$

$$= 4\pi n_0 v^2\, e^{-\frac{1}{2}mv^2\beta}\, \delta v.$$

Replacing δv by dv and n_0 by f gives

$$f(v)dv = Bv^2 e^{-\frac{1}{2}mv^2\beta} dv,$$

the same as before, with B a constant obtained by normalisation, that is by writing

$$\int_0^\infty f(v)dv = 1,$$

or $\qquad B\int_0^\infty v^2 e^{-\frac{1}{2}mv^2\beta} = 1.$

Evaluating this integral by the methods of § 12.6 gives

$$B = 4\pi\left(\frac{m\beta}{2\pi}\right)^{\frac{3}{2}} = 4\pi C^3, \qquad\qquad 5.10.1$$

where C is the constant given by 5.8.15.

The parameter β has already been shown to be $1/kT$ by applying the principle of equipartition to the one-dimensional case. In three dimensions, evaluation of β involves writing that the mean energy of translational motion of a particle of mass m is

$$\frac{1}{2}m\overline{v^2} = \frac{1}{2}m\int_0^\infty v^2 f(v)dv$$

$$= \frac{1}{2}m \times 4\pi\left(\frac{m\beta}{2\pi}\right)^{\frac{3}{2}}\int_0^\infty v^4 e^{-\frac{1}{2}mv^2\beta} dv$$

$$= \frac{3}{2\beta} \qquad \text{(using 12.6.9)}$$

$$= \frac{3}{2}kT \qquad \text{(from equipartition)}$$

whence $\beta = 1/kT$ as before.

The function

$$f(v)dv = 4\pi\left(\frac{m}{2\pi kT}\right)^{\frac{3}{2}} v^2 e^{-mv^2/2kT} dv \qquad\qquad 5.10.2$$

is called *Maxwell's distribution law* (1860) and is shown in *fig. 5.6*. In this form it is normalised; it is often easier, however, to use it unnormalised. For example, writing

$$f(v)dv = Bv^2 e^{-mv^2/2kT} dv,$$

10

where B is a constant, we have the mean-square speed:

$$\overline{v^2} = \frac{\displaystyle\int_0^\infty v^2 f(v)dv}{\displaystyle\int_0^\infty f(v)dv}$$

$$= \frac{\displaystyle\int_0^\infty Bv^4\, e^{-\mu v^2}\, dv}{\displaystyle\int_0^\infty Bv^2\, e^{-\mu v^2}\, dv},$$

where $\mu = m/2kT$.

In this form the integrals are most readily evaluated by logarithmic differentiation (§ 12.3). Thus

$$\overline{v^2} = -\frac{\partial}{\partial\mu} \ln \int_0^\infty v^2\, e^{-\mu v^2}\, dv$$

$$= -\frac{\partial}{\partial\mu} \ln \tfrac{1}{4} \frac{\sqrt{\pi}}{\mu^{\frac{3}{2}}}$$

$$= \frac{3}{2\mu} = \frac{3kT}{m}, \qquad\qquad 5.10.3$$

as we know already.

The mean speed

$$\bar{v} = \frac{\displaystyle\int_0^\infty v f(v)dv}{\displaystyle\int_0^\infty f(v)dv}$$

$$= \frac{\displaystyle\int_0^\infty Bv^3\, e^{-\mu v^2}\, dv}{\displaystyle\int_0^\infty Bv^2\, e^{-\mu v^2}\, dv}.$$

Here the quotient is not evaluable by logarithmic differentiation and it is necessary to calculate numerator and denominator separately by the methods of § 12.6. Hence

$$\bar{v} = \frac{1}{2\mu^2}\bigg/ \frac{\pi^{\frac{1}{2}}}{4} \cdot \frac{1}{\mu^{\frac{3}{2}}}$$

$$= 2/(\mu\pi)^{\frac{1}{2}}$$

$$= 2(2kT/m\pi)^{\frac{1}{2}} \qquad\qquad 5.10.4$$

and $(\overline{v^2})^{\frac{1}{2}}/\bar{v} = \frac{1}{2}(3\pi/2)^{\frac{1}{2}}$

$$\simeq 1\cdot09,\qquad\qquad\qquad 5.10.5$$

which proves the point, used in § 1.16 and § 2.2, that the ratio of the root-mean-square to the mean speed is constant. Since the ratio is close to unity it is often immaterial which is used.

The ratio of $\bar{v}$ (5.10.4), the mean speed of all molecules, to $|\,\overline{v_x}\,|$ (5.8.22), the mean speed of molecules in the x- or any given direction, is then

$$\bar{v}/|\,\overline{v_x}\,| = 2 .\qquad\qquad\qquad 5.10.6$$

Thus the expression (1.15.6) for the number of molecules striking unit area of a surface per second should read

$$\Gamma = \tfrac{1}{2}n\,|\,\overline{v_x}\,| = \tfrac{1}{4}n\bar{v},\qquad\qquad 5.10.7$$

as was obtained by other methods in § 4.10. We have already noted (§§ 2.5–11) that it is rare to find experimental data sufficiently accurate to distinguish this formula from 1.15.6, which we used in chapter 2.

The most probable velocity v_m is the maximum of $f(v)$. It is most readily obtained by differentiation with respect to v^2. Thus

$$\frac{d}{d(v^2)}\{v^2\,e^{-\mu v^2}\}$$

$$= -v^2\mu\,e^{-\mu v^2} + e^{-\mu v^2}$$

$$= 0 \text{ for a maximum}.$$

So $v_m^2 = 1/\mu,$

$$v_m = (2kT/m)^{\frac{1}{2}}.\qquad\qquad 5.10.8$$

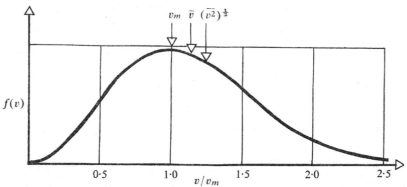

Figure 5.6. Maxwell's distribution law. Speeds are plotted as fractions of the most probable speed v_m (equation 5.10.8).

The ordinates corresponding to v_m, $\bar{v}$ and $(\overline{v^2})^{\frac{1}{2}}$ are all indicated in *fig.* 5.6. The ratios

$$v_m : \bar{v} : (\overline{v^2})^{\frac{1}{2}} = 1 : 2/\pi^{\frac{1}{2}} : (\tfrac{3}{2})^{\frac{1}{2}}$$

$$\simeq 1 : 1\cdot13 : 1\cdot23 \qquad\qquad 5.10.9$$

are all independent of mass and temperature.

The fraction of molecules having speeds $> v_0$ is

$$\frac{\displaystyle\int_{v_0}^{\infty} f(v)\,dv}{\displaystyle\int_{0}^{\infty} f(v)\,dv} = \frac{\displaystyle\int_{v_0}^{\infty} v^2\, e^{-\mu v^2}\, dv}{\displaystyle\int_{0}^{\infty} v^2\, e^{-\mu v^2}\, dv},$$

where $\qquad\qquad \mu = m/2kT.$

The denominator can be integrated as usual; the numerator can be integrated by parts by writing

$$\int_{v_0}^{\infty} v^2\, e^{-\mu v^2}\, dv = \int_{v_0}^{\infty} v[v\, e^{-\mu v^2}]\,dv$$

$$= \frac{v_0}{2\mu}\, e^{-\mu v_0^2} + \frac{1}{2\mu}\int_{v_0}^{\infty} e^{-\mu v^2}\, dv.$$

The integral $\displaystyle\int_{v_0}^{\infty} e^{-\mu v^2}\, dv$ cannot be evaluated explicitly but it can be written

$$\int_{v_0}^{\infty} e^{-\mu v^2}\, dv = \int_{0}^{\infty} e^{-\mu v^2}\, dv - \int_{0}^{v_0} e^{-\mu v^2}\, dv. \qquad 5.10.10$$

The first of these integrals has the value $\frac{1}{2}(\pi/\mu)^{\frac{1}{2}}$. The second is available from tables as the *error function* (§ 12.7), which is usually tabulated as

$$\text{erf } x = \frac{2}{\pi^{\frac{1}{2}}}\int_{0}^{x} e^{-x^2}\, dx. \qquad\qquad 5.10.11$$

The results of such a calculation are given in table 8.

TABLE 8 : % of molecules with speeds greater than certain multiples of the mean

$v/\bar{v}$	0·5	1·0	1·5	2·0	2·5	3·0
%	88·8	46·7	12·6	1·7	0·12	0·01

Table 8 shows that only 1 molecule in 10⁴ has a speed more than three times the mean. The ordinates corresponding to various values of $v/\bar{v}$ are indicated in *fig.* 5.6.

In this section we have derived the Maxwell distribution law by purely statistical reasoning using a model which assumes nothing but the laws of probability and the laws of conservation of particles and energy. We have made no assumptions about the nature of the gas molecules or the collisions between them. In § 5.14 we give a brief account of direct experimental tests of the distribution law. Meantime, in the next section we look at a shorter proof.

§ 5.11   Maxwell's derivation of the velocity distribution law

Maxwell originally derived the distribution law which bears his name by assuming no more than that the velocities were distributed randomly. It is instructive to follow through his arguments, feeding in the assumptions as required.

We first draw vectors from a common origin, each vector representing the velocity of one molecule. The resulting figure (*fig.* 5.7) re-

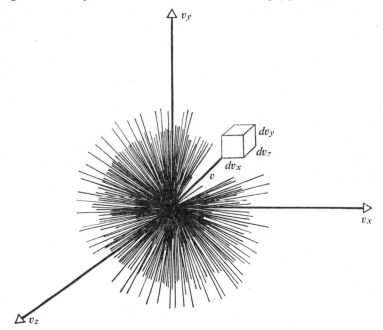

Figure 5.7. Maxwell's derivation of his distribution law.

sembles a spiny sea-urchin and from what we know already we shall expect that there will be relatively few very short spines, more with intermediate length and again few very long ones.

If we assume as we did before that all directions of motion are equally probable, and that the number of molecules is very large, then the probability that a given vector ends in a small element of volume, such as that indicated, depends only on the length of the radius vector, that is on v, and on the size of the volume element which is $dv_x dv_y dv_z$. We may write the dependence on v as $\phi(v^2)$ and the combined probability as

$$\phi(v^2)dv_x dv_y dv_z .$$

By our definition of probability the same expression represents the fraction of radius vectors which end in this element of volume.

We now add the assumption that the probability of a molecule having a given velocity in any direction is independent of the velocity in any perpendicular direction. If the probability that a molecule has x-component of velocity in the range v_x to $v_x + dv_x$ is written as $f(v_x)dv_x$, then the probability that it has components of velocity within the ranges v_x to $v_x + dv_x$, v_y to $v_y + dv_y$, and v_z to $v_z + dv_z$ is the product of three independent probabilities and can be written as $f(v_x)dv_x f(v_y)dv_y f(v_z)dv_z$. This probability is the same as that which we have already obtained in terms of v, so

$$f(v_x)f(v_y)f(v_z)dv_x dv_y dv_z = \phi(v^2)dv_x dv_y dv_z . \qquad 5.11.1$$

Further $v^2 = v_x^2 + v_y^2 + v_z^2$, $\qquad\qquad\qquad\qquad\qquad$ 5.11.2

so $\qquad f(v_x)f(v_y)f(v_z) = \phi(v_x^2 + v_y^2 + v_z^2)$. $\qquad\qquad$ 5.11.3

The function f is thus required to have the property that the product of three functions of different variables is a function of the sum of the variables. This identifies f as an exponential. We shall follow Maxwell in not attempting to solve the functional equations 5.11.1–3 analytically but simply noting that they are satisfied by

$$f(v_x) = C\, e^{-\mu v_x^2}, \qquad\qquad\qquad\qquad\qquad 5.11.4$$

which we now know to be correct. C and μ are obtained the same way as in § 5.8.

Boltzmann criticised Maxwell's derivation on the grounds that molecular collisions were never even mentioned. He argued that the distribution obtained would be the same if there were no collisions, whereas we know that equilibrium is established as a result of collisions. Boltzmann's derivation, therefore, makes a feature of elastic collision theory, perhaps at the cost of hiding the purely statistical nature of the result. A simplified derivation on the lines of Boltzmann's is given in § 10.8.

The derivation in §§ 5.8–10 attempts to get the best of both approaches: the result is purely statistical but the collisions are required to move the representative points from cell to cell in momentum space. Given a means of changing the complexion of the system we can assume that all microscopic configurations allowed by the conservation laws will be tried if we wait long enough. Of these configurations, some occur so much more frequently than others as to be effectively the only ones ever observed. These give our distribution law.

§ 5.12   Generalisation of the Maxwell distribution

The distribution law we have just found can be written in the form

$$f(v_x,v_y,v_z)dv_xdv_ydv_z = \frac{e^{-\varepsilon(v_x,v_y,v_z)/kT} \, dv_xdv_ydv_z}{\displaystyle\int_{-\infty}^{\infty}\int_{-\infty}^{\infty}\int_{-\infty}^{\infty} e^{-\varepsilon(v_x,v_y,v_z)/kT}dv_xdv_ydv_z}, \quad 5.12.1$$

where $\varepsilon(v_x,v_y,v_z) = \tfrac{1}{2}mv_x^2+\tfrac{1}{2}mv_y^2+\tfrac{1}{2}mv_z^2$ 5.12.2

is simply the (kinetic) energy of a molecule expressed in terms of v_x, v_y and v_z. The triple integral in the denominator ensures that f is a true probability in that the probability that a given molecule has velocity components each between $-\infty$ and $+\infty$ is a certainty. While it is convenient to write the denominator as a triple integral, the form of the integrand and the limits are such that the triple integral is simply the product of three single integrals:

$$\int_{-\infty}^{\infty}\int_{-\infty}^{\infty}\int_{-\infty}^{\infty} e^{-\varepsilon(v_x,v_y,v_z)/kT} \, dv_xdv_ydv_z$$

$$= \int_{-\infty}^{\infty}\int_{-\infty}^{\infty}\int_{-\infty}^{\infty} e^{-\frac{1}{2}m(v_x^2+v_y^2+v_z^2)/kT} \, dv_xdv_ydv_z$$

$$= \int_{-\infty}^{\infty} e^{-\frac{1}{2}mv_x^2/kT} \, dv_x \times \int_{-\infty}^{\infty} e^{-\frac{1}{2}mv_y^2/kT} \, dv_y \times$$

$$\times \int_{-\infty}^{\infty} e^{-\frac{1}{2}mv_z^2/kT} \, dv_z$$

$$= \sqrt{\frac{2\pi kT}{m}} \times \sqrt{\frac{2\pi kT}{m}} \times \sqrt{\frac{2\pi kT}{m}}. \quad 5.12.3$$

Now in §§ 1.6–9 we extended the law of equipartition to include forms of energy other than translational. We may in similar fashion generalise the distribution law 5.12.1. First, we take account of the possibility that the energy of the particle may depend on its position or orientation and include co-ordinates x, y, z, etc., among the variables contributing to ε. We generalise these co-ordinates by calling them $q_1, q_2, \ldots, q_m$. Then we introduce generalised momenta $p_x = mv_x, p_y = mv_y, \ldots$ instead of velocities so that we can deal with rotations, vibrations, etc. The momenta are likewise generalised by the notation $p_1, p_2, \ldots, p_n$.

Then the probability that a particle has co-ordinates in the range q_1 to $q_1 + dq_1$, q_2 to $q_2 + dq_2$, and so on, and momenta in the range p_1 to $p_1 + dp_1$, p_2 to $p_2 + dp_2$, and so on, is

$$f(q_1, \ldots, q_m, p_1, \ldots, p_n)dq_1 \ldots dq_m dp_1 \ldots dp_n =$$

$$= \frac{\exp\{-\varepsilon(q_1, \ldots, q_m, p_1, \ldots, p_n)/kT\}dq_1 \ldots dq_m dp_1 \ldots dp_n}{\int \ldots \int \exp\{-\varepsilon(q_1, \ldots, q_m, p_1, \ldots, p_n)/kT\}dq_1 \ldots dq_m dp_1 \ldots dp_n}.$$

$$5.12.4$$

The integration in each case is over all possible values of the variable; thus a momentum could take all values from $-\infty$ to $+\infty$ but co-ordinates might be more limited: for example, a gravitational potential energy mgz would be integrated over the vertical dimension of the system, an angle over the range 0 to 2π, and so on.

Equation 5.12.4 is the Maxwell-Boltzmann distribution and its proof is no more difficult in principle than the proof for the three components p_x, p_y, p_z. We construct a set of mutually perpendicular axes in a space of $m+n$ dimensions and draw planes as before dividing all space up into multidimensional cells. Representative points are again put in these cells in a random manner but subject to conservation of representative points and energy. The procedure is exactly as before in § 5.8.

§ 5.13   Applications of the Maxwell-Boltzmann distribution

The linear harmonic oscillator. To illustrate the use of the generalised expression, consider an assembly of identical particles of mass m vibrating in one dimension about their positions of equilibrium to which they are fixed by springs with spring constant (force/unit displacement) λ. The energy of each particle is

$$\varepsilon(q, p) = \tfrac{1}{2}\lambda q^2 + p^2/2m, \qquad\qquad 5.13.1$$

where q is the displacement from the position of equilibrium and p

the momentum. The mean energy is

$$\bar{\varepsilon}(q,p) = \frac{\int_{-\infty}^{\infty}\int_{-\infty}^{\infty} \varepsilon(q,p)f(q,p)dqdp}{\int_{-\infty}^{\infty}\int_{-\infty}^{\infty} f(q,p)dqdp} \qquad 5.13.2$$

$$= \frac{\int_{-\infty}^{\infty}\int_{-\infty}^{\infty} (\tfrac{1}{2}\lambda q^2 + p^2/2m)\, e^{-(\tfrac{1}{2}\lambda q^2 + p^2/2m)/kT}\, dqdp}{\int_{-\infty}^{\infty}\int_{-\infty}^{\infty} e^{-(\tfrac{1}{2}\lambda q^2 + p^2/2m)/kT}\, dqdp}$$

$$= \frac{\int_{-\infty}^{\infty} \tfrac{1}{2}\lambda q^2\, e^{-\tfrac{1}{2}\lambda q^2/kT}\, dq \times \int_{-\infty}^{\infty} e^{-p^2/2mkT}\, dp}{\int_{-\infty}^{\infty} e^{-\tfrac{1}{2}\lambda q^2/kT}\, dq \times \int_{-\infty}^{\infty} e^{-p^2/2mkT}\, dp} +$$

$$+ \frac{\int_{-\infty}^{\infty} e^{-\tfrac{1}{2}\lambda q^2/kT}\, dq \times \int_{-\infty}^{\infty} (p^2/2m)\, e^{-p^2/2mkT}\, dp}{\int_{-\infty}^{\infty} e^{-\tfrac{1}{2}\lambda q^2/kT}\, dq \times \int_{-\infty}^{\infty} e^{-p^2/2mkT}\, dp}.$$

Cancelling the integrals which are the same in numerator and denominator and evaluating the integral quotients as shown in § 12.6, we obtain

$$\bar{\varepsilon}(q,p) = \tfrac{1}{2}kT + \tfrac{1}{2}kT = kT, \qquad 5.13.3$$

which proves the assumption we made when we extended the law of equipartition of energy in § 1.9. A similar proof shows that the mean value of any term which occurs in the expression for the energy as the square of a co-ordinate or momentum is $\tfrac{1}{2}kT$.

The barometer formula. The usefulness of the Maxwell-Boltzmann distribution is not confined to terms involving squares: for example, the gravitational potential energy of a gas molecule is mgz, where z is the height above the Earth. The mean value of this energy is

$$\bar{\varepsilon}(z) = \frac{\int_0^l \varepsilon(z)f(z)dz}{\int_0^l f(z)dz} = \frac{\int_0^l mgz\, e^{-mgz/kT}\, dz}{\int_0^l e^{-mgz/kT}\, dz}, \qquad 5.13.4$$

where l is the co-ordinate corresponding to the top of the container.

The integrals are of the same type as we met (§ 4.1) in connection with mean free paths; so writing $\alpha = mg/kT$ we have

$$\bar{\varepsilon} = -mg\frac{\partial}{\partial\alpha}\ln\int_0^l e^{-\alpha z}\,dz$$

$$= -mg\frac{\partial}{\partial\alpha}\ln\frac{1}{\alpha}(1-e^{-\alpha l}). \qquad 5.13.5$$

The interesting cases are

(i) *l is small*, being a dimension of a normal container of gas. Then substituting $e^{-\alpha l}\simeq 1-\alpha l$ in 5.13.5 gives

$$\bar{\varepsilon} = 0, \qquad 5.13.6$$

so that, as we would have expected, the gravitational energy does not contribute to the total thermal energy of a small mass of gas. The meaning of the word 'small' in this context is defined by the requirement

$$\alpha l \ll 1$$

or $$\frac{mgl}{kT} \ll 1.$$

For an air molecule $m \sim 10^{-25}$ kg while $g \simeq 10$ m/sec² and kT at room temperature $\simeq 5\times 10^{-21}$ J.
Hence

$$\frac{mgl}{kT} \sim \frac{l}{5}\times 10^{-3};$$

so $l < 1$ km will satisfy the condition '*l* is small'.

(ii) *l is large*: let $l\to\infty$. Then

$$\bar{\varepsilon} = mg\frac{\partial}{\partial\alpha}\ln\alpha \qquad 5.13.7$$

$$= kT,$$

a rather academic result for gravitational energy but serving to show that the mean (equipartition) value of the energy corresponding to any term which is directly proportional to a co-ordinate or momentum is kT.

The mean height of a gas molecule in the atmosphere. If we take it that the atmosphere is all at one temperature T we can immediately write down the mean height of a molecule:

$$\bar{z} = \frac{\displaystyle\int_0^\infty z\, e^{-V(z)/kT}\, dz}{\displaystyle\int_0^\infty e^{-V(z)/kT}\, dz}.$$ 5.13.8

$V(z)$ is the potential energy of a molecule at height z and $\exp\{-V(z)/kT\}dz$ is consequently the fraction of molecules at heights between z and $z+dz$.

Now $V(z) = mgz$, so we have the same integrals as in the previous example. Evaluating them either by elementary methods or by differentiation (§ 12.1–3), we obtain

$$\bar{z} = kT/mg\,.$$ 5.13.9

In this form $\bar{z}$ has the less academic interpretation that the mean height of an air molecule above the surface of the earth is determined by a compromise between the ordering effect of the gravitational field, which tends to bring all air molecules to a state of equilibrium on the ground, and the disordering effect of thermal energy, which tends to distribute them throughout space. We used this argument in § 3.1 to explain why the atmosphere did not fall down.

The Langevin theory of paramagnetism. A more interesting case is one where the energy of a particle depends on its orientation.

Consider now a gas of N molecules each possessing a permanent magnetic dipole moment μ placed in a uniform magnetic field B. The dipoles will tend to line up parallel to the field in the same way as compass needles do, and the alignment will be opposed by thermal vibrations which tend to give random orientation. We have to calculate the mean resultant magnetic moment $N\bar{\mu}$.

Let θ be the angle between the axis of a given dipole and the direction of the field. Then the component of the dipole moment in the direction of the field is $\mu \cos \theta$ and the mean resultant moment is

$$\bar{\mu} = \frac{\displaystyle\int \mu \cos \theta\, e^{-V(\theta)/kT}\, d\Omega}{\displaystyle\int e^{-V(\theta)/kT}\, d\Omega},$$ 5.13.10

where $d\Omega$ is the element of solid angle between cones with semi-angles θ and $\theta+d\theta$, as shown in *fig.* 5.8, and $V(\theta)$ is the potential energy of a dipole at angle θ to the field. The integrals are to be taken over all Ω. We note that the derivation of 5.13.10 involves using the

Maxwell-Boltzmann statistics (5.12.4) to give the fraction f of dipoles which lie within the element of solid angle $d\Omega$ to be

$$f\,d\Omega = \frac{e^{-V(\theta)/kT}\,d\Omega}{\int e^{-V(\theta)/kT}\,d\Omega}.$$

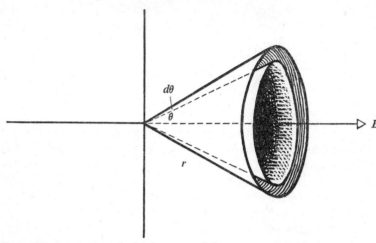

Figure 5.8. *Orientation of a dipole at an angle θ to a magnetic field B.*

Now the area of the shaded region in *fig.* 5.8 is $r^2\,d\Omega$ in terms of Ω and $2\pi r \sin\theta \cdot r\,d\theta$ in terms of θ. Thus

$$d\Omega = 2\pi \sin\theta\,d\theta \qquad\qquad 5.13.11$$

and the limits of integration are $0 \leqslant \theta \leqslant \pi$, this result, obtained here from first principles, being essentially the same as 4.9.2.

$V(\theta)$ is the work to displace a dipole from being parallel to the field to being at an angle θ to the field. Since from elementary physics the couple on a magnet of magnetic moment μ at angle θ to a field B is $\mu B \sin\theta$, we have

$$V(\theta) = \int_0^\theta \mu B \sin\theta\,d\theta$$
$$= \mu B(1 - \cos\theta). \qquad\qquad 5.13.12$$

Substituting 5.13.12 and 5.13.11 in 5.13.10 gives (cancelling constant factors)

$$\bar\mu = \frac{\mu\displaystyle\int_0^\pi \cos\theta \sin\theta\, e^{(\mu B/kT)\cos\theta}\,d\theta}{\displaystyle\int_0^\pi \sin\theta\, e^{(\mu B/kT)\cos\theta}\,d\theta},$$

whence, writing $a = \mu B / kT$, we have

$$\bar{\mu} = \mu \frac{\partial}{\partial a} \ln \int_0^{\pi} \sin \theta \, e^{a \cos \theta} \, d\theta$$

$$= \mu \frac{\partial}{\partial a} \ln \left[-\frac{1}{a} e^{a \cos \theta} \right]_0^{\pi}$$

$$= \mu \frac{\partial}{\partial a} \ln \frac{1}{a} (e^a - e^{-a})$$

$$= \mu \frac{\partial}{\partial a} \ln \frac{2}{a} \sinh a$$

$$= \mu \left(\frac{\cosh a}{\sinh a} - \frac{1}{a} \right)$$

$$= \mu \left(\coth a - \frac{1}{a} \right)$$

$$= \mu L(a).$$

The function $L(a) = \coth a - 1/a$ is called the Langevin function. In practice, magnetic fields available to us are so small that

$$\mu B \ll kT,$$

that is

$$a \ll 1,$$

and in this case $L(a)$ reduces to $a/3$.

So, if we have N dipoles, the total magnetic moment is

$$M = N\bar{\mu} = \tfrac{1}{3} N\mu \cdot \frac{\mu B}{kT}, \qquad\qquad 5.13.13$$

a result which shows that the orientation of a dipole is a balance between the magnetic energy μB, which tends to give order and the thermal energy kT, which opposes order. A similar result with a corresponding formula is obtained for the orientation of an electric dipole in an electric field.

§ 5.14 Experimental tests of the Maxwell distribution of velocities of gas molecules

We shall briefly describe two experiments which test the truth of the Maxwell distribution, one using the technique of molecular beams, the other a more direct but less sensitive technique.

Molecular beams. In the molecular beam techniques, the gas to be studied – usually a metallic vapour – is maintained at a high temperature in an oven. Atoms or molecules of the gas are allowed to leave the oven through a small hole and pass as a beam of particles into an evacuated enclosure where their times of flight over fairly long distances can be measured free from the complications introduced by molecular collisions.

One such technique, due to Hall, and carried out by Zartmann and Ko, used the apparatus shown schematically in *fig.* 5.9: metal vapour

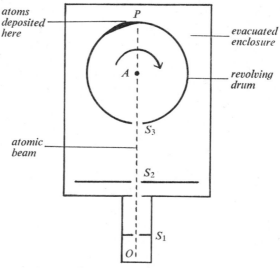

Figure 5.9. *Zartmann and Ko's apparatus for investigating the distribution of molecular speeds.*

atoms leave the oven O by the slit S_1 and pass into a highly evacuated region. The atomic beam is defined by further slits S_2 and then impinges on a revolving drum which rotates at high speed around an axis A parallel to the slits. Once every revolution a slit S_3 in the drum allows a batch of particles to enter it and continue their flight to the opposite side. If there were any particles with infinite speed they would hit the drum at P, exactly opposite to their entry point, but in general the time for a particle to cross the drum is inversely proportional to its speed (problem 5.15.6) so that slower particles reach the drum at points further from P in the direction shown. A glass plate fixed to the drum receives the deposited metal atoms in amounts which vary with distance from P in a manner related to the function $f(v)$. Photometry of the glass plate allows these amounts to be measured.

In Zartmann and Ko's experiments the oven contained bismuth at 827°C and the drum, 10 cm in diameter, revolved at 6000 rpm. The deposit of bismuth spread over a few centimetres, the peak occurring about 1 cm from the point diametrically opposite the entrance slit. Some of the complications of the interpretation of the resulting distribution, in particular those relating to the facts that the molecules have components of velocity in directions other than that of the beam, and that not all the bismuth occurs as atomic Bi, are discussed in problem 5.15.6. Another complication was one common to all atomic beam experiments: this is that the exit slit of the furnace has to be narrower than a mean free path of the vapour at the pressure in the furnace; otherwise molecular collisions may occur within the slit and the beam assumptions become invalid. On the other hand, the slit cannot be too narrow or the beam intensity becomes too low to allow measurable deposits to be collected in times of the order of hours.

Doppler line breadth. Tests of the Maxwell distribution involving the use of molecular beams, while straightforward, do involve artificial separation of the various speeds. It is interesting, therefore, to consider a phenomenon where the distribution reveals itself. One of these is the broadening of spectral lines by the motion of the gaseous atoms emitting them.

The optical spectrum from a gas of atoms and molecules consists of lines which have width determined by three main factors: first there is a natural width determined by the electronic processes which produce the light; this width is usually too small to observe. Then there is the width determined by the optics and dimensions of the spectroscope; this is under our control and can be limited. Finally there is a broadening of the lines due to motion of the molecules emitting them; this is readily observable and is due to the Doppler effect whereby the wavelength of a source, emitting light of wavelength λ_0, and moving with velocity v_x along the line of sight between the source and the observer, is seen as

$$\lambda = \lambda_0(1+v_x/c),\qquad\qquad 5.14.1$$

where c is the speed of light. If the source is moving away from the observer, $\lambda > \lambda_0$; if towards him, $\lambda < \lambda_0$.

If then there are $nf(v_x)dv_x$ molecules per unit volume emitting light of natural wavelength λ_0 and moving with velocities between v_x and $v_x + dv_x$ in the direction joining the source to the observer, the observer will see light with wavelengths between λ and $\lambda + d\lambda$, where λ is given by 5.14.1 and $d\lambda$ by

$$d\lambda = \lambda_0 \frac{dv_x}{c}.$$ 5.14.2

The intensity $I\,d\lambda$ of the light within the range λ to $\lambda + d\lambda$ will be proportional to $nf_x(v_x)dv_x$, that is

$$I\,d\lambda = An f(v_x)dv_x,$$ 5.14.3

where A is a constant.

Substituting 5.14.2 in 5.14.3, writing $f_x(v_x) = \text{const.} \times e^{-mv_x^2/2kT}$ and substituting for v_x the expression from 5.14.1,

$$v_x = c(\lambda - \lambda_0)/\lambda_0,$$

gives $I = I_0 \exp\left\{-mc^2(\lambda - \lambda_0)^2/2\lambda_0^2 kT\right\},$ 5.14.4

where I_0 is a constant.

Experimentally, the variation of intensity I with λ on either side of λ_0 is measured photometrically. Assuming that sources of broadening other than Doppler can be eliminated or allowed for, a plot of $\ln I$ against $(\lambda - \lambda_0)^2$ should give a straight line, the slope of which is proportional to the reciprocal of the absolute temperature of the source. The results of such an experiment are shown in *fig.* 5.10. Here a discharge was passed through heated helium gas at a pressure of 1 torr, and the 5016 Å spectral line photometered. In the figure, the logarithm of the intensity at each wavelength has been plotted against $(1/\lambda - 1/\lambda_0)^2$ which, since $\lambda - \lambda_0 \sim 0 \cdot 1$ Å $\ll \lambda_0$, is equivalent to plotting against $(\lambda - \lambda_0)^2 \lambda_0^{-4}$. The left-hand line, which corresponds to Doppler shifts towards shorter wavelengths, is accurately straight, and its slope corresponds to a temperature of $400°K$; the right-hand, longer, wavelength line is almost straight and corresponds to a temperature of $480°K$. The discrepancy in slopes and the failure to find exact linearity mean that the speed distribution was distorted from Maxwellian; this was ascribed to thermal gradients in the helium gas which it was the real object of the experiment to study.

Since the slope of the line depends on T, such a plot can be used to measure temperature, though the method would hardly be used if any simpler one were available. A common example of its use is to measure the temperature of gases in stellar atmospheres: here the temperature is likely to be higher than from terrestrial sources, so the Doppler width of the line is larger, effectively swamping other sources of broadening. A recent application has been to estimate the

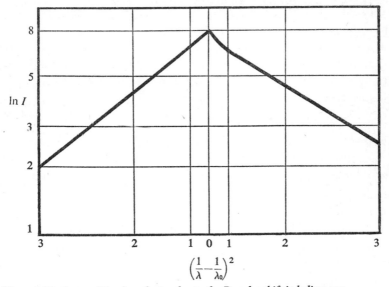

Figure 5.10. Spectral line broadening due to the Doppler shift in helium gas. Each unit of abscissa corresponds to 0·0011 cm⁻² (from L. S. Ornstein and W. R. van Wyk, Zeits. f. Physik 78, 734, 1932).

temperature of a plasma: atoms of a heavy gas, not likely to be completely ionized by the high temperature, were mixed with the components of the plasma and measurements made of the breadth of the spectral lines then emitted. If it could be assumed that the heavy gas atoms were in equilibrium with the plasma components, the resulting line widths gave the required temperature, which was of the order of millions of degrees.

§ 5.15 Problems

1. In § 3.1 we discussed a model of the atmosphere where molecules left the ground with vertical speed v_0, did not collide with each other and consequently all reached a maximum height

$$z_0 = v_0^2/2g \,.$$

11

The fact that the atmosphere does not stop abruptly at height z_0, but falls off in density according to the barometric law,

$$n(z) = n_0 \exp(-mgz/kT),$$

where T is assumed constant, must then arise because molecules do not all leave the ground with the same speed. Thus v_0 is not a constant.

Write the flux of molecules leaving the ground with vertical speed between v_0 and $v_0 + dv_0$ as $n v_0 f(v_0) dv_0$ and equate this to the difference between the fluxes crossing planes at heights z_0 and $z_0 + dz_0$ respectively. This equation, together with the two others already quoted in this problem, will give the one-dimensional velocity distribution in the form

$$f(v_0) = (m\bar{v}/kT) \exp(-mv_0^2/2kT),$$

where $\bar{v}$ is the mean speed and is constant everywhere, since T is constant. Since z_0 can be any height, not necessarily the ground, the subscript zero can be dropped to give the usual form of $f_z(v_z)$.

2. Show that it is not necessary to assume, as we did in § 5.7, that the differences in energy between successive cells are all the same.

To do this, consider three cells corresponding to energies ε_1, ε_2 and ε_3, in ascending order of magnitude, and assume that small numbers m_1 and m_3 can be found such that

$$m_1\varepsilon_1 + m_3\varepsilon_3 = (m_1 + m_3)\varepsilon_2.$$

Then the transfer of m_1 particles from cell ε_1, together with m_3 particles from cell ε_3, all to cell ε_2, will conserve energy. Write down expressions for w and w^* before and after the transfer and compare them as in equation 5.7.5. This serves to prove equation 5.7.9.

3. In a two-dimensional gas show that the relationship between the most probable speed v_m, the mean speed $\bar{v}$, and the root-mean-square speed $(\overline{v^2})^{\frac{1}{2}}$ is

$$v_m : \bar{v} : (\overline{v^2})^{\frac{1}{2}} = 1 : (\tfrac{1}{2}\pi)^{\frac{1}{2}} : 2^{\frac{1}{2}}.$$

4. Use the approximation 12.7.3 to the complementary error function

$$(\pi^{\frac{1}{2}}/2)\operatorname{erfc} x = \int_{x_0}^{\infty} e^{-x^2}\, dx \simeq (1/2x_0)\, e^{-x_0^2},$$

valid for $x_0 \gg 1$, to test the results given in table 8, which were obtained from a better approximation. Show that the condition $x_0 \gg 1$ is not very severe.

5. A metallic vapour is held at temperature T within an oven and allowed to escape through a small hole into an evacuated enclosure, as in the experimental arrangements described in §5.14.

(i) Show that the mean energy of the molecules emitted from the hole is

$$\overline{\tfrac{1}{2}mv^2} = \frac{\tfrac{1}{2}m\displaystyle\int_0^\infty v^5\, e^{-mv^2/2kT}\, dv}{\displaystyle\int_0^\infty v^3\, e^{-mv^2/2kT}\, dv}$$

$$= 2kT,$$

whereas the mean (equipartition) energy within the oven is $\tfrac{3}{2}kT$.

(ii) Show further that the most probable speed of a molecule in the beam is $(3kT/m)^{\frac{1}{2}}$ as compared with the value $(2kT/m)^{\frac{1}{2}}$ given by 5.10.8 for the equilibrium distribution. When the speed distribution is displayed as a distribution of atoms in space, as described in § 5.14, the most probable speed determines the position of the maximum intensity. An actual calculation of this appears in the next problem.

6. The diameter of the drum in a Zartmann and Ko apparatus is d and it revolves at n revolutions per second.

(i) Show that the displacement of the point at which a molecule with velocity v is deposited is

$$s = \pi n d^2 / v,$$

where $s = 0$ is the point directly opposite the entrance slit. Thus, molecules having speeds in the range v to $v + dv$ will be spread over a distance ds given by

$$ds = -\pi n d^2\, dv / v^2.$$

(ii) If I is the number of molecules deposited per unit length, use the same methods as in problem 5 to show that

$$I\, ds = -Cv^3\, e^{-Mv^2/2RT}\, dv,$$

where C is a constant and thus that I is given by

$$I = C's^{-5} \exp\left(-\pi^2 n^2 d^4 M / 2RTs^2\right),$$

where C' is another constant, so that the maximum intensity is found when

$$s^2 = \tfrac{1}{5}\pi^2 n^2 d^4 M / RT.$$

(iii) In Ko's experiments on Bi ($M = 209$), for which data are given in § 5.14, the measured distribution was analysed to show peaks at $s = 0.7$ cm and 1.0 cm with a smaller peak at 2.0 cm. Show that these results are consistent with the presence of the molecules Bi, Bi_2 and Bi_8 in the molecular beam.

(iv) Could a Zartmann and Ko-type apparatus be used to separate the isotopes of any element?

§ 5.16   Further reading

The methods used in § 5.7 were first developed in the first chapter of
R. W. Gurney *Introduction to Statistical Mechanics* McGraw-Hill,
New York and London, 1949.
This book subsequently proceeds to a very clear exposition of more advanced topics.

Chapter 6

THE RANDOM WALK

Suppose a man moves along a straight line, taking random steps to left or right. For example, he might toss a coin before each step; if the coin lands heads he takes the next step to the left if tails he goes to the right. The problem is to find the relative probabilities of his being 0, 1, 2, . . ., n steps from his starting point after n tosses of the coin. This is the problem of the random walk in one dimension; we shall first treat it as a mathematical problem, extending it to two and three dimensions. From time to time we shall seek to apply our results to various physical problems, of which the first and the most directly related to random walking is that of diffusion. Here we set up a model in which marked molecules, say impurities, are introduced at one point in the system and make successive flights each a free path in length but with random direction; we can then use the results of the random-walk theory to calculate how the impurities are distributed after a given time.

Later we shall see that when we measure any quantity there are many sources of error, some of which lead us to measure too high, some too low; application of random-walk theory will show us how to find the most probable sum of a large number of errors where the sign of each is determined by chance.

In a third application we shall re-derive the Maxwell velocity distribution by noting that a gas molecule is subject to impulses of random size and random direction due to impacts from other molecules. We shall use random-walk theory to calculate the most probable momentum of a molecule and the distribution of momenta.

§ 6.1 The random walk in one dimension

Suppose for simplicity that all steps are of equal length; at the start the random walker is certainly at the origin, after one step he cannot possibly be at the origin and has equal chances each with probability $\frac{1}{2}$ of being one step to left or right. After two steps the probability that he is two steps to the right is the same as the probability of obtaining tails with two successive tosses of a coin; there is zero probability of being one step from the origin and as to the chance of being back at the origin this is the same as the probability of obtaining a head followed by a tail, or a tail followed by a head. We can show this in a table:

TABLE 9 : probability of being q steps from the origin after n random steps

	q to left						q to right				
n	5	4	3	2	1	0	1	2	3	4	5
0						0	1	0			
1					0	$\frac{1}{2}$	0	$\frac{1}{2}$	0		
2				0	$\frac{1}{4}$	0	$\frac{2}{4}$	0	$\frac{1}{4}$	0	
3			0	$\frac{1}{8}$	0	$\frac{3}{8}$	0	$\frac{3}{8}$	0	$\frac{1}{8}$	0
4	0	$\frac{1}{16}$	0	$\frac{4}{16}$	0	$\frac{6}{16}$	0	$\frac{4}{16}$	0	$\frac{1}{16}$	0
5	$\frac{1}{32}$	0	$\frac{5}{32}$	0	$\frac{10}{32}$	0	$\frac{10}{32}$	0	$\frac{5}{32}$	0	$\frac{1}{32}$

In this table the denominators in each row are the quantities 2^n, the numerators are the numbers ^nC_q which appear in Pascal's triangle (§ 3.3) with zeros between them. From the table we see that:

(i) the probability that after n steps and n tosses the random walker is q steps to the right is the same as the probability that in his n tosses he has a majority of q tails or that he has obtained $\frac{1}{2}(n+q)$ tails and $\frac{1}{2}(n-q)$ heads.

(ii) after an even number of steps the most probable place for the walker to be is back at his starting point. This corresponds to the fact that equal distributions of heads and tails are most likely.

(iii) the sum of the probabilities across a row is unity as is obvious since the non-zero entries are the terms in the expansion of $(\frac{1}{2}+\frac{1}{2})^n$. This corresponds to the fact that the walker must be somewhere.

(iv) the mean displacement of the walker from the origin is zero.

(v) the mean-*square* displacement from the origin after n steps of length a is na^2. For example, after 4 steps we have

$$\overline{q^2a^2} = a^2(\tfrac{1}{16}\times 4^2 + \tfrac{4}{16}\times 2^2 + \tfrac{6}{16}\times 0^2 + \tfrac{4}{16}\times 2^2 + \tfrac{1}{16}\times 4^2)$$
$$= 4a^2 = na^2.$$

This result is true for all n though a general proof is best left until we have an explicit expression for the probability $P_n(q)$ that after n steps the random walker is q steps from the origin.

We can obtain a formula for $P_n(q)$ in the same way as we did in § 5.5 to obtain the relative probabilities of deviations from the most probable distribution of molecules between two equally probable boxes. Thus

$$P_n(q) = (\tfrac{1}{2})^n \frac{n!}{[\tfrac{1}{2}(n-q)]![\tfrac{1}{2}(n+q)]!}, \qquad 6.1.1$$

which is of course a maximum for $q = 0$. To put 6.1.1 in more tractable form we proceed exactly as in § 4.6 and § 5.5 except that, to avoid difficulties with the zeros in our table, we now form $P_n(q+2)$, the probability that after n steps the walker is $q+2$ from his starting point. We have

$$P_n(q+2) = (\tfrac{1}{2})^n \frac{n!}{[\tfrac{1}{2}(n-q-2)]![\tfrac{1}{2}(n+q+2)]!},$$

$$\frac{P_n(q+2)}{P_n} = \frac{P_n+(dP/dq).2}{P_n}$$

$$= 1 + \frac{2}{P}\frac{dP}{dq} = \frac{\tfrac{1}{2}(n-q)}{\tfrac{1}{2}(n+q)+1},$$

$$\frac{1}{P}\frac{dP}{dq} = \frac{-q-1}{n+q+2}$$

$$\simeq -\frac{q}{n}, \qquad 6.1.2$$

if $n \gg q \gg 1$. We can justify the assumption that $n \gg q$ since we already know from (v) above that the root-mean-square value of q is $n^{\frac{1}{2}}$.

Integrating 6.1.2 gives

$$P_n = P_{n0}\, e^{-q^2/2n}, \qquad 6.1.3$$

where P_{n0} is a constant which can in principle be obtained by normalising, that is by writing

$$\sum_{q=-n}^{q=n} P_{n0}\, e^{-q^2/2n} = 1. \qquad 6.1.4$$

Formula 6.1.3 can easily be shown to be the same as we obtained in § 5.5 for the probability of deviations from the mean distribution of balls between boxes. The superficial difference is due to difference in the definitions of q.

Sums such as 6.1.4 are difficult to handle and it is easier to convert them to integrals. To do this, suppose that the numbers of steps n and q become very large and the length of each step very short so that we may measure distance from the origin by the continuous variable $x = aq$. Equation 6.1.2 then becomes

$$\frac{1}{P}\frac{dP}{dx} = -\frac{x}{a^2 n},$$ 6.1.5

which integrates to

$$P(x) = P_0\, e^{-x^2/2a^2 n},$$

so that $P(x)dx$, the probability that after n steps of length a the random walker is between distance x and $x+dx$ from the starting point, is

$$P(x)dx = P_0\, e^{-x^2/2a^2 n}\, dx.$$

In this form it can readily be normalised by writing

$$\int_{-an}^{an} P_0\, e^{-x^2/2a^2 n}\, dx = 1.$$

As in § 5.5, we assume that since n is large the upper and lower limits can be taken as $\pm\infty$, that is

$$\int_{-\infty}^{\infty} P_0\, e^{-x^2/2a^2 n}\, dx = 1,$$

which using § 12.6 gives

$$P_0 = 1/(2a^2 n\pi)^{\frac{1}{2}}.$$ 6.1.6

Thus the normalised probability $P(x)$ is

$$P(x)dx = \frac{1}{(2a^2 n\pi)^{\frac{1}{2}}}\, e^{-x^2/2a^2 n}\, dx.$$ 6.1.7

The mean displacement $\bar{x}$ is

$$\bar{x} = \int_{-\infty}^{\infty} xP(x)dx = 0.$$

The mean-square displacement is

$$\overline{x^2} = \int_{-\infty}^{\infty} x^2 P(x)dx = a^2 n,$$ 6.1.8

the same result (v) as we obtained before for the first few steps. This is the most important result in random-walk theory.

Unequal steps. The above argument assumed that the steps were equal. We shall not attempt to generalise it to one where the steps are unequal but of random size except to see the effect on the most important formula 6.1.8. This can be read to mean that the mean-square number of steps from the origin after n^2 steps is n whatever the length of each step. Thus if, of our n steps from the origin,

n_1 were of length a_1,

n_2 were of length a_2,

. . . .

n_i were of length a_i,

then the quantity na^2, which represents the mean distance from the origin, becomes

$$\sum_{i=1}^{n} a_i^2 n_i = n\overline{a^2}, \qquad\qquad 6.1.9$$

so that 6.1.8 appears to be valid for unequal steps if we use the mean-square value of the step length. The importance of this result arises in diffusion of gases and liquids, where, as we shall see in § 6.4, the quantity we need is not Λ the mean free path, but $\sqrt{2}\Lambda$ the root-mean-square free path. An alternative 'proof' of 6.1.9 appears in problem 6.11.1.

§ 6.2 Application to diffusion

Suppose we have a row of equally-spaced boxes in one of which we have a large number N of red balls. All other boxes contain N white balls. Each ball is then caused to execute a random walk to-and-fro along the row by giving it, at equal intervals of time, the chance of making a random jump into the next box on its right or left, the probability of jumping being the same for both red and white balls. Thus the number of jumps made by any ball is proportional to time t:

$$n = vt.$$

The distance any ball moves in n jumps is given by the probability distribution 6.1.3.

This model is a credible one-dimensional representation of the mechanism of diffusion. Thus the central box initially full of balls represents the introduction of a high concentration of foreign atoms or molecules into a system. In a solid, the process of jumping to neighbouring boxes would represent some process whereby an atom can move to an adjacent lattice site, and the constant jump frequency v would mean that the probability of such a move was always the same. In a fluid, the mechanism would crudely represent the process whereby atoms or molecules go one free path at constant speed and are then stopped; the next free path is executed in an unpredictable direction which, in our one-dimensional model, has to be either straight on or straight back.

The first result of our theory is the obvious one that the total number of balls in any box remains constant. Indeed, this is already known from § 5.4, where we saw that the most probable distribution of balls (gas molecules) amongst boxes was one of constant density. To simplify the mathematics we assume that the number of boxes is very large so that instead of N balls per box we can use $\rho\,dx$ to mean the number of balls in the element of length from x to $x + dx$; ρ, the line density of balls, is a constant, if it refers to balls of either colour. The function $P(x)dx$ is then the fraction of our original set of red balls which have travelled a distance between x and $x + dx$ from the starting point after a time $t = n/v$, and the number of red balls in the element will be $\rho P(x)dx$, where $P(x)$ is given by

$$P(x)dx = (2a^2 v t \pi)^{-\frac{1}{2}}\, e^{-x^2/2a^2 v t}\, dx, \qquad\qquad 6.2.1$$

that is, by equation 6.1.7 with vt written for n; a is of course the spacing between boxes.

From equation 6.2.1 we can draw some conclusions about how the fraction of red balls will vary with time.

(i) At $x = 0$ the concentration of red balls will fall with time since red balls are spreading out along the line. The rate of fall is proportional to $t^{\frac{1}{2}}$.

(ii) At a given time t the concentration of red balls will fall as we go away from $x = 0$. At distance $x = (2a^2 v t)^{\frac{1}{2}}$, the concentration has fallen to e^{-1} of the $x = 0$ value.

(iii) *Fig.* 6.1 shows how the concentration varies with time. If we arbitrarily decide that we can detect the reddening of the mass of white balls when 1 % of red ones become mixed with them, then, ignoring the pre-exponential factor for the meantime on the principle (§ 12.8) that the 'exponential takes charge', we can see this occurs when

$$e^{-x^2/2a^2 v t} = 1\% \simeq e^{-5},$$

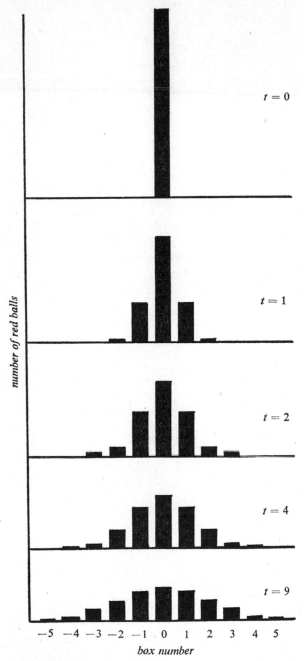

Figure 6.1. *Variation of concentration with duration of diffusion.*

that is, when

$$x \simeq (10a^2vt)^{\frac{1}{2}}, \qquad\qquad 6.2.2$$

so that the advance of the reddened zone proceeds proportional to $t^{\frac{1}{2}}$.

6.2.2. also shows that, in a diffusion or random-walk process, it is the square of the distance gone which is proportional to time. It is for this reason that the mean-square displacement was described in § 6.1 as 'the most important formula' in random-walk theory.

§ 6.3 Diffusion in solids

The one-dimensional model of a diffusing system is by no means purely academic. Thus the normal method of measuring diffusion coefficients (§ 2.8) in solid systems is to sandwich a thin layer (*fig. 6.2a*) containing a proportion of radioactive atoms between two inactive cylinders. At temperatures close to the melting point the atoms become mobile, and can make jumps to neighbouring lattice sites for reasons and at a rate discussed in § 10.9. Thus the initial concentration of active atoms shown in *fig. 6.2b* which corresponds to our initial concentration of red balls, spreads with time in the

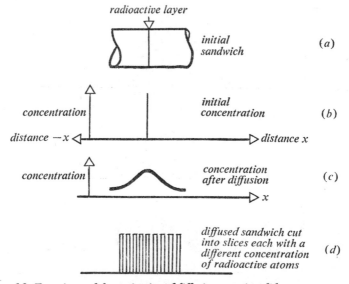

Figure 6.2. *Experimental determination of diffusion rates in solids.*

manner shown in *fig. 6.2c*. If the experiment is stopped after time *t* the concentration contour can be determined by turning off sections of equal thickness parallel to the original interface (*fig. 6.2d*). The concentration *c* of radioactive atoms in each section is found to obey a law of the form

$$\ln c = Cx^2, \qquad\qquad 6.3.1$$

where *C* is a constant. The results of such an experiment, where radioactive antimony was allowed to diffuse into copper for about four days at 758°C, are shown in *fig. 6.3*.

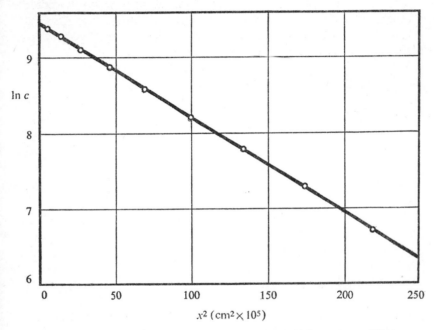

Figure 6.3. *Plot of* ln (*concentration*) *against* (*penetration*)^2 *for antimony diffusing into copper. The numerical data used in this graph are given in problem* 7.22.3.

Equation 6.3.1 is, of course, the same as 6.2.1. Similarly, the time one has to wait before a given concentration is observed at a given distance *x* from the original interface is found experimentally to vary with x^2. This is the experimental justification of 6.2.2.

To express these results in terms of the diffusion coefficient or diffusivity *D* in a one-dimensional system we start from the situation where a gradient of concentration dn/dx exists in the solid. In the examples above, n would represent the number of red balls per unit volume, or the number of radioactively tagged atoms per unit volume. n varies with distance x along the specimen, but for the one-dimensional case does not vary in the y or z directions. Then we recall from § 2.8 that D is defined by

$$\Gamma = -D\frac{dn}{dx},$$
6.3.2

where Γ is the flux (number per unit area per second) of tagged atoms.

We now assume that the atoms are arranged in a regular cubic array, the spacing between nearest neighbour atoms being a, and consider transport of tagged atoms between two planes perpendicular to the x-axis and distance a apart (*fig.* 6.4).

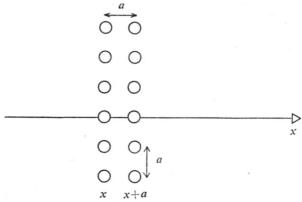

Figure 6.4. *One-dimensional diffusion in a cubic solid.*

If there are $n(x)$ tagged atoms per unit volume then there are $an(x)$ per unit area on the plane at distance x and $an(x+a)$ on the plane at $x+a$. If v, as defined in § 6.2, is the frequency with which atoms jump to neighbouring sites then nav tagged atoms per unit area are jumping per second. Of these jumps, two thirds are to positions in the same plane, in directions perpendicular to the concentration gradient. Of those one third of jumps which are in the direction of the concentration gradient, half are in the direction of the other plane. Thus, the number of tagged atoms jumping per second from unit area from the x plane to the plane at $x+a$ is $\frac{1}{6}avn(x)$. Similarly, the rate of jumping in the reverse direction is $\tfrac{1}{6}avn(x+a)$ and the net flux is

$$\Gamma = \tfrac{1}{6}avn(x) - \tfrac{1}{6}avn(x+a) \qquad \qquad 6.3.3$$

$$= -\tfrac{1}{6}a^2v\left\{\frac{n(x+a)-n(x)}{a}\right\} \qquad \qquad 6.3.4$$

$$= -\tfrac{1}{6}a^2v\frac{dn}{dx}, \qquad \qquad 6.3.5$$

since the quantity in brackets in 6.3.4 is the finite difference expression for the differential coefficient in 6.3.5.

Hence comparing 6.3.2 with 6.3.5 we have

$$D = \tfrac{1}{6}a^2v \qquad \qquad 6.3.6$$

or $\qquad D = \tfrac{1}{6}a^2/\tau, \qquad \qquad 6.3.7$

where $\tau = 1/v$ is the mean time between successive jumps.

6.3.7 is the formula for diffusivity originally derived by Einstein in his work on Brownian motion. It is valid for any random-walk process provided only that successive steps are uncorrelated, that is, are random with respect to direction.

If the jumps are strictly one-dimensional so that atoms cannot jump in directions perpendicular to the concentration gradient, then the numerical factor in the expression for D is easily seen to be $\tfrac{1}{2}$, so that

$$D = \tfrac{1}{2}a^2v. \qquad \qquad 6.3.8$$

These were the conditions applicable to the derivation of 6.2.1, which, with 6.3.8, becomes

$$P(x)dx = (4\pi Dt)^{-\frac{1}{2}} e^{-x^2/4Dt}\, dx. \qquad \qquad 6.3.9$$

6.3.9 enables us to re-interpret in terms of D, the results summed up in conclusions (i) to (iii) of § 6.2. For example, if diffusion takes place from a thin plane source, the depth at which the concentration has fallen to $1/e$ of the value at the source is $2(Dt)^{\frac{1}{2}}$ – an important parameter in diffusion theory and often called the *diffusion depth*. Equation 6.3.9 further shows that the constant C in 6.3.1 is given by

$$C = -1/4Dt. \qquad \qquad 6.3.10$$

This is the slope of a line such as that plotted in *fig.* 6.3. Finally, we may use 6.3.9 in conjunction with 6.1.8 to give the mean-square displacement of a particle moving in Brownian motion:

$$\overline{x^2} = 2Dt \qquad \qquad 6.3.11$$

166   THE RANDOM WALK

§ 6.4 Diffusion in gases

Equation 6.3.6 was derived for the special case where all jumps a are of equal length. We note that the expression obtained (2.8.4) for one-dimensional diffusion in gases was

$$D = \tfrac{1}{3}\bar{v}\Lambda, \qquad\qquad 6.4.1$$

where Λ was the mean free path. We shall now show that 6.4.1 and 6.3.6 are identical.

If we replace $\bar{v}$ by Λ/τ, where τ is the mean time between collisions, we obtain

$$D = \tfrac{1}{3}\Lambda^2/\tau,$$

which is not the same as 6.3.6 if Λ is taken to be the constant jump distance a. The discrepancy is resolved if we note that what is required is not Λ^2 but $\overline{s^2}$, where

$$\overline{s^2} = \int_0^\infty s^2 f(s)\,ds$$
$$= \frac{1}{\Lambda}\int_0^\infty s^2 e^{-s/\Lambda}\,ds$$
$$= 2\Lambda^2.$$

Thus, for one-dimensional diffusion in gases, we have once again the Einstein expression

$$D = \tfrac{1}{6}\overline{s^2}/\tau,$$

the same as we obtained (6.3.7) for the simple solid where all atom movements were of equal length. The same expression is valid for liquids.

§ 6.5 The random walk in two dimensions

In two dimensions the random walker may be assumed to start from the origin of co-ordinates and move randomly in either direction parallel to either the x or y axis. He might, for example, draw a card from a pack and move up, down, left or right, according to the suit drawn. The probability of any one such move is of course $\tfrac{1}{4}$.

It is instructive to draw up a two-dimensional table of probabilities in the same way as we did for the one-dimensional random walk. The tables corresponding to the first four steps in such a two dimensional random walk are shown in *fig.* 6.5 and from these it is clear that the new tables are a generalisation of Pascal's triangle in that the number to be written in each position–the coefficient of $(\tfrac{1}{4})^n$–is obtained by

Figure 6.5 (opposite). *The first four steps of a random walk in two dimensions.*

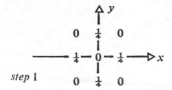

step 1

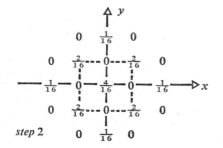

step 2

Note that the probability that the random walker is $a\sqrt{2}$ from the origin is the sum of four exclusive events and is $\frac{8}{16}$, or twice the probability of being at the origin

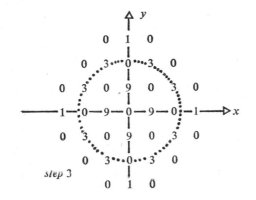

step 3

Here relative probabilities only are shown: each number should have divisor $4^3 = 64$. Note the high probability of being on the dotted circle

```
                    y
                    |
                    1
                    |
     0    4    0    4    0
                    |
0    6    0    15   0    6    0
                    |
4    0    24   0    24   0    4
                    |
-1-0-15----0---36----0---15--0--1---->
                    |              x
4    0    24   0    24   0    4
                    |
0    6    0    15   0    6    0
                    |
     0    4    0    4    0
                    |
step 4              0
                    |
                    1
```

Relative probabilities after four steps show that the probability of being $a\sqrt{2}$ from the origin is now $\frac{96}{36}$ times that of being at the origin

12

adding the numbers in the four surrounding positions of the previous $(n-1)$th step.

From even as few as 4 steps it is apparent that a new feature has emerged in two dimensions, that is that the importance of the origin declines with the number of steps, so that by steps 3 and 4 the most probable position has moved out to about one step from the origin. For example, by step 4, the probability of the origin has declined to $36/256$, while after step 6 it is $400/4096$. At the same time the combined probability of points in a ring 1–2 units from the origin has increased. The reason for the decline in the relative popularity of the origin as an end point of a random walk is, of course, that there is only one origin point, while the larger the ring the more points are there in it and the more ways by which the walker can reach them. This is the property we called degeneracy in our velocity space (§ 5.8). If we indicated probability by density of shading we would observe that the region of maximum probability density was a ring centred on the origin, the ring increasing in diameter with number of steps and at the same time becoming more diffuse. The probability ring behaves like a smoke-ring and in fact is a good model of a smoke-ring.

To calculate the probability $P(r)dr$ that the random walker has arrived in a ring contained between circles of radii r and $r+dr$ we note that $r = r(x,y)$ and

$$P(r)dr = P(x)P(y)dxdy, \qquad 6.5.1$$

that is, the required probability is equal to the product of the independent probabilities that the end of the random walk has occurred at any of the points (x,y) which are within the ring. Introducing values of $P(x)$ and $P(y)$ from 6.1.7, we find

$$P(r)dr = \frac{1}{2a^2n\pi} e^{-x^2/2a^2n} e^{-y^2/2a^2n} dxdy. \qquad 6.5.2$$

Now, $x^2+y^2 = r^2$ and $dxdy$, the element of area in terms of x and y, can be replaced by the element of area in terms of r, that is $2\pi r\, dr$. Thus

$$P(r)dr = \frac{r}{a^2n} e^{-r^2/2a^2n} dr. \qquad 6.5.3$$

In this form the function $P(r)$ is already normalised. That is

$$\int_0^\infty P(r)dr = \frac{1}{a^2n} \int_0^\infty r\, e^{-r^2/2a^2n} dr$$
$$= -\left[e^{-r^2/2a^2n}\right]_0^\infty = 1.$$

The mean distance from the origin is

$$\bar{r} = \int_0^\infty r P(r) dr$$

$$= \frac{1}{a^2 n} \int_0^\infty r^2 e^{-r^2/2a^2 n} dr$$

$$= a\sqrt{(\tfrac{1}{2} n \pi)}. \qquad \qquad 6.5.4$$

The mean-square distance from the origin is

$$\overline{r^2} = \int_0^\infty r^2 P(r) dr$$

$$= \frac{1}{a^2 n} \int_0^\infty r^3 e^{-r^2/2a^2 n} dr$$

$$= 2a^2 n. \qquad \qquad 6.5.5$$

The most probable distance r_m from the origin is given by

$$\frac{d}{dr} P(r) = 0 \quad \text{at} \quad r = r_m,$$

which leads to

$$r_m = a\sqrt{n}. \qquad \qquad 6.5.6$$

The least probable distance is $r = 0$. This result together with formulae 6.5.4–6 confirm what had been suggested by considering detailed probabilities for the first few steps, that is that the ring of maximum probability moves out as n increases (6.5.6) and at the same time becomes more diffuse since, as equations 6.5.4–5 show, the mean and the root-mean-square of the probability density move out faster than the maximum.

This is what we see with a smoke ring: a small disc-shaped concentration of smoke particles is introduced into the atmosphere and moves randomly under the impact of air molecules. As a result of the random motion the disc thins in the middle and becomes a ring which expands and at the same time becomes more diffuse.

§ 6.6   The random walk in three dimensions

By a similar argument to that used to obtain equation 6.5.3 we obtain the result for the three-dimensional random walk

$$P(r) dr = \frac{4\pi r^2}{(2a^2 n \pi)^{\frac{3}{2}}} e^{-r^2/2a^2 n} dr, \qquad \qquad 6.6.1$$

where in this case the element of volume in three dimensions is $4\pi r^2 dr$, the volume of a shell between spheres of radii r and $r+dr$. $P(r)$ was constructed from normalised functions and is thus already normalised, that is $\int_0^\infty P(r)dr = 1$, as can readily be tested using the integrals of § 12.6.

The mean distance from the origin is

$$\bar{r} = \int_0^\infty rP(r)dr = 2\sqrt{\frac{2}{\pi}}\,a\sqrt{n}\,.$$

6.6.2

The mean-square distance from the origin is

$$\overline{r^2} = \int_0^\infty r^2 P(r)dr = 3a^2 n\,,$$

6.6.3

and the most probable distance from the origin is

$$r_m = a\sqrt{(2n)}\,.$$

6.6.4

§ 6.7   Rates of diffusive processes

We can use any of equations 6.6.2–4 to estimate the rate at which a random walk process proceeds.

To take a definite example, suppose some evil-smelling gas is released from a point source in still air and we wish to calculate how long it will be before the peak of its effect has passed a given point distance l away. From 6.6.4, the peak of the distribution goes a distance l after a single molecule has made n jumps, each taking place in time τ where

$$l = a\sqrt{(2n)} = a\sqrt{(2t/\tau)}\,.$$

If we identify the jumps with mean free paths as discussed in the first paragraph of this chapter then

$$a = \Lambda$$

and $n = t/\tau = t(\bar{v}/\Lambda)\,,$

where $\bar{v} = \Lambda/\tau$ is the mean speed of molecular motion. So

$$l = 2t\bar{v}(\Lambda/l)$$

and the 'velocity' l/t at which the peak travels is

$$l/t = 2\bar{v}(\Lambda/l)\,.$$

6.7.1

Calculation on the basis of any ordinate other than the maximum of the distribution curve simply changes the numerical constant in 6.7.1. This constant is likewise changed if we are dealing with one- or two-dimensional systems or if, as in §6.4, allowance is made for variable jump length. Thus, whatever is being transported over a given distance by a diffusive process is transported with a velocity which is equal to the random velocity of the transport particles diminished in the ratio of the mean free path of the particles to the distance. In symbols

$$v_D \sim \bar{v}\frac{\Lambda}{l} \sim \frac{D}{l},\qquad\qquad 6.7.2$$

where v_D is the diffusive velocity defined as above and D is the diffusivity related to $\bar{v}\Lambda$ by 2.8.4. Relations 6.7.2 are typical of a diffusive process and are of quite general application.

§ 6.8   Heat conduction as a diffusive process

First consider transport of heat by conduction in a column of gas of unit cross-sectional area and length l. The rate of transport of heat is given by (2.6.1)

$$Q/t = K(T_2 - T_1)/l,\qquad\qquad 6.8.1$$

where T_2 and T_1 are respectively the temperatures at the high and low temperature ends and K is the thermal conductivity.

Now from 2.6.2, K is given by

$$K \sim C\bar{v}\Lambda,$$

where $C(= nC_V')$ is the specific heat per unit volume and the constant $\frac{1}{3}$ which appeared in equation 2.6.2 was somewhat uncertain. Thus

$$Q/t \sim C(T_2 - T_1)\bar{v}(\Lambda/l).\qquad\qquad 6.8.2$$

Now $C(T_2 - T_1)$ can be regarded as the excess of energy density of the hot end over the cold end, and relation 6.8.2 thus tells us that this excess energy is propagated down the column of gas at a speed given by the mean speed of molecular motion diminished by Λ/l. Hence, we may look on the mechanism of heat conduction in gases as follows: excess energy is given to the molecules at the hot end and this energy is transferred down the column of gas by random walk process. In this, a molecule with extra energy carries it for one free path which is terminated by a collision after which the energy may be sent off in any direction. The net flow of energy from hot end to cold end is produced by the greater concentration of energetic molecules at the hot end. Thus, although the movement of any one molecule is random, there is a greater probability that an energetic molecule will be moving down the thermal gradient. Moreover, since the speed at which the heat is transported is proportional to Λ/l, the time required for, say, a pulse of heat to become perceptible at distance l is proportional to Λ/l^2, the constant of proportionality depending on the sensitivity of the instrument detecting the arrival of the pulse. The distance the pulse goes is thus proportional to the square root of the time. These are exactly the conclusions predicted by our diffusion model in § 6.2.

In metals, heat is carried mainly by free electrons which can be thought of as a gas moving at random and colliding with the metallic ions. A mean free path Λ and mean velocity $\bar{v}$ can be defined as in an ordinary gas, and once again it can be shown that the rate of heat transport is governed by a relation like 6.8.2. In non-metals there are no free electrons and heat is transferred by lattice vibrations; we suppose that the ions at the hot end vibrate harder about their positions of equilibrium and pass on energy to their neighbours and so on down the solid without any ion actually changing its equilibrium position. Now quantum theory tells us that lattice vibrations can be treated as if they were particles called phonons (by analogy with the photons which are quantized light vibrations). These phonons are supposed to travel with the velocity v of sound and to have mean free paths Λ. A relation like 6.8.2 can be derived for the rate at which heat travels in a non-metal and this allows us to conclude that heat transport by lattice vibrations, as is known by other considerations, is a diffusive process. We picture energetic phonons being injected from the source of heat and diffusing down to the cold end of the solid.

Thus, heat conduction in solids, whether metallic or non-metallic, is a diffusive process. Experimental evidence of this is given by a modern method whereby heat conductivities of solids are measured by pulse-heating one end and measuring how long it takes the pulse to rise to a given fraction of its final height at the other end. This time depends on the square of the length of the specimen.

§ 6.9 Brownian motion

A further application of 6.7.2 explains why Brownian particles (§ 1.13) appear to move so slowly. If we assume that Brownian particles, while much larger than molecules, are in thermal equilibrium with the gas or liquid in which they are suspended (this point is discussed in the next section) then the mean energy of such particles is $3kT/2$ and their mean speed $\bar{v} \sim \sqrt{(3kT/m)}$. For a particle of diameter $0.1\ \mu$ (10^{-5} cm) the mass will be $\sim 10^9$ times that of a single molecule, so its speed is $\sim 10^4$ times less; that is, $\bar{v} \sim 1$ cm/sec. Now, when Brownian particles are observed under the microscope, they appear to travel several orders of magnitude slower than this. The reason is that we cannot observe the zig-zag of the true path between collisions and the path we observe is a smoothed-out version. The speed v_m we actually measure is

$$v_m \sim \bar{v}(\Lambda/l), \qquad\qquad 6.9.1$$

where Λ is the mean free path for the Brownian particles.

Now in Perrin's classic experiments on the distribution of gum particles in water which are described in §§ 1.12–13 and which led to the first determination of Avogadro's number N_0, he noted that a typical particle with size $\sim 10^{-5}$ cm moved distances of $\sim 3 \times 10^{-4}$ cm in successive time intervals of 30 sec. Thus $v_m \sim 10^{-5}$ cm/sec. In water the mean free path of the gum particles must be of the order of the distance between water molecules or 10^{-8} cm, so $\Lambda/l \sim 10^{-5}$, and equation 6.9.1 is thus justified at least in order of magnitude. As mentioned in § 1.12, the particles used by Perrin to measure N_0 were about 5 times larger than those used for Brownian motion studies and consequently less mobile by a factor of $\sim 5^{\frac{3}{2}}$.

§ 6.10 The random walk in momentum space

Equation 6.6.1 expresses the distribution law for particles which have spread out from a source into a space of three dimensions. It is formally the same as equation 5.10.2, which expresses Maxwell's law for the distribution of particles in three-dimensional velocity space. Similarly, equations 6.6.2–4 express certain consequences of the shape of the particle distribution in ordinary space and these are formally the same as equations 5.10.4, 5.10.3, and 5.10.8 respectively, which arise from the distribution in velocity space. The formal identity of the relations in ordinary space and in velocity or momentum space suggests that we might derive the Maxwell-Boltzmann distribution by a random impulse method.

Suppose particles could be injected into a gas in such a way that they were initially at rest. This state of affairs could not last for long since each particle will receive random increments of momentum imparted by collisions with moving molecules. Suppose further for simplicity that all impulses are equal and are p_0, so that the particles start from the origin of momentum space and make random jumps of magnitude p_0 in each of the three directions p_x, p_y, p_z. Then, after each of the injected particles has received n impulses, each of magnitude p_0 but with random direction, the distribution of momentum amongst the particles will be

$$f(p)dp = \frac{4\pi p^2}{(2p_0^2 n\pi)^{\frac{3}{2}}} e^{-p^2/2p_0^2 n} \, dp \, , \qquad 6.10.1$$

which is the same as equation 6.6.1 but with p written for r and p_0 for a.

The mean-square momentum after n impulses is, from 6.6.3,

$$\overline{p^2} = 3p_0^2 n \, . \qquad 6.10.2$$

This formula might suggest that the energy of one of our particles would increase indefinitely, proportional to the number of impacts, that is, proportional to time. This is, of course, incorrect since $\overline{p^2}$ must approach the equilibrium value of $3m_p kT$ where m_p is the mass of the particle, the error being in the assumption that we can indefinitely add constant impulses with random direction. This assumption is justified as long as the particle is near to the origin of momentum space; but when it acquires a speed comparable with that of the gas molecules, an impulse where it is overtaken by a molecule will be less effective than a head-on collision. Thus the jumps in momentum space are no longer random. A similar restriction would have to be made on the random walk in a finite container, for the distance of the random walker from his starting point cannot exceed the dimensions of the container. When his walk takes him to the wall his next step is no longer random.

Equation 6.10.2 is thus to mean that, after an average of n impulses each imparting momentum with magnitude p_0 but random direction, the particle of mass m_p reaches the equipartition value of energy corresponding to the temperature of the gas. By the arguments of § 6.1, p_0^2 corresponding to equal steps of momentum can be replaced by $\overline{p_0^2}$, where $\overline{p_0^2}$ is the mean-square value of random-sized impulses. n is thus given by

$$n = m_p kT / \overline{p_0^2} \, . \qquad 6.10.3$$

Equation 6.10.3 can be used to estimate how long it will take a large particle, for example of smoke or pollen, to come to equilibrium with the gas in a Brownian motion experiment. Putting $\overline{p_0^2} = mkT$, that is taking the impulses to be of the same order of magnitude as the momenta of the molecules, we obtain

$$n \sim m_p/m \,. \qquad\qquad 6.10.4$$

For the Brownian motion particles of § 6.9 with diameter $\sim 0 \cdot 1 \mu$, $m_p/m \sim 10^9$, so n is of this order of magnitude.

The number of impacts a particle receives per second is given in § 2.2 and was around $10^9/\sec$ for a gas molecule at N.T.P. A particle with linear dimension 10^{-5} cm would have cross-section 10^6 greater than a gas molecule and so would receive about 10^{15} impacts per second. Thus a particle of this size will come into thermal equilibrium with a gas at N.T.P. in $\sim 10^{-6}$ sec. With larger particles and gases at lower pressures, the time to reach equilibrium might be so long that the system could never be in equilibrium.

A further application of the approximate relation 6.10.4 enables us to calculate the mean free path for a large particle in a gas consisting of molecules. Obviously the formulae of § 2.2 are inapplicable since a single impact with a gas molecule cannot be said to end the free path of a heavy particle. Instead we may take n as derived in 6.10.4 as the number of impacts required to do so. Then, using the values derived above for the particles of diameter $0 \cdot 1 \mu$ we have that the required n impacts take place in $\sim 10^{-6}$ sec. In this time the heavy particle has gone $\sim 10^{-6}$ cm at its speed of ~ 1 cm/sec. This distance is then the mean free path Λ of the Brownian particles in a gas at N.T.P. and it is about two orders of magnitude greater than the assumed free path in a liquid. Hence, from 6.9.1 we would expect v_m, the apparent speed to be two orders of magnitude greater than in a liquid. Once again experiment shows that our reasoning is on the right lines.

§ 6.11   Problems

1. A random walk consists of unequal steps $a_1, a_2, a_3, \ldots, a_N$ each of random direction. Develop qualitative arguments to show that, if $N \gg 1$,

$$\bar{x} \equiv \sum_{n=1}^{N} a_n = 0 \,, \qquad\qquad 6.11.1$$

$$\overline{x^2} \equiv \sum_{n=1}^{N} a_n \sum_{m=1}^{N} a_m \,,$$

$$= \sum_{n=1}^{N} a_n^2 + \sum_{\substack{n=1 \\ m=1}}^{N}{}' a_n a_m \,, \qquad\qquad 6.11.2$$

where the dash on the second sum indicates that the summation excludes terms for which $n = m$. Then show that

$$\sum_{\substack{n=1 \\ m=1}}^{N}{}' a_n a_m = 0, \qquad 6.11.3$$

so that

$$\overline{x^2} = N\overline{a^2}, \qquad 6.11.4$$

the same result as 6.1.9.

2. The barometer formula (1.12.2) tells us that the number n of molecules of mass m per unit volume of the atmosphere falls off with height z according to the law

$$n = n_0 \exp\left(-mgz/kT\right). \qquad 6.11.5$$

The concentration of molecules is thus not uniform, so we expect that the random walk process known as diffusion will result in a flux of molecules from high concentration to low. This flux is (§ 2.8)

$$\Gamma = -D\frac{dn}{dz}, \qquad 6.11.6$$

or, since $\Gamma = nv$, where v is the mean drift speed in the direction down the concentration gradient, that is towards greater heights,

$$v = -\frac{D}{n}\frac{dn}{dz}. \qquad 6.11.7$$

The flux Γ is balanced in equilibrium by an equal and opposite flux of molecules falling towards the ground under the influence of gravity.

Now a particle falling in a viscous medium acquires a constant speed given by

$$v = mg\mu, \qquad 6.11.8$$

where μ is the mobility defined as the velocity per unit force. To illustrate this concept we note that if we assume Stokes' law, then v is also given by

$$v = \frac{mg}{6\pi\eta a}, \qquad 6.11.9$$

where a is the radius of the particle and η the viscosity of the medium, so that in this case

$$\mu = 1/(6\pi\eta a). \qquad 6.11.10$$

Use equations 6.11.5–8 to show that

$$D = \mu kT. \qquad 6.11.11$$

This formula, originally derived by Einstein in his work on Brownian motion, shows the relationship between the random-walk process called diffusion and the dissipative processes of viscosity or friction. The relation is much more general than our derivation of it and has been applied to spontaneous electron movements in metals and semiconductors, the phenomenon called Johnson noise in § 11.5, in which case μ is simply the electrical conductivity.

To relate 6.11.10 to Brownian motion we use the relationship 6.3.11, giving the mean square displacement in one dimensional diffusion

$$\overline{x^2} = 2Dt,$$

so that the mean-square displacement in Brownian motion is

$$\overline{x^2} = 2\mu kTt. \qquad\qquad 6.11.12$$

Chapter 7

THE THEORY OF ERRORS

§ 7.1 Estimation of the accuracy of physical measurements

The aim of most physical experiments is to obtain a numerical value for some quantity. This numerical value is much more useful if its accuracy is known, that is if it can be quoted in the form

$$A \pm a,$$

which means that the value is 'round about A–most probably between $A-a$ and $A+a$'. The larger the value of a the less sure we are of our result. A more precise definition of the expression in inverted commas is the aim of a theory, popularly called the 'theory of errors'. This name is unfortunate since 'error' is used for several different things, ranging from gross mistakes in calculation to random fluctuations in the length of scales due to thermal movement of the atoms in them. The former can easily be avoided, the latter cannot be avoided at all.

The errors likely to be encountered in any physical experiment can be roughly classified (not necessarily in order of importance) as follows:

(i) mistakes, gross errors
(ii) constant errors
(iii) systematic errors
(iv) random errors.

(i) *Mistakes, gross errors, etc.* This group consists of arithmetical errors, misreading of scales, neglect of obvious precautions, etc., and simply needs ordinary care for its elimination.

(ii) *Constant errors* affect all the results of a series of experiments by the same amount. Thus, the presence of such errors cannot be detected by analysing the results. For example, if the centimetre scale used in some determination of g were assumed correct at 0°C when it had actually been calibrated to be correct at 20°C, then all the estimates made of the gravitational acceleration would be in error on this account by nearly equal amounts. A similar constant error would be obtained if in these experiments the clock had been running slow.

(iii) *Systematic errors* vary in a regular manner. For example, if the hand of a watch is not pivoted in the centre of the dial but is pivoted nearer to 12 o'clock the watch will apparently run too slow from 9 o'clock to 3 o'clock and too fast over the other half of the dial. Integral rotations of the hand will be recorded correctly however and the relative error will decrease as the period of timing increases. A similar effect is given by the zero error in micrometers, etc.–the relative error is reduced as the distance being measured is increased.

Constant errors and systematic errors can be thought of as corrections which have always to be made in experiments. In new experiments these corrections are often hidden and there is only one way to eliminate or at least minimise them. First, the experiment must be carefully considered from all angles for possible sources of systematic error. Then the experiment is performed, all known corrections made, and a result $A_1 \pm a_1$ obtained. This method of quoting the result means 'provided there are no undiscovered constant or systematic errors the best estimate of the quantity is A_1; but, as a result of random, uncontrollable errors in our measurements, we can only say that the value of the quantity is most probably between $A_1 - a_1$ and $A_1 + a_1$'. Finally, the same physical quantity must be measured in a radically new way (in which different sources of systematic error are present) and a new result $A_2 \pm a_2$ obtained. If A_1 and A_2 agree 'within the random errors a_1 and a_2' then it is reasonable to believe that both methods are free from uncorrected systematic error. This process can, of course, be further checked by new experiments giving $A_3 \pm a_3$, $A_4 \pm a_4$, etc. Thus it is essential for an estimate of the important class of systematic error that a knowledge of random error be gained. This is the most important justification of the time spent in obtaining and minimising the random errors. But the fact that random error can be treated mathematically and apparently calculated accurately does not mean that it is the most important error.

§ 7.2 Repeated measurements

We can illustrate the ideas of the theory of random errors by anticipating a result to be obtained in § 7.8. This is that successive measurements of a quantity enable a result to be deduced more accurately than any single measurement, indeed more accurately than the calibration of the measuring instrument.

Suppose, for example, we wished to measure the distance D between lines in a co-planar system of equally-spaced parallel rulings and that the only measuring instrument available is a coin of diameter d such that $d < D$. If the coin is thrown at random on to the rulings, then its centre may fall anywhere in the distance D between two successive lines and it will overlap a line if the centre falls within a distance $d/2$ from either of the two. The probability of overlapping a line (a hit) is thus $(2 \times d/2)/D = d/D$. The probability of not overlapping a line (a miss) is similarly $(D-d)/D = 1-d/D$. If a large number of trials are made and the numbers of hits n_{H} and of misses n_{M} are recorded, we have

$$\frac{d}{D} = \frac{n_{\mathrm{H}}}{n_{\mathrm{H}}+n_{\mathrm{M}}}$$

or $\qquad D = d(n_{\mathrm{H}}+n_{\mathrm{M}})/n_{\mathrm{H}}.$ $\qquad\qquad\qquad$ 7.2.1

Common sense suggests that we shall obtain more accurate values of D/d the more trials we make. In fact the accuracy increases proportional to $(n_{\mathrm{H}}+n_{\mathrm{M}})^{\frac{1}{2}}$, as we can see by considering a specially simple case and using results we already have.

Suppose for simplicity that the true value of D/d is exactly 2 so that from 7.2.1 the coin has equal probability of lying across a line or missing the lines. The mean number of events we called 'hits' is $\frac{1}{2}N$, where N is the number of trials, and the probability of deviations from the mean obeys exactly the same law as we found in § 5.5 for the deviations from the mean numbers of molecules in two equal boxes. This law was (5.5.7)

$$P(q) = (\bar{n}\pi)^{-\frac{1}{2}} \exp{(-q^2/\bar{n})},$$

where $P(q)$ is now the probability that, instead of the mean number $\bar{n} = \frac{1}{2}N$ of 'hits', we obtain $n = \bar{n}+q$. A convenient measure of the probable deviation from the mean is the quantity we called the standard deviation or root-mean-square fluctuation $(\overline{\delta^2})^{\frac{1}{2}}$, where

$$(\overline{\delta^2})^{\frac{1}{2}} \propto N^{-\frac{1}{2}} \propto (n_{\mathrm{H}}+n_{\mathrm{M}})^{-\frac{1}{2}}.$$

The probable accuracy of our experiment in measurement will vary inversely as the chance of making errors, so the accuracy may be expected to increase proportionately to the square root of the number of trials.

In the calculation just made it was assumed that the true probability of hit or miss was known to be $\frac{1}{2}$. By the definition of probability (3.2.1) this is the experimental result which would be obtained from an infinite number of trials. We cannot, however, make an infinite number of trials and we must content ourselves with a relatively small number – a *sample* of all those we might have made. Our result tells us that accuracy is proportional to the square root of the size of the sample.

Apparently, then, D can be determined in terms of d to any desired accuracy by making enough trials and it appears that the crudest possible measuring apparatus can give results to any number of decimal places. Naturally accuracy is in practice limited by the finite thickness of the lines, uncertainty in whether a border-line case is a hit or a miss – involving an element of human decision – irregularities in line spacing or in the coin, and many other factors.

A similar problem is that of measuring the distance between two lamp posts, say a hundred metres apart, using a car distance indicator calibrated say, in integral kilometres. If the observer simply notes the number of times he happens to pass the two lamp posts and the fraction of times that his distance indicator clicks up a new kilometre when between them, then, with the figures given, this fraction should be $\frac{1}{10}$ if measured over a large number of journeys. Once again limitations are easy to list. There is also the qualification that the distance the observer goes between successive experiments must be random; this qualification corresponds to the assumption made above that the coin can be thrown at random on to a sheet of ruled paper.

§ 7.3   The theory of random errors

The theory of random errors is based on the assumption that if we measure a quantity a very large number of times and our measurements are subject only to errors which are truly random, then the result we obtain most frequently is the correct one and the further a result is from the correct value the less frequently we shall obtain it. In other words large random errors are less likely than small ones.

We may illustrate this by a simple example where we are measuring a quantity for which an exact value is available. Consider an experiment to measure π by rolling a coin along a table. The actual measurements are the diameter D of the coin, which might be measured with callipers, and the length of the trace of its circumference C on the table. Having measured D and C we obtain $\pi = C/D$. Measurements of D and C are subject to error, a few possible sources of which are listed in table 10.

TABLE 10 : sources of error in the measurement of π from the ratio of the circumference to the diameter of a coin.
Errors giving too large values are indicated by (+); errors giving too small values by (−).

uncertainties in the measurement of D	effect on D	effect on π
callipers pressed too tight	−	+
callipers too slack	+	−
coin not a circle	+ −	+ −
and so on		

uncertainties in the measurement of C	effect on C	effect on π
coin not rolled along straight line	−	−
small bumps on surface	+	+
coin slipping	−	−
coin sliding	+	+
and so on		

---

§ 7.4   Random errors and the random walk

From a list such as that in table 10, which with a little imagination can be extended indefinitely, we see that the random error is the sum of a very large number of small errors which may as likely be positive as negative. Suppose for simplicity that all these errors are equal and can be written $\pm\delta$, then instead of the correct value Q of the quantity we are trying to measure, we obtain:

$$Q \pm \delta \pm \delta \pm \delta \pm \delta \pm \ldots$$
$$= Q \pm \sum(\pm)\delta, \qquad\qquad 7.4.1$$

where the symbol ($\pm$) means here that the sign of each term in the summation is determined by pure chance. The resemblance to the random walk is obvious: we set out from the correct value, departing from it by steps which are as likely to be towards larger values as towards smaller. Thus the result of our measurement of the quantity Q is

$$Q \pm \Delta,$$

where Δ is the random sum $\sum(\pm)\delta$ defined by 7.4.1.

Now if we measured Q a great many times we would make different errors each time: this is implied in our assumption that the errors are of random sign. Thus, we can speak of a distribution of values of Δ, this distribution expressing the relative probabilities of obtaining values of Δ within a given range. Since $\sum(\pm)\delta$ is exactly the quantity we evaluated in our discussion of the random walk in § 6.1, we can say that the probability of making an error between Δ and $\Delta + d\Delta$ is given by

$$P(\Delta)d\Delta = \frac{h}{\sqrt{\pi}} e^{-h^2\Delta^2} d\Delta, \qquad 7.4.2$$

where h is a constant given by (6.1.6)

$$h^2 = 1/2n\delta^2, \qquad 7.4.3$$

n being the number of errors in the sum in 7.4.1. $(h/\sqrt{\pi})$ is a normalising constant (6.1.7), which ensures that

$$\int_{-\infty}^{\infty} P(\Delta)d\Delta = 1,$$

or that the probability of making an error between $+\infty$ and $-\infty$ is a certainty.

Equation 7.4.2 is called the *normal law* of distribution of errors.

§ 7.5 The normal law

If indeed errors are distributed according to 7.4.2 then the most probable error is zero, and we can write down expressions for the probability of making an error greater than some amount Δ_0, noting that, because of the form of the function P, the probability of making a large error is much less than the probability of making a small error. This is the assumption with which this chapter began.

If then we really did measure the ratio of the circumference C of a coin to its diameter D to three decimal places a very large number of times, and if our measurements were subject to truly random errors, we would expect to obtain values of C/D between 3·130 and 3·150 much more frequently than we obtained values between, say, 3·010 and 3·030. We might plot our results as a histogram, as in *fig.*

13

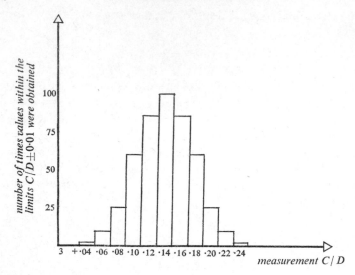

Figure 7.1. *Histogram of measurements of the ratio of the circumference C to the diameter D of a coin.*

7.1, and our considerations above suggest that if the number of measurements were large enough, the shape of the histogram would be very close to that of the exponential curve represented by the function

$$F(\Delta\pi) = \frac{h}{\sqrt{\pi}} \, e^{-h^2(\pi - \Delta\pi)^2}, \qquad\qquad 7.5.1$$

that is, the same function as P in equation 7.4.2. but now centred on π instead of on the origin. The most probable value of the measured quantity is π, and h is a measure of the precision with which our measurements have been made. If h is large the function F falls rapidly from a high maximum towards zero; this corresponds to accurate measurement, as can also be seen from the fact that

$$h^2 = 1/2n\delta^2,$$

which means that large h corresponds to few or small errors. Similarly h small means that our histogram is a wide bell-shaped curve, indicating that large errors of measurement are relatively frequent. h is thus a measure of the width of the curve. We shall call h the *precision index.*

§ 7.6 Measures of precision

Besides h, other measures of precision are frequently used including:
(i) *the standard deviation* (σ) or root-mean-square error. If the probability of making an error between Δ and $\Delta + d\Delta$ is $P(\Delta)d\Delta$ then

$$\sigma^2 = \int_{-\infty}^{\infty} \Delta^2 P(\Delta)d\Delta .$$

(ii) *the average error* (η). This is obtained by simply taking the arithmetic mean of the errors, all negative signs being ignored, that is

$$\eta = 2\int_0^{\infty} \Delta P(\Delta)d\Delta .$$

η thus corresponds to the quantity $|\overline{v_x}|$ (1.15.1 and 5.8.22) in the Maxwellian speed distribution and the factor 2 in its definition is explained in the same way. The true 'average error', if account is taken of signs, is zero.

(iii) *the probable error* (r) or *quartile*. This is defined as being such that the probability of making an error in the range $-r$ to $+r$ is the same as of making any numerically larger error. This should not be confused with the quantity we called the most probable error, which corresponds to the maximum of the normal distribution curve and is, of course, zero.

Partly as an exercise in the use of the normal distribution, partly because the numerical results are required later, we shall now calculate the relationship between the various measures of precision h, σ, η and r. Assuming that the errors Δ are distributed according to the normal law we have

$$P(\Delta)d\Delta = \frac{h}{\sqrt{\pi}} e^{-h^2\Delta^2} d\Delta ,$$

whence we obtain the following results:
(i) the root-mean-square error or standard deviation σ is

$$\sigma = (\overline{\Delta^2})^{\frac{1}{2}} , \qquad\qquad 7.6.1$$

where $\quad \overline{\Delta^2} = \dfrac{h}{\sqrt{\pi}} \displaystyle\int_{-\infty}^{\infty} \Delta^2 e^{-h^2\Delta^2} d\Delta$

$$= 1/(2h^2) \qquad\qquad 7.6.2$$

$$= n\delta^2 , \qquad\qquad 7.6.3$$

in the notation of equation 7.4.3, so that

$$\sigma = \frac{0.707}{h}.$$ 7.6.4

(ii) The average error η is

$$\eta = \frac{2h}{\sqrt{\pi}} \int_0^\infty \Delta \, e^{-h^2\Delta^2} \, d\Delta$$

$$= \frac{1}{\sqrt{\pi}} \cdot \frac{1}{h} = \frac{0.565}{h}.$$ 7.6.5

(iii) The probable error r is given by

$$\frac{h}{\sqrt{\pi}} \int_{-r}^r e^{-h^2\Delta^2} \, d\Delta = \tfrac{1}{2}$$

or $$\frac{2h}{\sqrt{\pi}} \int_0^r e^{-h^2\Delta^2} \, d\Delta = \tfrac{1}{2}.$$ 7.6.6

The integral is the error function

$$\frac{2}{\sqrt{\pi}} \int_0^x e^{-x^2} \, dx = \operatorname{erf} x,$$

which we met (5.10.11) when discussing the fraction of molecules with speeds within various ranges. It cannot be evaluated explicitly (§ 12.7) but can be obtained from tables, whence

$$r = \frac{0.480}{h}.$$ 7.6.7

The standard deviation is the most commonly used index of precision, but the probable error shows most clearly what is involved: thus for observations which obey normal law, probably half will have negative errors and probably three-quarters will not have positive errors of more than r. The meaning of r is made clear in table 11, while the relations between σ, η, r and $1/h$ are given in table 12.

TABLE 11 : probabilities of errors

The probability that the error of any observation chosen at random shall be outside the range		
	$-r$ to r	0.5
	$-2r$ to $2r$	0.18
	$-3r$ to $3r$ } is	0.04
	$-4r$ to $4r$	0.007
	$-5r$ to $5r$	0.0007

An error as great as five times the 'probable error' is only to be expected about once in 1400 observations.

TABLE 12 : relations between measures of precision

	σ	η	r	$1/h$
σ	1·000	1·250	1·481	0·707
η	0·800	1·000	1·183	0·565
r	0·675	0·845	1·000	0·480
$1/h$	1·414	1·770	2·083	1·000

Here, for example, the first row is to be read:
$\sigma = \sigma = 1\cdot250\eta = 1\cdot481r = 0\cdot707/h.$

§ 7.7 The best estimate of a measured quantity; principle of least squares

We cannot normally make sufficient measurements of a physical quantity to be able to plot a histogram, see if it has the normal law form suggested by equations 7.4.2 or 7.5.1, and measure its width to find h. We can, however, assume that the few measurements we have made are representative of the larger number and that, if we had more measurements, the distribution would have been of the normal form. We can then use the few results to estimate h. Again, we have so far assumed that the correct value is known and that the errors in measurement can be calculated from it. It was to keep this in mind that the quantity we measured was chosen to be π. In physical measurements we do not in general know the correct value, and we have to have some method of estimating the best value. If we define the 'best value' as the 'most probable value' then it is clear from the discussion above that *provided the measurements are distributed according to normal law*, the mean is the best value.

We can demonstrate this in a way which brings out the probability aspects of error theory and introduces some new concepts. Suppose we have n measurements, $x_1, x_2, \ldots, x_n$ of a physical quantity where the true value is x. We wish to find the best estimate of x. If the measurements are distributed according to normal law then the probabilities of obtaining the values $x_1, x_2, \ldots, x_n$ are, from equation 7.5.1,

$$F(x - x_1) = \frac{h_1}{\sqrt{\pi}} e^{-h_1^2(x-x_1)^2},$$

. . . .

$$F(x - x_n) = \frac{h_n}{\sqrt{\pi}} e^{-h_n^2(x-x_n)^2},$$

where the h_i are the precision indices of each measurement.

Now, if all the measurements are independent but of the same quantity x, the probability of making them all is

$$F(x-x_1)F(x-x_2)\ldots F(x-x_n)$$

$$= \frac{h_1 h_2 \ldots h_n}{\pi^{n/2}} \exp\left\{-\sum_{i=1}^{n} h_i^2 (x-x_i)^2\right\},$$

that is, the required probability is the product of n independent probabilities. For this probability to be a maximum requires

$$\sum_{i=1}^{n} h_i^2 (x-x_i)^2 = \text{minimum}, \qquad 7.7.1$$

which if all the h_i are equal, that is all the measurements are of equal precision, reduces to

$$\sum_{i=1}^{n} (x-x_i)^2 = \text{minimum}. \qquad 7.7.2$$

This is Legendre's *principle of least squares* (1820), which requires the mean to be the most probable value. To show this, note that the mean is

$$\bar{x} = \frac{\sum x_i}{n},$$

and find what value of x makes the quantity $\sum(x-x_i)^2$ a minimum. Write

$$\sum_{i=1}^{n} (x-x_i)^2 = \sum_{i=1}^{n} \{(x-\bar{x})+(\bar{x}-x_i)\}^2$$

$$= \sum_i (x-\bar{x})^2 + 2(x-\bar{x})\sum_i(\bar{x}-x_i) + \sum(\bar{x}-x_i)^2$$

$$= n(x-\bar{x})^2 + 2(x-\bar{x})(n\bar{x}-\sum x_i) + \sum(\bar{x}-x_i)^2 .$$

The middle term vanishes since $n\bar{x} = \sum_i x_i$ and the remaining terms are a minimum if $x = \bar{x}$; for the first then vanishes leaving the third, which is independent of x.

This result, that the mean is the most probable value, would not necessarily be still valid if we had continued as in equation 7.7.1 to deal with measurements of varying precision. We shall return to this point in § 7.16.

§ 7.8 Precision of the arithmetic mean; residuals

It is commonly assumed that the best thing to do with more than one measurement of a physical quantity is to take the mean. In the last section we saw that the mean is indeed the most probable value provided the measurements are of equal accuracy and are distributed according to the normal law. We can now show that the mean is more accurate than any single value.

Suppose we have n measurements $x_1, x_2, \ldots, x_n$ of a quantity and that the corresponding root-mean-square errors (7.6.1–3) are $\sigma_1, \sigma_2, \ldots, \sigma_n$. If these errors are as likely to be positive as negative then the mean value $\bar{x}$ is given by

$$\bar{x} = \frac{1}{n}\left\{ \sum_{i=1}^{n} x_i \pm \sum_{i=1}^{n} (\pm)\sigma_i \right\},$$

where the symbol $(\pm)$ denotes, as in § 7.4, that the sign of each term is determined by chance. The right-hand sum in the brackets is the formula (§ 6.1) for a random walk with unequal steps, so its most probable value is zero; this shows once again that the mean is the most probable value of a series of measurements. Further, the mean-square value of the random sum is $n\overline{\sigma^2}$, where

$$\overline{\sigma^2} = \frac{1}{n} \sum_{i=1}^{n} \sigma_i^2;$$

so the root-mean-square error of the mean is given by

$$\sigma_m = \frac{1}{n} n^{\frac{1}{2}} (\overline{\sigma^2})^{\frac{1}{2}}$$

$$= (\overline{\sigma^2})^{\frac{1}{2}} / n^{\frac{1}{2}}.$$

Hence the arithmetic mean is more accurate than any single measurement and if there are n measurements of equal precision the increase in accuracy is by a factor $n^{\frac{1}{2}}$.

We have now seen how from a small number of measurements we can find the most probable value, which, if the measurements are distributed according to the normal law, is the arithmetic mean. We have also seen that the arithmetic mean is more accurate than any single measurement and becomes more accurate the more measurements we have. We have still however retained the original assumption that we know the true errors. This is obviously incorrect: the true errors can never be known because we do not in general know the true value of the quantity we are measuring. We therefore distinguish the *true* value, which we do not know, and the errors in its measurement from the *best* value and the deviations from it which occur in our measurements. We call the deviations from the best value *residuals*, where a residual v_i is given by

$$v_i = \bar{x} - x_i.$$

The principle of least squares then leads to the assumption that the best value, the mean, is found by making the sum of squared residuals, $\sum v_i^2$, a minimum, the residuals being treated as if they were errors. It is further assumed that the few residuals obtained from a limited number of measurements can be used, as if they were derived from a complete normal distribution, to calculate h, σ, and the other parameters which measure the width of the normal-law curve.

Thus the mean-square error ((i) in § 7.6) is taken to be

$$\Delta^2 = \frac{\sum v_i^2}{n},$$

so that $\sigma = \sqrt{\dfrac{\sum v_i^2}{n}}.$

This is at best an approximation, since our Δ^2 was obtained in § 7.6 on the assumption that we had a very large number of observations. It is manifestly wrong if we have only one observation, for then

$$\sum v_i^2 = 0$$

and $\sigma = 0,$

which would imply that $h \to \infty$ and that our solitary observation was free from error.

We can remove this absurdity by replacing the n in the denominator by $n-1$, that is by writing

$$\sigma = \sqrt{\frac{\sum v_i^2}{n-1}}. \qquad\qquad 7.8.1$$

Justification of this step, which involves showing that the residuals give too small an estimate of error involves no more than an algebraic trick and is not really relevant to this book. Since, however, formula 7.8.1 is basic to the theory of errors a simple justification appears as an appendix (§ 7.21) to this chapter. σ as given by 7.8.1 is a measure of the accuracy of the method of measuring: it is a measure of the accuracy of a single measurement.

We saw earlier that the root-mean-square error of the arithmetic mean of n observations was $n^{-\frac{1}{2}}$ times the error of a single observation. Assuming that we can treat residuals as errors this gives

$$\sigma_{\text{a.m.}} = \sqrt{\frac{\sum v_i^2}{n(n-1)}}. \qquad\qquad 7.8.2$$

For completeness we quote without proof the formula for the standard deviation of σ. It is:

$$\text{standard deviation of } \sigma = \frac{\sigma}{\sqrt{(2n)}}.\qquad\qquad 7.8.3$$

This last formula is important in practice since it enables us to decide to how many significant figures it is worth quoting σ. The formulae derived above are known as *Bessel's formulae* and are summarized in the next section.

§ 7.9 Bessel's formulae

If we have a set of n equally reliable measurements $x_1, x_2, \ldots, x_n$ of a quantity and can assume that they form a random sample of the normal frequency distribution, then our theory gives the following results.

(i) The most probable value of the quantity is the arithmetic mean:

$$\bar{x} = \frac{1}{n} \sum_{i=1}^{n} x_i.\qquad\qquad 7.9.1$$

Denote by v_i the residuals $\bar{x} - x_i$; then:
(ii) the standard deviation of a single measurement is

$$\sigma_1 = \sqrt{\frac{\sum v_i^2}{n-1}},\qquad\qquad 7.9.2$$

(iii) the arithmetic mean is more accurate than any one measurement and its standard deviation is

$$\sigma_{\text{a.m.}} = \sqrt{\frac{\sum v_i^2}{n(n-1)}}.\qquad\qquad 7.9.3$$

(iv) The standard deviation of σ is $\sigma/(2n)^{\frac{1}{2}}$. 7.9.4

§ 7.10 Peters' formulae

Bessel's formulae are generally accepted to be the most accurate. However, working with a sum of squares is rather tedious, so a less laborious method is to be preferred for all but the most accurate work. Such a method is due to Peters and is based on an estimate of the mean error rather than the mean-square error.

Assuming as before that we have n measurements $x_1, x_2, \ldots, x_n$ of a quantity x, and that these can be treated as a random sample of a normal distribution, then the arithmetic mean $\bar{x} = \frac{1}{n} \sum x_i$ is the most probable value of x. We now form the residuals

$$|v_i| = |\bar{x} - x_i|, \qquad\qquad 7.10.1$$

where the vertical strokes denote as usual that the quantity they enclose is to be taken as positive. We note in passing that the mean $\bar{x}$ does not necessarily correspond to a minimum of $\sum |v_i|$: if a proof of this negative proposition is required, it is only necessary to consider a set of measurements such as 3, 3, 3, 4, 7 (where the mean is not also the median). Here the mean is 4 and $\sum |v_i| = 6$, which is not a minimum since a smaller $\sum |v_i|$ is obtained if the v_i are calculated relative to some quantity between 3 and 4, say $3\frac{1}{2}$.

The mean residual is $\sum |v_i|/n$ and, assuming we can identify this approximately with the average error η as defined in § 7.6 for a complete normal distribution, we have

$$\eta \simeq \frac{\sum |v_i|}{n}. \qquad\qquad 7.10.2$$

Once again this formula is an approximation and is absurd for $n = 1$, since then $\sum |v_i| = 0$. We remove the absurdity with the minimum disturbance by writing $\sqrt{n(n-1)}$ for n, so that

$$\eta \simeq \frac{\sum |v_i|}{\sqrt{n(n-1)}}; \qquad\qquad 7.10.3$$

the standard deviation of a single observation is (using table 12)

$$\sigma_1 = \frac{5 \sum |v_i|}{4\sqrt{n(n-1)}}, \qquad\qquad 7.10.4$$

and the standard deviation of the arithmetic mean is $1/n^{\frac{1}{2}}$ of this last quantity, that is

$$\sigma_{\text{a.m.}} = \frac{5 \sum |v_i|}{4n\sqrt{n-1}}. \qquad\qquad 7.10.5$$

The standard deviation of σ is, as before, $\sigma/\sqrt{(2n)}$.

A useful check on numerical working is to note that the sum of positive residuals is equal numerically to the sum of the negative residuals.

§ 7.11 Combination of errors; standard deviation of a sum or difference

Suppose we have two quantities A and B, the results of independent measurement, and estimates of their accuracy, say standard deviations, $\pm a$ and $\pm b$ respectively. We wish to estimate the accuracy of

$A+B$. Clearly the best estimate is not $\pm(a+b)$ since this would imply that every positive error in measuring A was automatically accompanied by a positive error in measuring B. The same considerations lead us to expect that the accuracy of $A-B$, whatever it is, will be the same as that of $A+B$.

Using the same arguments as in § 7.4, suppose that the measurement of A involved n_A errors each of the same size δ and the measurement of B, n_B errors each of size which for simplicity we also take to be δ. Then, from 7.6.3,

$$a = \delta\sqrt{n_A}, \qquad b = \delta\sqrt{n_B},$$

if a and b are taken to be standard deviations. The measurement of $A\pm B$ then involves n_A+n_B errors, so that the root-mean-square error or standard deviation of this measurement is

$$\delta(n_A+n_B)^{\frac{1}{2}} = (\delta^2 n_A + \delta^2 n_B)^{\frac{1}{2}} = (a^2+b^2)^{\frac{1}{2}}.$$

If the observations obey the normal law then probable errors and mean errors are proportional to the root-mean-square errors. The result is that for any of these measures of error

$$(A\pm a)+(B\pm b)-(C\pm c)+ \ldots$$
$$= A+B-C+ \ldots \pm \sqrt{(a^2+b^2+c^2+ \ldots)}. \qquad 7.11.1$$

§ 7.12   Standard deviation of a product or quotient

A similar argument gives a formula for the estimate of error of a product. Suppose we have two quantities and their respective standard deviations $A\pm a$ and $B\pm b$ as before. We now require to find the standard deviation of the product AB.

As before, let δ be one of the n_A or n_B errors involved in the measurement of A and B respectively, where δ can be either positive or negative. On account of these micro-errors only, the product AB can be written

$$(A+\delta)(B+\delta) = AB\left(1+\frac{\delta}{A}\right)\left(1+\frac{\delta}{B}\right) = AB\left(1+\frac{\delta}{A}+\frac{\delta}{B}\right),$$

neglecting the term in δ^2, which is, by hypothesis, small compared with the others. The error in AB is thus

$$(A+\delta)(B+\delta)-AB = AB\left(\frac{\delta}{A}+\frac{\delta}{B}\right)$$

and the relative error is $\dfrac{\delta}{A} + \dfrac{\delta}{B}$. Thus the total error in the product AB is the sum of n_A terms each δ/A with random sign and n_B terms each correspondingly $\pm\delta/B$. The mean-square error in AB is thus, by 7.6.3,

$$\overline{\Delta^2_{AB}} = (AB)^2\left\{n_A\left(\frac{\delta}{A}\right)^2 + n_B\left(\frac{\delta}{B}\right)^2\right\} = (AB)^2\left\{\left(\frac{a}{A}\right)^2 + \left(\frac{b}{B}\right)^2\right\};$$

so, writing $\sigma_{AB} = (\overline{\Delta^2_{AB}})^{\frac{1}{2}}$, we have

$$\frac{\sigma_{AB}}{AB} = \left\{\left(\frac{a}{A}\right)^2 + \left(\frac{b}{B}\right)^2\right\}^{\frac{1}{2}}.$$ 7.12.1

The same proof gives for $\sigma_{A/B}$

$$\frac{\sigma_{A/B}}{A/B} = \left\{\left(\frac{a}{A}\right)^2 + \left(\frac{b}{B}\right)^2\right\}^{\frac{1}{2}}.$$ 7.12.2

§ 7.13 Standard deviation of a power

Now consider the standard deviation of A^2. We cannot simply put $A = B$ and $a = b$ in equation 7.12.1 since the assumption there was that the errors in A and B were independent, so that a positive error in A could be combined with a negative error in B. In the case of $A \times A$, instead of the random sums $\sum\limits^{n}(\pm)\dfrac{\delta}{A} + \sum\limits^{n}(\pm)\dfrac{\delta}{A}$, we have $\sum\limits^{n}(\pm)\dfrac{2\delta}{A}$,

so that $$\frac{\sigma_{A^2}}{A^2} = \frac{2a}{A}.$$ 7.13.1

Thus squaring a quantity doubles its relative error. It is easy to extend this result to any power so that we have

$$\frac{\sigma_{A^m}}{A^m} = m\frac{\sigma_A}{A}.$$ 7.13.2

The derivation of 7.13.1 illustrates why it was necessary in § 7.11 to stress that the measurements of A and B were independent. Combination of independent measurements involves the possibility that the errors of measurement may cancel each other. Thus

$$\frac{\sigma_{AB}}{AB} < \frac{\sigma_A}{A} + \frac{\sigma_B}{B},$$

whereas

$$\frac{\sigma_{AA}}{A \times A} = \frac{\sigma_A}{A} + \frac{\sigma_A}{A},$$

for in this case an error in measurement of one of the terms in the product is necessarily associated with the same error in the other term. By the same argument, if m is a numerical factor subject to no error then

$$\sigma_{mA} = m\sigma_A.$$
7.13.3

§ 7.14   General formula for combination of errors

The techniques developed in §§ 7.11–13 for use in special cases can be applied to the general case of an arbitrary mathematical function. Suppose we have independent measurements of quantities $A,B, C,\ldots$ and their respective standard deviations $\sigma_A,\sigma_B,\sigma_C,\ldots$. We wish to estimate the standard deviation of $f(A,B,C,\ldots)$ where f denotes some function of the quantities $A,B,C,\ldots$.

Let $\delta_A,\delta_B,\delta_C,\ldots$ be one of the micro-errors involved in the measurement of $A,B,C,\ldots$ respectively; to show that there is no difficulty involved in taking them to be different, we now drop this assumption. Then

$$f\{A+\delta_A,\ B+\delta_B,\ C+\delta_C,\ldots\}$$

$$= f\{A,B,C,\ldots\}+\frac{\partial f}{\partial A}\delta_A+\frac{\partial f}{\partial B}\delta_B+\frac{\partial f}{\partial C}\delta_C+\ldots,$$

where the expansion is by Taylor's theorem, and neglects terms of orders δ^2 and higher. The error in f due to these micro-errors is thus

$$\frac{\partial f}{\partial A}\delta_A+\frac{\partial f}{\partial B}\delta_B+\frac{\partial f}{\partial C}\delta_C+\ldots.$$

Summing all these terms, each with random sign, gives for the total error in f

$$\sum^{n_A}(\pm)\frac{\partial f}{\partial A}\delta_A+\sum^{n_B}(\pm)\frac{\partial f}{\partial B}\delta_B+\sum^{n_C}(\pm)\frac{\partial f}{\partial C}\delta_C+\ldots,$$

where each sum is a random walk over all $n_A+n_B+n_C+\ldots$ sources of error. By 7.6.3 the mean-square value of this sum is

$$\left(\frac{\partial f}{\partial A}\right)^2 n_A\delta_A^2+\left(\frac{\partial f}{\partial B}\right)^2 n_B\delta_B^2+\left(\frac{\partial f}{\partial C}\right)^2 n_C\delta_C^2+\ldots$$

with bars over the δ_i^2 if, as in 6.1.9, the micro-errors in each quantity are not to be assumed equal. As before $n_A\delta_A^2$ is the mean-square value of error in A, that is

$$n_A\delta_A^2 = \sigma_A^2,$$

so that $$\sigma_f^2 = \sigma_A^2\left(\frac{\partial f}{\partial A}\right)^2+\sigma_B^2\left(\frac{\partial f}{\partial B}\right)^2+\sigma_C^2\left(\frac{\partial f}{\partial C}\right)^2+\ldots.$$
7.14.1

§ 7.15   Summary of formulae for combination of errors

It is useful to have the final formulae of §§ 7.11–14 collected together, free from complexities of derivation.

If we have independently measured quantities $A,B,\ldots$ and their standard deviations $\sigma_A, \sigma_B, \ldots$, then, if

(i) $f = mA$,

where m is a number subject to no error,

$$\sigma_f = m\sigma_A \quad \text{or} \quad \frac{\sigma_f}{f} = \frac{\sigma_A}{A};$$ 7.15.1

(ii) $f = A \pm B$,

$$\sigma_f = (\sigma_A^2 + \sigma_B^2)^{\frac{1}{2}};$$ 7.15.2

(iii) $f = lA \pm mB$,

$$\sigma_f = (l^2\sigma_A^2 + m^2\sigma_B^2)^{\frac{1}{2}};$$ 7.15.3

(iv) $f = mAB$ or $f = mA/B$,

$$\frac{\sigma_f}{f} = \left\{\left(\frac{\sigma_A}{A}\right)^2 + \left(\frac{\sigma_B}{B}\right)^2\right\}^{\frac{1}{2}};$$ 7.15.4

(v) $f = lA^m$,

$$\frac{\sigma_f}{f} = m\frac{\sigma_A}{A};$$ 7.15.5

(vi) general formula

$$f = f(A,B,\ldots),$$

$$\sigma_f^2 = \left(\frac{\partial f}{\partial A}\sigma_A\right)^2 + \left(\frac{\partial f}{\partial B}\sigma_B\right)^2 + \ldots.$$ 7.15.6

§ 7.16   Weighting of observations

In § 7.7 we established that the most probable value of a set of observations was the mean, provided the observations were distributed according to the normal law and were of equal precision.

Suppose now we have n observations

$$x_1, x_2, \ldots, x_i, \ldots, x_n$$

not all of the same precision. If h_i, as defined in §§ 7.4–5 is the precision index of the ith observation then (as in 7.7.1) the most probable value of x is that which makes the quantity

$$\sum_{i=1}^{n} h_i^2(x - x_i)^2$$

a minimum. Now, in a similar manner to that in § 7.7, let X be the estimate of x which makes this sum a minimum, and write

$$\sum h_i^2(x-x_i)^2 = \sum h_i^2\{(x-X)+(X-x_i)\}^2$$
$$= \sum h_i^2(x-X)^2 + 2(x-X)\sum h_i^2(X-x_i) +$$
$$+ \sum h_i^2(X-x_i)^2.$$

Again, as in § 7.7, we look for the value of X which makes the middle term vanish. This is

$$X = \frac{\sum h_i^2 x_i}{\sum h_i^2}.$$ 7.16.1

Now, from 7.6.1 and 7.6.2,

$$h_i^2 = 1/2\sigma_i^2,$$

where σ_i is the standard deviation of x_i. Thus the best estimate of x is

$$X = \frac{\sum x_i/\sigma_i^2}{\sum 1/\sigma_i^2}.$$ 7.16.2

Since, with a normal distribution, the probable error r and average error η are proportional to σ, either of these can be substituted for σ in 7.16.2.

X is a *weighted mean*, the weight of each term being related to an estimate of its reliability obtained by statistical reasoning. We are of course familiar with weighted means: for example, in § 3.10 we evaluated the mean potential energy of molecules in the atmosphere by weighting the potential energy of a molecule at height z, that is mgz, by its probability of being there, that is $\exp(-mgz/kT)$. Naturally 7.16.2 is not the only possible weighted mean of the x_i. We could, for instance, weight the observations according to our own prejudices about the reliability of the methods used to obtain the various x_i or about the skill of the various observers. In any case we have

$$X = \frac{\sum w_i x_i}{\sum w_i},$$ 7.16.3

where w_i is the weight of the ith observation. It is frequently convenient to normalise such an expression (compare § 3.8) by multiplying all the w_i by the same factor $1/\sum w_i$, giving new weights w_i' such that $\sum w_i' = 1$.

To obtain an estimate of the standard deviation of a weighted mean we may consider a special case. Suppose we have $n_1 + n_2 + n_3 + \ldots$ observations of a quantity. The mean value $\bar{x}$ is, of course,

$$\bar{x} = \frac{\sum x_i}{n_1 + n_2 + n_3 + \ldots},$$

where the index i runs over all the $n_1 + n_2 + \ldots$ quantities x_i.

We might, however, have divided the observations into groups containing $n_1, n_2, \ldots, n_j, \ldots$ observations. The means of each group may be denoted by $\bar{x}_1, \bar{x}_2, \ldots, \bar{x}_j, \ldots$, where

$$\bar{x}_1 = \frac{\sum_{i=1}^{n_1} x_i}{n_1}, \qquad \bar{x}_2 = \frac{\sum_{i=n_1+1}^{n_1+n_2} x_i}{n_2}, \text{, etc.}$$

The mean of all the observations can then be obtained from the $\bar{x}_j$ by writing

$$X = \frac{n_1 \bar{x}_1 + n_2 \bar{x}_2 + \ldots}{n_1 + n_2 + \ldots}.$$

X is then a weighted mean, with the quantities $n_1, n_2, \ldots$, playing the part of weights. Obviously $X = \bar{x}$, and the standard deviation σ_X of X is the same as that of $\bar{x}$.

The first step in calculating σ_X is to estimate the precision of the $\bar{x}_j$, knowing that the $\bar{x}_j$ are not of equal precision. To do this we remember from § 7.8 that the mean of n_j quantities is $n_j^{\frac{1}{2}}$ times more accurate than that of any one. Thus we may expect to find a common measure of precision σ', say a standard deviation, such that the precision of any $\bar{x}_j$ is given by $\sigma'/n_j^{\frac{1}{2}}$. Such a quantity is, by analogy with § 7.8, the square root of the mean of the squares of the weighted residuals $(X - \bar{x}_j)$, the weights being the $n_j^{\frac{1}{2}}$. Thus

$$\sigma' = \sqrt{\frac{\sum n_j (X - \bar{x}_j)^2}{n}},$$

where n is the number of $\bar{x}_j$. As in § 7.8 we correct this by replacing n by $n-1$. Further, it may not be known how many observations went to produce the average $\bar{x}_j$ and there is only a measure, or estimate, w_j of its weight. This being so, we drop the bars on the x_j and obtain for the common measure of precision of quantities x_j, each having weight w_j,

$$\sigma' = \sqrt{\frac{w_j (X - x_j)}{n-1}}. \qquad 7.16.4$$

The corresponding measure of precision of x_j is, as stated already, $\sigma'/w_j^{\frac{1}{2}}$, while that of X is $\sigma'/(n_1+n_2+ \ldots)^{\frac{1}{2}}$, or $\sigma'/(\sum w_j)^{\frac{1}{2}}$ if we do not know the n_j. Thus, finally, the standard deviation of the weighted mean of n observations x_j each having weight w_j is

$$\sigma_X = \sqrt{\frac{\sum w_j v_j^2}{(n-1)\sum w_j}}, \qquad 7.16.5$$

where $v_j = X - x_j$. If all w_j are equal this formula reduces to Bessel's formula 7.9.3.

If we prefer to work with the quantities $|v_j|$ the corresponding equation may readily be seen to be

$$\sigma_X = \frac{5\sum w_j^{\frac{1}{2}} |v_j|}{4\sqrt{\{n(n-1)\sum w_j\}}}, \qquad 7.16.6$$

which, if all w_j are equal, reduces to Peters' formula 7.10.5.

§ 7.17 Best straight line

Suppose we have n pairs of measurements $(x_1,y_1),(x_2,y_2),\ldots,(x_i,y_i),\ldots$ which are believed to be connected by a linear relationship of the form

$$y = mx+c, \qquad 7.17.1$$

where m and c are constants. For example, y_i might be the length of a rod loaded with weights x_i. c would then be the length with $x = 0$, that is, the unloaded length while, if the material of the rod obeyed Hooke's law, m would be an elastic modulus. If we had only two pairs of measurements (x_1,y_1) and (x_2,y_2), then m and c would be determined by solving a pair of simultaneous equations. If we have more than two measurements, then, since all the x_i and y_i are subject to error, we shall obtain a variety of values of m and c by solving the equations in pairs. The problem is to find the best or most probable values of m and c.

One method of doing this is to plot the n points (x_i,y_i) on paper and draw what appears to be the best straight line through them, the line being drawn in such a way that the experimental points are roughly equally distributed on either side of it and all points as close as possible to it. In statistical terms, we might extend the result of § 7.7 and try to arrange that the sum of the squares of the distances of the points from the line is a minimum.

We first simplify the problem by postulating that one of the variables, say x, is exact and the errors are all in the other. This

14

simplification is indeed quite common in practice: for example, in the elasticity example with which this section began, the weights x can be known with great precision; the inaccuracies arise in measurements of length and small changes in length.

Suppose that m and c have been determined in some way. If we now substitute experimental values $x = x_i$ and $y = y_i$ in the expression $y - mx - c$, the result will not in general be zero because of errors in measurement of y_i (and x_i if we do not make the simplifying assumption). Write

$$y_i - mx_i - c = v_i. \qquad 7.17.2$$

The principle of least squares (§ 7.7) then suggests that we make

$$\sum_{i=1}^{n} v_i^2 = \text{minimum} \qquad 7.17.3$$

or $$\sum_{i=1}^{n} (y_i - mx_i - c)^2 = \text{minimum}. \qquad 7.17.4$$

Differentiating partially with respect to m and c gives two equations for this minimum. These are called *normal equations* and are

$$\sum_{i=1}^{n} x_i(y_i - mx_i - c) = 0 \qquad 7.17.5$$

and $$\sum_{i=1}^{n} (y_i - mx_i - c) = 0. \qquad 7.17.6$$

These equations may be re-written

$$\sum x_i y_i - m\sum x_i^2 - c\sum x_i = 0 \qquad 7.17.7$$

and $$\sum y_i - m\sum x_i - cn = 0. \qquad 7.17.8$$

Solving 7.17.7 and 7.17.8 as simultaneous equations for m and c gives

$$m = \frac{n\sum x_i y_i - \sum x_i \sum y_i}{n\sum x_i^2 - (\sum x_i)^2} \qquad 7.17.9$$

and $$c = \frac{\sum x_i \sum x_i y_i - \sum y_i \sum x_i^2}{(\sum x_i)^2 - n\sum x_i^2}. \qquad 7.17.10$$

7.17.9 and 7.17.10 can be used to calculate m and c. The process, however, is somewhat laborious, so for practical purposes it is useful to indicate a simpler method. Thus, 7.17.8 can be written

$$\frac{1}{n}\sum y_i - \frac{m}{n}\sum x_i - c = 0,$$

which tells us that the point given by

$$\bar{x} = \frac{1}{n}\sum x_i \quad \text{and} \quad \bar{y} = \frac{1}{n}\sum y_i$$

satisfies the equation and thus lies on the best straight line. This point $(\bar{x},\bar{y})$ is the centre of gravity of the n experimental points and corresponds in the two-dimensional case to the mean in the case of one variable.

We may take a hint from this result and define a best straight line as the line joining the centre of gravity of the first $\frac{1}{2}n$ points to the centre of gravity of the second $\frac{1}{2}n$ points, where 'first' and 'second' refer to values of x_i or y_i in order of magnitude. This is the *centre of gravity method*, and with it we have

$$m = \frac{\bar{y}_2 - \bar{y}_1}{\bar{x}_2 - \bar{x}_1},\qquad\qquad 7.17.11$$

where $(\bar{x}_1,\bar{y}_1)$ and $(\bar{x}_2,\bar{y}_2)$ are the centres of gravity of the two sets of points.

It is easy to see that this line passes through the centre of gravity of all the points: for, if the number of points is even, then

$$\left(\frac{\sum\limits_{i=1}^{\frac{1}{2}n} x_i}{\frac{1}{2}n}, \ \frac{\sum\limits_{i=1}^{\frac{1}{2}n} y_i}{\frac{1}{2}n} \right) = (\bar{x}_1,\bar{y}_1)$$

and

$$\left(\frac{\sum\limits_{i=\frac{1}{2}n+1}^{n} x_i}{\frac{1}{2}n}, \ \frac{\sum\limits_{i=\frac{1}{2}n+1}^{n} y_i}{\frac{1}{2}n} \right) = (\bar{x}_2,\bar{y}_2)$$

are the centres of gravity of the first $\frac{1}{2}n$ and second $\frac{1}{2}n$ points respectively. The co-ordinates of the mid-point of the line joining them are then

$$(\tfrac{1}{2}(\bar{x}_1+\bar{x}_2), \tfrac{1}{2}(\bar{y}_1+\bar{y}_2)) = \left(\frac{\sum\limits_{i=1}^{n} x_i}{n}, \ \frac{\sum\limits_{i=1}^{n} y_i}{n} \right),$$

$$= (\bar{x},\bar{y}),$$

which is the centre of gravity of all the points. c is then given by

$$\bar{y} = m\bar{x} + c.\qquad\qquad 7.17.12$$

No attempt will be made to give a general proof that the slope m and intercept c found by the centre of gravity method are almost the same as the corresponding parameters found from equations 7.17.9 and 7.17.10, that is by use of the principle of least squares. A numerical example such as problem 7.22.3 may help to make the assumption plausible.

§ 7.18 Accuracy of coefficients

We may use the results of the centre of gravity method to estimate the accuracy of the coefficients m and c. The estimates so obtained can be used on results obtained by other methods.

Using the experimental values of x_i, which were assumed accurate, and the calculated values of m and c we can find a quantity y_i' defined by

$$y_i' = mx_i + c, \qquad 7.18.1$$

but which will in general differ from the experimental y_i because of experimental error. Denoting by v_i the residuals

$$v_i = y_i' - y_i, \qquad 7.18.2$$

we then have, in the same way as in 7.10.2, that the mean residual is

$$\eta = \frac{\sum |v_i|}{n}.$$

This is a measure of the width of the distribution of residuals and as such a measure of the accuracy of the measurements of the y_i.

Now if n is only 2, the two points define a single straight line uniquely. Thus $\sum v_i = 0$; so this formula would suggest that the two measurements were free of the possibility of error. As in § 7.8 and § 7.10 we remove this absurdity by writing $\sqrt{n(n-2)}$ for n. The standard deviation of a single y is thus (using table 12)

$$\sigma_y = \frac{5 \sum |v_i|}{4\sqrt{n(n-2)}}. \qquad 7.18.3$$

Now the accuracy of c, which is the intercept on the y axis, is obviously the same as the accuracy of $\bar{y}$, the mean of n observations of y, that is

$$\sigma_c = \sigma_y / n^{\frac{1}{2}}. \qquad 7.18.4$$

The accuracy of m is determined from 7.17.11. If we assume that the number of points n is even then the standard deviations of $\bar{y}_1$ and $\bar{y}_2$ are both

$$\sigma_{\bar{y}_1} = \sigma_{\bar{y}_2} = \frac{\sigma_y}{\sqrt{(n/2)}},$$

since each is the mean of $\frac{1}{2}n$ observations. Using 7.15.2 we then find that the standard deviation of $\bar{y}_2 - \bar{y}_1$ is

$$\sigma_{(\bar{y}_2 - \bar{y}_1)} = \sqrt{2}\frac{\sigma_y}{\sqrt{(n/2)}} = \frac{2\sigma_y}{\sqrt{n}}.$$

Finally, since the factor $\bar{x}_2 - \bar{x}_1$ is by hypothesis free from error, we may use rule 7.15.1 and obtain as our estimate of the standard deviation of m

$$\sigma_m = \frac{2\sigma_y}{(\bar{x}_2 - \bar{x}_1)\sqrt{n}}. \qquad 7.18.5$$

§ 7.19 Curve fitting

The same method as in § 7.17 may be used to fit data to polynomial expressions involving powers higher than the first. Suppose for definiteness we wish to fit n pairs of values $(x_1,y_1),(x_2,y_2),\ldots,(x_n,y_n)$, to a quadratic expression of the form

$$y = a + bx + cx^2. \qquad 7.19.1$$

By exactly the same argument as for equation 7.17.4, the constants a, b and c are determined by minimising the expression

$$\sum_{i=1}^{n} (y_i - a - bx_i - cx_i^2)^2.$$

Differentiating partially with respect to a, b and c gives the following normal equations:

$$\sum y_i - na - b\sum x_i - c\sum x_i^2 = 0,$$
$$\sum x_i y_i - a\sum x_i - b\sum x_i^2 - c\sum x_i^3 = 0, \qquad 7.19.2$$
$$\sum x_i^2 y_i - a\sum x_i^2 - b\sum x_i^3 - c\sum x_i^4 = 0,$$

and their solution gives the most probable values of a, b and c. This method can obviously be extended to polynomials of any order, although, as the number of constants increases, the computation becomes increasingly laborious. Computer programmes are available to help.

§ 7.20 Correlation

In § 7.17 we found that if experimental values of x and y were assumed to be related by an equation of the form

$$y = mx + c, \qquad 7.20.1$$

then the principle of least squares gave the best estimate of m to be (7.17.9)

$$m = \frac{n\sum x_i y_i - \sum x_i \sum y_i}{n\sum x_i^2 - (\sum x_i)^2}.$$ 7.20.2

We may simplify this expression by moving the origin to the centre of gravity of the n observed points, which lies on the best straight line. We write

$$X_i = x_i - \bar{x},$$
$$Y_i = y_i - \bar{y}.$$

The assumed straight line relating the new variables is then

$$Y = mX,$$ 7.20.3

where m is still given by expression 7.20.2 but with the simplification that now

$$\sum X_i = \sum Y_i = 0,$$

so that $\quad m = \dfrac{\sum X_i Y_i}{\sum X_i^2}.$ 7.20.4

Suppose, however, we had written the assumed equation connecting the variables as

$$X = m' Y;$$ 7.20.5

then going through exactly the same reasoning as used in 7.17.1–9 gives

$$m' = \frac{\sum X_i Y_i}{\sum Y_i^2}.$$ 7.20.6

If all our assumptions are correct, then equations 7.20.3 and 7.20.5 represent the same line, so that

$$m = 1/m' \quad \text{or} \quad mm' = 1.$$

If, however, m and $1/m'$ are very different we are led to question the assumption that the variables X and Y (or x and y) are related by a linear law. The quantity r defined by the relation

$$r = mm' = \frac{\sum X_i Y_i}{\sqrt{(\sum X_i^2 \sum Y_i^2)}},$$

is a measure of the accuracy of this asumption and is called the *correlation coefficient*. The limiting cases are

(i) $r = 1$: this corresponds to perfect correlation, that is X and Y (or x and y) are linearly related, X increasing with Y.

(ii) $r = -1$: this again corresponds to perfect correlation except that X now increases as Y decreases. In such a case $\sum X_i Y_i$ is the sum of negative quantities only.

(iii) $r = 0$: this means the variables X and Y are not related or are related by some law which cannot be even approximately represented by a straight line. $r = 0$ requires

$$\sum X_i Y_i = 0,$$

which means that a given X_i is as likely to be associated with a negative Y_i as with a positive Y_i. Alternatively $r = 0$ could be interpreted as meaning that one or both of the lines relating x and y were parallel to the axis so that m or m' was zero. Once again this means that the variables are independent.

Between these limits, definition of what value of r corresponds to good correlation is somewhat arbitrary. For example, E. S. Barr * asked himself the question 'does index of refraction of glass vary directly with density?'. He plotted various values obtained from tables and produced the answer shown in *fig.* 7.2. If numerical data are taken from this figure, the correlation coefficient is found to be -0.09. Barr's answer is thus apparently correct.

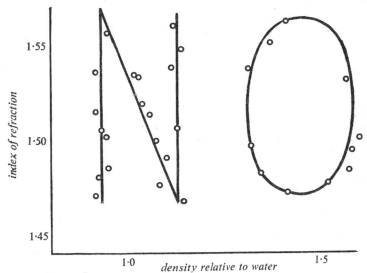

Figure 7.2. '*Does index of refraction of glass vary directly with density?*'

* *American Journal of Physics*, **23**, 623 (1955).

In general, the correlation coefficient is not a very useful concept in physics or other exact sciences where theory exists, or should exist, to explain why and how one quantity depends on another. Its value in the social sciences is illustrated by problem 7.22.4 which lists the scores obtained by physics students in: (a) a verbal reasoning test suggested for use as a means of student selection, and (b) and (c), two physics examinations differing in time and content. The correlation r obtained between (a) and (c) was $+0\cdot24$, which suggests that the proposed test is of little value for predicting success in physics examinations. Better correlation is obtained between the marks obtained in two similar examinations. Whether the physics examinations themselves predict success has not yet been examined statistically.

§ 7.21 Appendix: errors and residuals

Justification of formula 7.8.1. Let there be n observations $x_1, x_2, \ldots, x_i,$ $\ldots, x_n$ and suppose the true value x is known (compare the measurement of π in § 7.3). The true error e_i in observation i may be written

$$e_i = x - x_i,$$

while if $\bar{x}$ is the mean of the x_i, that is,

$$\bar{x} = \frac{1}{n}\sum x_i,$$

the residuals are

$$v_i = \bar{x} - x_i.$$

Consider now the quantities $\sum e_i^2$ and $\sum v_i^2$:

$$\sum e_i^2 = \sum_{i=1}^{n} (x - x_i)^2$$
$$= nx^2 - 2x\sum x_i + \sum x_i^2$$
$$= nx^2 - 2x(n\bar{x}) + \sum x_i^2,$$

$$\sum v_i^2 = \sum_{i=1}^{n} (\bar{x} - x_i)^2$$

$$= n(\bar{x})^2 - 2\bar{x}\sum x_i + \sum x_i^2$$
$$= n(\bar{x})^2 - 2\bar{x}(n\bar{x}) + \sum x_i^2,$$

$$\sum e_i^2 - \sum v_i^2 = nx^2 - n(\bar{x})^2 - 2n\bar{x}(x - \bar{x})$$
$$= nx^2 + n(\bar{x})^2 - 2n\bar{x}x$$
$$= n(x - \bar{x})^2, \qquad\qquad 7.21.1$$

which is essentially positive or zero. Thus the sum of squared residuals is always less than the sum of squared true errors unless the mean is also the true value. Moreover

$$\frac{1}{n}\sum e_i^2 = \frac{1}{n}\sum v_i^2 + (x - \bar{x})^2.$$

Now x can reasonably be thought of as yet another measurement of the quantity for which we have n measurements $x_1, x_2, \ldots, x_n$. Hence $x - \bar{x}$ is another residual or

$$\frac{1}{n}\sum e_i^2 \simeq \frac{1}{n-1}\sum v_i^2, \qquad\qquad 7.21.2$$

which makes the substitution of $n-1$ for n in the derivation of 7.8.1 a little more plausible. More careful calculation replaces the approximate relation 7.21.2 by an exact equation with a correction factor on the right hand side. This factor is unity when n is large (more than about 10), rising to about 1·2 when n is 4, and to about 1·5 when n is 2. Since it is unlikely to be wise to apply a theory of errors to so few observations we shall regard the divergencies from unity in this factor as entirely academic.

§ 7.22 Problems

1. In an experiment such as that described in § 7.2, the width D of identical rectangular strips (like tickets) was measured as follows: the strips were thrown down at random on the floor and a bag of coins of diameter d emptied over them. Denoting 'hits' as those coins which lay entirely on a strip without overlapping a side and 'misses' those coins which overlapped a side, show that in the notation of § 7.2

$$\frac{D}{d} = \frac{2n_{\mathrm{H}} + n_{\mathrm{M}}}{n_{\mathrm{M}}}.$$

2. In an experiment to measure Young's modulus E by the formula

$$E = \frac{3}{4}\frac{M}{x}\frac{gaL^2}{bd^3},$$

where M is a mass, g is the gravitational acceleration (9·81 m s^{-2}), and x, a, L, b and d all have the dimensions of a length, the following readings were made:

TABLE 13 : results of an experiment to measure Young's modulus

$b = 2\cdot075, 2\cdot084, 2\cdot072, 2\cdot076, 2\cdot076, 2\cdot081$ cm
$d = 1\cdot029, 1\cdot025, 1\cdot025, 1\cdot026, 1\cdot022, 1\cdot024$ cm

M(kg)	x(cm)
$L = 39\cdot0$ cm **$a = 15\cdot5$ cm**	
0·5	0·024
1·0	0·052
1·5	0·080
2·0	0·098
$L = 46\cdot6$ cm **$a = 11\cdot7$ cm**	
0·5	0·030
1·0	0·062
1·5	0·088
2·0	0·120
$L = 42\cdot0$ cm **$a = 14\cdot0$ cm**	
0·5	0·026
1·0	0·056
1·5	0·082
2·0	0·116

Find the best value of E and its standard deviation. (*Answer*: $E = (1\cdot486 \pm 0\cdot007) \times 10^{10}$ Nm^{-2}.)

3. The results in the table below were obtained by L. W. Barr (Ph.D. thesis, Edinburgh 1959), in his work on diffusion of antimony into

TABLE 14 : results of a diffusion experiment

ln c	x^2
(c in counts per min/gm)	(cm$^2 \times 10^5$)
9·393	1·82
9·265	12·28
9·116	26·12
8·905	45·11
8·587	69·27
8·217	98·60
7·814	133·08
7·315	172·72
6·757	217·53
6·254	267·50

silver carried out as described in § 6.3. Analyse these results, which are plotted in *fig.* 6.3, so as to find the best straight line relating ln *c* to x^2. Show that almost the same slope and standard deviation are obtained whether the analysis is by least squares or by the centre of gravity method (§ 7.17).

TABLE 15 : correlations between examination marks

Student no.	(a) verbal reasoning	(b) term exam	(c) degree exam
1	117	34	55
2	129	44	68
3	90	31	51
4	134	73	81
5	112	54	69
6	138	44	55
7	134	42	36
8	116	54	84
9	110	51	37
10	138	68	90
11	138	43	59
12	133	43	59
13	119	34	46
14	112	40	51
15	122	31	20
16	138	34	29
17	125	32	38
18	128	55	56
19	111	48	64
20	133	53	56
21	126	47	59
22	131	58	69
23	139	76	85
24	135	66	79
25	137	56	73
26	125	69	69
27	132	61	61
28	121	42	51
29	135	47	66

4. The marks in table 15 were obtained by a class of 29 students in (*a*) a verbal reasoning 'intelligence' test proposed for student selection; (*b*) a term examination in physics a few months after the start of a year;

(*c*) a degree examination at the end of the year.

Show that there is little correlation ($r = +0.24$) between (*a*) and (*c*) but fairly good correlation ($r = +0.8$) between (*b*) and (*c*).

§ 7.23   Further reading

J. Topping *Errors of observation and their treatment*, Institute of Physics, and the Physical Society, London 1955. In addition to theory and formulae this book contains many worked examples and problems.

Chapter 8

ENTROPY

We have seen in § 5 that an isolated system of non-interacting particles settles into the configuration of maximum probability. Another way of saying the same thing is that if we enumerate the complexions (§ 3.3) which the system of particles can have, then the equilibrium state is one of the configurations which contains the greatest number of complexions. Any less probable configuration will rapidly be abandoned in favour of a more probable one.

Since we shall shortly wish to see how interactions between the particles affect the way they behave, it is as well to remind ourselves that by 'non-interacting' we meant that interactions were supposed to be the minimum required to allow the particles to scatter each other into different cells in real space or phase space. In particular we assumed that the probability that a particle was in a given cell was entirely independent of the number of particles in that cell. The particles we have been dealing with so far could collide, but were not allowed to stick together or to repel each other.

§ 8.1   The statistical definition of entropy

Consider then a system of non interacting particles and define a quantity S by the equation

$$S = k \ln w, \qquad\qquad 8.1.1$$

where k is Boltzmann's constant and w is the number of ways of arranging the system, that is the number of complexions it can take. The most probable state of the system is that for which the quantity S is a maximum. We saw in § 5.3 that the number of complexions in the most probable configuration was so enormously larger than the number in any other that it was immaterial whether w referred to it or to all configurations.

We now wish to show that S is the same quantity as the *entropy* as used in thermodynamics. A general proof is not difficult, but it will be sufficient here to show for a special case that the above definition of S gives the same answer as is obtained by the thermodynamic definition. We shall later meet other examples where the two definitions are seen to be equivalent.

§ 8.2 Thermodynamic entropy

The thermodynamic definition of entropy tells us that if a system follows a reversible path, that is a path consisting only of equilibrium states, from state 1 to state 2, then the change of entropy between these states is

$$S_2 - S_1 = \int_1^2 \frac{dQ}{T}, \qquad\qquad 8.2.1$$

where dQ is the heat taken in in an infinitesimal change and T is the temperature at which the change takes place.

If we consider the special case of one kg-mole of a perfect gas expanding isothermally at a given temperature from volume V_1 to volume V_2, we can calculate $S_2 - S_1$ provided we can find a reversible path for the expansion. This we do by allowing the expansion to take place very slowly; for example, we might arrange that the volume V_1 is closed on one side by a piston which is allowed to move out infinitely slowly until it encloses a volume V_2. During an infinitesimal increase in volume dV the gas does work $p\, dV$ and, from the first law of thermodynamics (law of conservation of energy) for a reversible process,

$$dQ = dU + p\, dV, \qquad\qquad 8.2.2$$

where dU, the change of internal energy, is here zero since the change is isothermal and the gas is perfect. The heat dQ, which reappears as work, must be supplied by the surroundings. From equation 8.2.1

$$S_2 - S_1 = \int_{V_1}^{V_2} \frac{p\, dV}{T}. \qquad\qquad 8.2.3$$

Since we are dealing with one kg-mole of a perfect gas we have

$$pV = RT,$$

whence

$$S_2 - S_1 = R \int_{V_1}^{V_2} \frac{dV}{V} = R \ln (V_2/V_1). \qquad\qquad 8.2.4$$

We recall at this stage that the thermodynamic entropy is a property of an equilibrium state and is independent of the method by which that state is reached. We had here to specify the detailed path between states 1 and 2, with the requirement that the path be reversible, only in order to have the use of equations 8.2.1 and 2. If we had chosen any other reversible path we should have obtained the same value for $S_2 - S_1$.

For example, suppose we had allowed the gas to expand adiabatically, but still reversibly, from volume V_1 to volume V_2. In this case no heat enters or leaves the system, so $dQ = 0$ and the work of expansion is supplied by the internal energy of the gas. This means that the temperature of the gas falls, say to temperature T_2. We now arrange to heat up the gas in a reversible manner at constant volume until the temperature is restored to T_1. During the adiabatic expansion there is no change of entropy, while during the heating the change is

$$S_2 - S_1 = \int_{T_2}^{T_1} \frac{dQ}{T} = \int_{T_2}^{T_1} \frac{c_V dT}{T}$$

$$= c_V \ln \frac{T_1}{T_2}. \qquad 8.2.5$$

Now we can express T_2 in terms of V, since in an adiabatic change a perfect gas obeys the equation

$$TV^{\gamma - 1} = \text{constant}, \qquad 8.2.6$$

where $\qquad \gamma = c_p / c_V$.

Thus $\qquad \dfrac{T_1}{T_2} = \left(\dfrac{V_2}{V_1}\right)^{\gamma - 1}$

and $\qquad c_V \ln (T_1 / T_2) = (c_p - c_V) \ln (V_2 / V_1)$

$$= R \ln (V_2 / V_1), \qquad 8.2.7$$

since for a kg-mole of a perfect gas $c_p - c_V = R$.

Thus $\quad S_2 - S_1 = R \ln (V_2 / V_1)$, $\qquad 8.2.8$

the same expression as 8.2.4.

§ 8.3 Equivalence of statistical and thermodynamic entropy

To obtain an expression for $S_2 - S_1$ by statistical means we need only concern ourselves with the end states, and we need not worry about whether the path taken between them is reversible or not. This is because the statistical definition allows us to calculate the entropy of equilibrium states directly without having to take account of how the system arrived there.

First, in general terms we note that the thermodynamic entropy has increased in the expansion. We shall expect the statistical entropy likewise to increase. That it does so can be seen by dividing the volumes V_1 and V_2 into equal small cells as we did before. If $V_2 > V_1$, there will be more cells in V_2 and consequently more ways of arranging the molecules in them. We use equation 8.1.1 to calculate S, first taking w to refer to all complexions and secondly taking account only of equilibrium complexions; we expect these two methods to give the same result for S.

To take account of all complexions it is mathematically convenient to take the cells to be so small that nearly all are empty and only an occasional cell contains a molecule. The probability that a cell contains more than one molecule is then negligibly small. The number of ways of arranging N molecules in n cells is then given by the number of arrangements of N occupied cells and $n - N$ empty cells. This is

$$w = \frac{n!}{N!(n-N)!},$$ 8.3.1

which is the number of permutations of the n cells divided by the numbers of permutations of the indistinguishable full and empty cells. From 8.3.1 using Stirling's formula (§ 12.5) we have:

$$\ln w = n \ln n - N \ln N - (n-N) \ln (n-N)$$

$$= -n \ln \frac{n-N}{n} + N \ln \frac{n-N}{N},$$ 8.3.2

which, since $n \gg N$, reduces to

$$\ln w = N + N \ln \frac{n}{N}.$$ 8.3.3

This last step is where we note the mathematical simplification brought about by using such small cells.

Now suppose that in volume V_1 we had n_1 cells, while in volume V_2 we have n_2 cells of the same size. That is $n_r \propto V_r$. Calling the numbers of arrangements of the same number N of molecules over n_1 and n_2 cells w_1 and w_2 respectively, we have

$$\ln w_2 - \ln w_1 = N \ln \frac{n_2}{N} - N \ln \frac{n_1}{N}$$

$$= N \ln \frac{n_2}{n_1}$$

$$= N \ln (V_2/V_1).$$ 8.3.4

Multiplying both sides by k gives

$$S_2 - S_1 = Nk \ln (V_2/V_1), \qquad 8.3.5$$

while if $N = N_0$, the number of molecules in a kg-mole,

$$S_2 - S_1 = R \ln (V_2/V_1), \qquad 8.3.6$$

the same expression as we obtained in 8.2.4 and 8.2.8 using the thermodynamic expression for entropy change.

To calculate w for an equilibrium configuration, suppose the volume V is divided into n' cells of equal size–but now large enough to allow us to write $N \gg n'$. In equilibrium, each equal cell contains an equal number N/n' of molecules. Then

$$w = \frac{N!}{[(N/n')!]^{n'}}, \qquad 8.3.7$$

which assumes that, as in § 5.2, we can distinguish molecules in different cells but do not count rearrangements within the same cell as different complexions. Taking logarithms gives

$$\ln w = \ln (N!) - n' \ln ([N/n']!),$$

whence by Stirling's formula we obtain

$$\ln w = N \ln N - N \ln (N/n') = N \ln n'. \qquad 8.3.8$$

Hence, by the same arguments as before, dividing the volume V_1 into n_1' cells and the volume V_2 into n_2' cells of equal size, we have

$$\ln w_2 - \ln w_1 = N \ln (V_2/V_1),$$

the same expression as 8.3.4 and giving the same answer for the entropy change.

The definition

$$S = k \ln w$$

is often called the *Boltzmann definition* of entropy. We shall see in § 9.5. that the Boltzmann and thermodynamic definitions give the same result for entropy of thermal vibration.

§ 8.4 Free energy

We can at once extend the results obtained above to more complicated and interesting cases than perfect gases.

In any reversible cycle

$$\oint \frac{dQ}{T} = 0.$$

15

The quantity inside the integral is what we called the entropy and the above equation tells us that the difference in entropy between any two states is independent of the path followed between them. This means that entropy is a property of the state of the system, a result which agrees with our statistical ideas. It is also in accord with our statistical ideas to observe that, in a system left to itself, the entropy will either remain constant or increase, for in the former case the system is in a state of maximum probability; in the latter case it is not and some rearrangement of the particles (in the widest sense of the term) will increase its probability.

Now even in the simple case of an isothermal expansion of a perfect gas we had to suppose that, during the reversible expansion, heat could be drawn as required from the surroundings. We did not enquire what happened to the entropy of the surroundings, but if we count the surroundings along with the system we would expect that the total entropy of the larger system would either increase or stay constant. As before, increase of entropy means that our system is moving into a state of equilibrium with its surroundings; no change means that it is in equilibrium. We thus have

$$dS + dS_{surr} \geqslant 0,$$

where the S without a suffix refers to our system, S_{surr} to the surroundings.

Suppose as before that our system absorbs heat dQ reversibly from the surroundings. Then

$$dS_{surr} = -\frac{dQ}{T},$$

the minus sign being in accord with the usual thermodynamic convention that heat given to a system (in this case the surroundings) is positive. Thus

$$dS - \frac{dQ}{T} \geqslant 0.$$

This heat dQ has gone into our system and from the First Law,

$$dQ = dU + p\,dV.$$

Thus for our system

$$T\,dS - dU - p\,dV \geqslant 0$$

or $\qquad dU - T\,dS + p\,dV \leqslant 0.$

The inequality is the condition for a change to take place. The condition for equilibrium is

$$dU - T\,dS + p\,dV = 0,\qquad\qquad 8.4.1$$

or at constant temperature and pressure

$$d(U - TS + pV) = 0.\qquad\qquad 8.4.2$$

The quantity

$$G = U - TS + pV\qquad\qquad 8.4.3$$

is called the *Gibbs free energy* or *thermodynamic potential*. At constant volume, 8.4.2 reduces to

$$d(U - TS) = 0,\qquad\qquad 8.4.4$$

or $\quad dF = 0.$

F is called the *Helmholtz free energy* or more usually just the *free energy*.

In dealing with solids, changes of volume are small, for even on melting the volume does not change by more than a few percent, while less drastic changes of state are accompanied by even smaller changes of volume. Under such conditions dF and dG are the same, so it is customary to use F as if it were the complete free energy function.

§ 8.5 Equilibrium of a system of interacting particles

Expression 8.4.4 shows that we can determine equilibrium conditions in a solid or other condensed system by finding the minimum of the quantity $F = U - TS$. This result is a generalisation of the one obtained in chapter 5 where we found that the equilibrium state of a system of non-interacting particles was the one of maximum probability, that is maximum entropy. It is likewise a generalisation of the result, used in elementary mechanics, that a system of strongly interacting bodies settles in the state of minimum potential energy. We now see that equilibrium for a general system of particles which may interact is determined by a compromise between a state of lowest energy ($U = $ min) and a state of maximum probability ($S = $ max). The compromise is expressed by the form of the function F.

In slightly more generality, equilibrium is determined by a compromise between minimum internal energy, minimum volume, and maximum probability, the compromise being expressed by the form of the function G.

Chapter 9

APPLICATIONS OF ENTROPY AND
FREE ENERGY

We shall now give examples of the use of the functions F and G derived in the last chapter, and of the idea that the equilibrium state of an assembly of particles is a compromise between a minimum of energy and a maximum of probability. We shall draw our examples mainly from the solid state, where the entropy concept is particularly easy to understand, because solids, which are nearly all crystalline, have an easily recognisable order. The state of maximum order is particularly obvious and departures from perfect order are easy to enumerate; there is no need to divide space up by arbitrary partitions, for the crystal lattice does this for us. Likewise we have a ready-partitioned phase space.

§ 9.1   Solid of non-interacting particles

We start with a simple model of a condensed state consisting of a large number of equal balls at rest in a box. For this system there are no forces between the balls and the equilibrium state is one where the balls lie on the bottom of the box in such a way that their total potential energy is a minimum. This state is also the one where the balls are as densely packed as possible, so it is also the state of minimum volume and maximum order.

If now the box is shaken gently, we simulate the effect of temperature: the total energy of the system is increased and at the same time disorder is introduced. More vigorous shaking leads to a state where the balls remain in contact with their neighbours but there is little recognisable order; this is the liquid state. Really violent shaking causes the balls to move freely throughout the box. Their arrangement is then determined by the state of maximum probability, which is a uniform distribution within the box.

§ 9.2 Crystal equilibrium

In a crystalline solid at low temperatures, the particles (atoms, molecules or ions) form a regular array like the balls in the box of the preceding section, except that there are now forces between the particles.

The binding energy of a crystal is usually taken as the negative of the amount of energy to dissipate the crystal into its free particles, so the condition of minimum energy becomes one of maximum negative binding energy. At low temperatures this minimum determines the crystal structure and the distances between particles. It very frequently happens that the equilibrium structure at low temperatures is also the one in which the particles are most closely packed but, if this is so, it is only because the close-packed structure is the one with greatest negative binding energy. That the pV term in the free energy expression (8.4.3) plays no part can be seen by noting that the binding energy of a metal is of the order of 10^5 kJ/kg-mole, whereas the molar volume is about 10^{-2} m^3, so pV at atmospheric pressure (10^5 N m^{-2}) is about 1 kJ/kg-mole. In a very weakly bound crystal, such as a molecular crystal or a crystal of a rare gas, the binding energy would be some 100 times less and the molar volume much the same as in a metal; so even in this extreme case pV can be neglected.

As the temperature is raised, the regular crystalline lattice persists right up to the melting point, but disorder is introduced in two ways.

(i) The particles oscillate about their positions of equilibrium; the energy U of the crystal thus rises with temperature (or the magnitude of the negative binding energy falls). This rise in energy is partly compensated by an increase in TS, which comes about not only because T increases but also because S increases. We shall be finding an expression for S in § 9.5, but the basic reason for the increase of S with temperature is that the more energy there is to distribute over the particles, the more ways there are of distributing it.

(ii) Some lattice sites become vacant, so that the number of positions available for particles is larger than the number of particles to occupy them. Since there are binding forces between the particles, work must be done to remove one from its lattice site, so the energy of a crystal with vacant lattice sites is higher than that of a perfect crystal. The compensating rise of entropy is due to there now being many more ways of arranging the particles on a greater number of sites. We shall, in § 9.11, use our result that equilibrium corresponds to a minimum of the quantity $U - TS$, and so calculate the number of vacant lattice sites in equilibrium at any temperature.

§ 9.3   Crystal consisting of a mixture of atoms

If the lattice sites of a crystal can be occupied by atoms of two or more types then a new contribution to the entropy must arise: this is the *entropy of mixing* S_m defined by

$$S_m = k \ln w_m, \qquad\qquad 9.3.1$$

where w_m is the number of ways of arranging the atoms of different kinds over a number of lattice sites equal to the total number of atoms. Considering only this entropy of mixing, various possibilities arise.

(i) The forces may be the same between similar and dissimilar atoms. In this case all atomic arrangements have the same energy, so the equilibrium state is determined by the condition that entropy of mixing be a maximum: our definition shows that this occurs when the atoms of various types are distributed at random over the lattice sites. This is called a *homogeneous mixture*; it also arises, if the forces between atoms are all small or zero, as in a mixture of nearly perfect gases. Indeed, the expression for the entropy of mixing is the same for an apparently ordered structure like a crystal as for a chaotic assembly like a gas. The only difference is that, in dealing with the crystal, we have a ready-made egg-box for the particles and do not have to create artificial divisions in space.

(ii) The forces between like atoms are very strong and those between unlike atoms very weak. In this case all atomic arrangements do not have the same energy and we can define an energy of mixing ΔU_m (§ 9.13), which is a maximum for the configuration where each atom is surrounded by others of the same kind. Such an arrangement is obviously of low entropy and, if $\Delta U_m \gg TS_m$, energy considerations alone will determine the equilibrium form as one in which a homogeneous mixture is impossible and the components are insoluble in each other. As the temperature rises, the term TS_m may cease to be negligible compared with ΔU_m, thus providing an explanation for increase of solubility with temperature. Once again results obtained for the solid state will have relevance to a non-condensed state.

(iii) The forces between unlike atoms are stronger than between like atoms. Here the tendency will be to form an ordered structure where each atom of one kind surrounds itself with atoms of another kind. Such an ordered structure must be of low entropy and may have to be given up at temperatures so high that TS_m becomes comparable with the binding energy of the ordered structure. Again it may not be possible to form the ordered structure unless the concentrations of the components are favourable. An extreme example of such an ordered structure is the crystal NaCl, when the Na^+ ions repel each other but attract Cl^- ions so strongly that order survives even beyond the melting point. If there is more of one ion than the other, the necessary disorder may be accommodated by leaving an appropriate number of lattice sites vacant.

Intermediate cases are of course common. In § 9.14 we shall indicate the lines on which the very extensive theory of alloy phases has developed.

§ 9.4   Variation of free energy with temperature: phase equilibrium

As an example of the use of the concept of free energy we shall consider what happens when a metal melts, calculating how the internal energy and entropy vary as the temperature passes from just below to just above the melting point.

Up to the melting point, the internal thermal energy U and the entropy S of one mole of a solid at constant pressure can be calculated from measured values of the molar heat c_p, since

$$U - U_0 = \int_{T_0}^{T} c_p dT; \quad S - S_0 = \int_{T_0}^{T} \frac{c_p dT}{T}. \qquad 9.4.1$$

Here U_0 and S_0 are the internal energy and entropy respectively at temperature T_0 and U_0 includes the binding energy of the solid at absolute zero as defined in § 9.2.

We may simplify the evaluation of the integrals in 9.4.1 by replacing c_p, the molar heat at constant pressure by c_V, the molar heat at constant volume: we saw in § 1.10 that the difference was not large. We further simplify by assuming that the temperature T_0 is sufficiently high for us to use the equipartition (1.9.3) value for c_V:

$$c_V = 3R.$$

We shall see in § 9.6 that, if T_0 is even a few tenths of the absolute melting point T_m, this assumption is fully justified. The integrals in 9.4.1 thus become

$$U - U_0 = \int_{T_0}^{T} c_V \, dT$$

$$= 3R(T - T_0) \qquad\qquad 9.4.2$$

and $\qquad S - S_0 = \int_{T_0}^{T} \frac{c_V \, dT}{T}$

$$= 3R \ln (T/T_0). \qquad\qquad 9.4.3$$

Values of c_V, U and S calculated thus, are shown in the solid lines which extend up to T_m in *fig.* 9.1.

At the melting point, the internal energy receives an increment, which we know as the latent heat of melting L_m, and the entropy a corresponding increase, L_m/T_m. This entropy increase is a measure of the additional disorder which arises when a solid passes at the melting point from the highly ordered solid state to the less ordered liquid state. These increments of energy and entropy at constant temperature are indicated on *fig.* 9.1 by vertical lines at T_m. Above the melting point, the measured molar heats of metals are only slightly greater than those for the corresponding solids, so the curves for c_V, U, and S will continue above the melting point as shown by the solid lines in *fig.* 9.1.

If we had not known that T_m marks a qualitative change in the state of the solid, we would have no reason to do other than extend the curves of U and S for the solid from temperatures below T_m to temperatures above T_m. This extrapolation is shown by the dashed lines above T_m in *fig.* 9.1, these extrapolations representing the thermodynamic functions of a hypothetical solid surviving at temperatures above T_m. Similar extrapolations of the properties of the liquid to temperatures below T_m are shown in *fig.* 9.1, the dashed lines there representing the values of U and S which we would expect if the disordered liquid state survived at temperatures less than T_m.

We can now calculate the free energies for the solid and liquid phases by using *figs.* 9.1*b* and 9.1*c* to give U and S respectively and hence calculating $F = U - TS$. The result appears as *fig.* 9.1*d*, which gives the variation of F with temperature for the two phases. As shown in *fig.* 9.1*d*, the solid phase has the lower free energy below the melting point and is therefore the stable phase. At the melting point the free energies of the liquid and solid phases are equal and the two

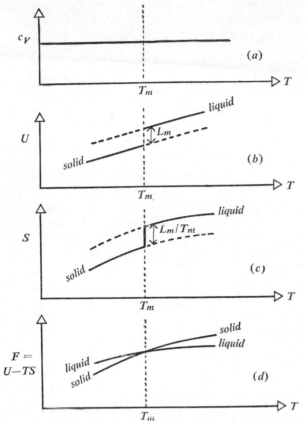

Figure 9.1. Idealised variation of (a) specific heat c_V, (b) binding energy U, (c) entropy S, and (d) free energy F of a condensed system at temperature around the melting point T_m.

phases are in equilibrium. Above T_m the liquid phase has the lower free energy and is thus stable relative to the solid.

Alternatively, when the phases are in equilibrium we can say that the solid is more stable as regards energy because the binding between particles is stronger than in the liquid. The liquid under the same conditions is more stable insofar as the entropy is concerned since the particles in the liquid are in greater disorder, have more ways of arranging themselves and therefore greater entropy. As always, in condensed systems, equilibrium is a compromise between minimum (maximum negative) energy and maximum probability. In non-condensed systems, the same considerations apply but the pV term in the free energy expression (8.4.3) must be included since the volume change may not be small.

§ 9.5 Free energy and entropy of a crystal

Our model of a crystal is the same as we used in chapter 1 to calculate its specific heat; we suppose it to consist of a regular three-dimensional array of N particles, all of the same kind. Each particle is supposed to vibrate about its position of equilibrium and the mean energy of its vibration in each of three perpendicular directions is kT. The total energy of the thermal motion is thus $U = 3NkT$, or, if our crystal contains one kilogram-molecule, N is N_0, Avogadro's number, and $U = 3RT$.

Now suppose that we measure the energy in multiples of a small unit which we call ε. We assumed this before in the calculation of the distribution of energy amongst particles and saw that, provided we can make ε small enough, there will be nothing we can observe which will be inconsistent with our conclusions. In fact, the assumption that the energy of vibration comes in small discrete units is in accord with Quantum Theory, which makes the unit or quantum of energy hv, where h is a universal constant (Planck's constant) and v is the frequency of vibration of the particle. Our model thus assumes that the frequency of vibration of each particle is a constant. A solid made up of particles which vibrate at a frequency v, which is constant at all temperatures but varies in amplitude, is called an *Einstein solid* and for such a solid $hv = k\Theta$, where Θ (often written Θ_E) is the *Einstein characteristic temperature*. We shall assume for the moment that the quantum of energy ε or hv is much smaller than the mean energy kT, that is that we are working at temperatures such that $T \gg \Theta$. This assumption will be re-examined in § 9.6 when we look at what happens to the energy of the crystal when our unit hv or ε is less than the mean energy so that not all particles can be given even one unit.

In the meantime, let us see how we can share out units ε of energy amongst the N oscillating particles. We shall find it convenient to treat each particle as 3 oscillators corresponding to the 3 directions into which its motion can be resolved and thus to share the energy amongst $3N$ oscillators. The number n of units of energy is given by

$$n = \frac{3NkT}{\varepsilon},$$ 9.5.1

and we can give any integral number of units to any of the $3N$ oscillators.

The number of ways w of distributing the energy is thus the same as the number of ways of distributing n identical balls over $3N$ boxes the formula for which is obtained in § 12.9 and is

$$w = \frac{(3N+n)!}{(3N)!n!}.$$ 9.5.2

The entropy is $S = k \ln w$, so using Stirling's formula (§ 12.5) to write

$$\ln (n!) \sim n \ln n - n$$

with similar expressions for the other factorials, we have

$$S = k\{(3N+n) \ln (3N+n) - 3N \ln (3N) - n \ln n\}$$

$$= 3Nk \ln \frac{3N+n}{3N} + nk \ln \frac{3N+n}{n}$$ 9.5.3

$$= 3Nk \ln \left(1 + \frac{n}{3N}\right) + nk \ln \left(1 + \frac{3N}{n}\right).$$ 9.5.4

Now, provided the units of energy are small enough, that is $\varepsilon \ll kT$, 9.5.1 shows that $n \gg 3N$ so that we can approximate to the two logarithms in 9.5.4 by

$$\ln \left(1 + \frac{n}{3N}\right) \simeq \ln \frac{n}{3N} = \ln (kT/\varepsilon),$$

and $\quad \ln \left(1 + \frac{3N}{n}\right) \simeq 3N/n.$ 9.5.5

Introducing approximations 9.5.5 into equation 9.5.4 gives

$$S = 3Nk\left(1 + \ln \frac{kT}{\varepsilon}\right),$$ 9.5.6

while $\quad S_0 = 3Nk\left(1 + \ln \frac{kT_0}{\varepsilon}\right),$ 9.5.7

where T_0 as defined in § 9.4 above is the lowest temperature at which we need our approximations to be valid. Thus

$$S - S_0 = 3Nk \ln (T/T_0),$$

which, if the model crystal contains Avogadro's number of particles, is the same result as obtained by thermodynamic means in equation 9.4.3.

§9.6   Further discussion of the Einstein model of a solid: the internal energy at low temperatures

Since we have already introduced the idea that our unit of energy cannot be arbitrarily small, it is worth while to see what happens to the energy and entropy of a system of oscillators all of the same frequency v at temperatures T such that hv is comparable with or greater than kT.

Taking the energy first, we have $3N$ oscillators each of which can be given an integral number of units ε of energy. If we consider oscillators with energy $r\varepsilon$, then, by the distribution law we discovered in § 5.7, the number of such oscillators will be much less when r is large than when r is small. In fact, the fraction of oscillators with energy $r\varepsilon$ is

$$f(r\varepsilon) = \frac{e^{-r\varepsilon\beta}}{\sum\limits_{r=0}^{\infty} e^{-r\varepsilon\beta}}, \qquad 9.6.1$$

where β is a constant which for the moment we take to be unknown.

The total energy of our $3N$ oscillators is thus

$$U = \frac{3N \sum\limits_{r=0}^{\infty} r\varepsilon\, e^{-r\varepsilon\beta}}{\sum\limits_{r=0}^{\infty} e^{-r\varepsilon\beta}}. \qquad 9.6.2$$

The upper limits of all the sums in these expressions have been taken as ∞. This is justified since the quantities $\exp(-r\varepsilon\beta)$ decrease rapidly as r becomes large and then contribute little to the total. We can evaluate the expression for U by writing

$$U = -3N\frac{\partial}{\partial\beta} \ln \sum\limits_{r=0}^{\infty} e^{-r\varepsilon\beta}, \qquad 9.6.3$$

where the sum is the geometric series

$$\sum\limits_{r=0}^{\infty} e^{-r\varepsilon\beta} \equiv 1 + e^{-\varepsilon\beta} + e^{-2\varepsilon\beta} + e^{-3\varepsilon\beta} + \ldots, \qquad 9.6.4$$

which is convergent as long as $\varepsilon\beta$ is positive. We know ε is positive and can guess and will show that $\beta > 0$. The sum is

$$\sum\limits_{r=0}^{\infty} e^{-r\varepsilon\beta} = \frac{1}{1 - e^{-\varepsilon\beta}}, \qquad 9.6.5$$

whence we obtain

$$U = 3N\frac{\varepsilon e^{-\varepsilon\beta}}{1 - e^{-\varepsilon\beta}} = \frac{3N\varepsilon}{e^{\beta\varepsilon} - 1}. \qquad 9.6.6$$

If $\beta\varepsilon \ll 1$, the exponential can be expanded, giving the result that

$$U = 3N/\beta, \qquad\qquad 9.6.7$$

or that the mean energy of one of our oscillators is

$$\frac{U}{3N} = \frac{1}{\beta}. \qquad\qquad 9.6.8$$

Now we know that this mean energy is kT, so

$$\beta = 1/kT, \qquad\qquad 9.6.9$$

a result which we obtained before and which we shall take to be quite general.

The condition for being able to simplify expression 9.6.6 by expanding the exponential was

$$\varepsilon\beta \ll 1,$$

which, using 9.6.9, gives the condition for equipartition to be valid:

$$kT \gg \varepsilon. \qquad\qquad 9.6.10$$

If we accept that our unit ε has the value stated in § 9.5,

$$\varepsilon = h\nu = k\Theta, \qquad\qquad 9.6.11$$

where Θ is an empirically determined characteristic temperature, then we see that the analytic condition for the equipartition value of the internal energy of a crystal to be correct is

$$T \gg \Theta. \qquad\qquad 9.6.12$$

At low temperatures, inequality 9.6.12 does not hold and the internal energy is given by equation 9.6.6 with

$$\beta = 1/kT \quad \text{and} \quad \varepsilon = h\nu = k\Theta.$$

Thus

$$U = 3N\frac{k\Theta}{e^{\Theta/T}-1}, \qquad\qquad 9.6.13$$

from which we obtain the molar heat at constant volume

$$c_V = \frac{\partial U}{\partial T} = 3Nk\left(\frac{\Theta}{T}\right)^2 \frac{e^{\Theta/T}}{(e^{\Theta/T}-1)^2} \qquad\qquad 9.6.14$$

$$= 3Nk f_E(\Theta/T). \qquad\qquad 9.6.15$$

The function $f_E(\Theta/T)$ is called the *Einstein specific heat function* and is shown in *fig. 9.2*. The form of the function predicts that the specific heat of a solid is not constant, as we found using the theory of equipartition, but falls exponentially to zero as the temperature falls to absolute zero. The equipartition value of the molar heat,

$$c_V = 3R,$$

is reached asymptotically as the temperature tends to large values.

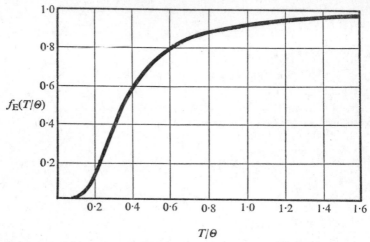

Figure 9.2. The Einstein function $f_E(T/\Theta)$.

By equating the measured value of c_V for any crystal at a given temperature to the theoretical value from equation 9.6.14, the Einstein characteristic temperature can be calculated; and, if the theory were exact, the theoretical curve would fit the experimental curve at all points. In practice the fit is not very good, particularly at temperatures near absolute zero. Better fit could be obtained by introducing several characteristic temperatures, that is by assuming that some fraction of the particles vibrated at one frequency, some at another; but really the model is too crude, the main fault being in the assumption that each particle vibrates independently of its neighbours. In reality the particles which make up a solid are not fixed to 'positions of equilibrium' but to each other. Each thus vibrates in sympathy with its neighbours.

However, the Einstein theory does give a qualitative explanation of why the specific heat of a solid tends to zero as the temperature falls towards absolute zero. It also explains why the c_V/T curves for all solids have the same shape–approximately the shape shown in *fig.* 9.2. Thus, if the molar heat of one crystal is c_V at T_1 then the molar heat of any other crystal should have the same value at temperature T_2, such that

$$T_2 = (\Theta_2/\Theta_1)T_1, \qquad\qquad 9.6.16$$

where Θ_1 and Θ_2 are the Einstein characteristic temperatures of the first and second crystals respectively. This result is known as the *law of corresponding states*.

Some values of Θ are given in table 16, with, for comparison, values of the melting points T_m.

TABLE 16 : melting points T_m and Einstein characteristic temperatures Θ for a few solids

solid element	M	$\Theta°K$	$T_m°K$
Na	23	160	770
Cr	52	405	2073
Zn	65	240	693
W	184	315	3653
Au	197	185	1231
Hg	201	90	230
Pb	207	86	600
Be	9	1200	1550
C (diamond)	12	1850	—

The vibration frequency corresponding to $\Theta = 200°K$ is, by 9.6.11, about 10^{12} sec^{-1}.

Fig. 9.2 shows that the Einstein function, which gives the ratio of the Einstein specific heat to the equipartition value, reaches 0·95 by $T/\Theta = 1·2$ and 0·98 by $T/\Theta = 1·6$. This shows that condition 9.6.12 is not very severe: as far as specific heat is concerned, for a temperature to be 'much greater than' the Einstein characteristic temperature, it need only be about 20% greater. A similar result can be obtained for the temperature dependence of the entropy.

§ 9.7 Entropy of an Einstein solid at low temperatures

The entropy of a system of $3N$ oscillators sharing n units or quanta of energy is given by equation 9.5.4 and is

$$S = 3Nk \ln\left(1 + \frac{n}{3N}\right) + nk \ln\left(1 + \frac{3N}{n}\right). \qquad 9.7.1$$

This expression, which is that for the entropy of an Einstein solid, is valid at any temperature.

Now the total energy U of an Einstein solid at any temperature was given by 9.6.13 as

$$U = 3N\frac{k\Theta}{e^{\Theta/T}-1},$$ 9.7.2

so the number n of quanta, each $k\Theta$, is given by

$$n = \frac{U}{k\Theta} = \frac{3N}{e^{\Theta/T}-1}.$$ 9.7.3

At temperatures so low that $T \ll \Theta$, 9.7.3 reduces to

$$n/3N = e^{-\Theta/T} \ll 1,$$ 9.7.4

so that we have now less units of energy than we have oscillators. Substituting $e^{-\Theta/T}$ for $n/3N$ in 9.7.1, we obtain

$$S = 3Nk \ln (1+e^{-\Theta/T})+3Nk\, e^{-\Theta/T}\ln (e^{\Theta/T}).$$ 9.7.5

Expanding the first logarithm and remembering that $\ln (e^x) = x$, we have

$$S = 3Nk\, e^{-\Theta/T}(1+\Theta/T)$$

$$\simeq 3Nk(\Theta/T)\, e^{-\Theta/T},$$

since $\Theta/T \gg 1$.

As $T \to 0$, $\Theta/T \to \infty$, so, knowing that (§ 12.8)

$$\lim_{x \to \infty} x\, e^{-x} = 0,$$

we see that the entropy of an Einstein solid tends to zero as the temperature approaches absolute zero. This result, which is of much greater generality and is sometimes referred to as the *third law of thermodynamics*, is, of course, what we would have expected from our statistical definition of entropy, since the crystal should be in a state of perfect order–every particle on its equilibrium lattice site–when there is no thermal energy to disorder it. We shall see in § 9.10 however that there are sources of disorder which may persist at absolute zero.

We have used our model of a solid to describe its properties at all temperatures. In fact, as we saw in § 9.6, the Einstein model, where every particle is supposed to vibrate independently of its neighbours, is not a good description of a solid at low temperatures where the number of quanta of energy would have to be less than the number of oscillators. If it were correct we would have to imagine that an occasional particle could vibrate while its neighbours remained at rest. A better approximation at low temperatures is the Debye model, where the chains of many atoms are supposed to vibrate in unison; there are then lower frequencies of vibration, because of the greater inertia of the chains, and, indeed, a whole spectrum of frequencies and so a variety of quanta with a range of sizes from zero up to a maximum which is roughly the same as our Einstein quantum. In the Debye model at high temperatures ($T \gg \Theta$), the most probable quantum is the Einstein quantum, which is why the Einstein model is so successful, but at very low temperatures this becomes frozen out leaving the lower energy quanta to carry the thermal energy. The greater possibilities of such a model are matched by greater mathematical difficulties.

Apart from the next two sections, all our examples will be at temperatures high enough for the Einstein model to be successful. In this way, we shall, with little mathematics, obtain results which can be tested by experiment.

§ 9.8 Breakdown of equipartition : quantum conditions

The expression (9.6.13) for the energy of a system of oscillators at low temperatures, that is at temperatures such that $\varepsilon > kT$, was one case of the breakdown of equipartition of energy. The derivation of 9.6.13 showed that, if the units or quanta of energy ε supplied by nature were larger than or comparable with kT, the mean energy $\bar{u}$ per oscillator was not kT but

$$ \bar{u} = \frac{\varepsilon}{e^{\varepsilon/kT} - 1} . \qquad 9.8.1 $$

Expanding the exponential as

$$ e^{\varepsilon/kT} = 1 + \frac{\varepsilon}{kT} + \frac{\varepsilon^2}{2k^2T^2} + \cdots $$

shows that

$$ \bar{u} < \frac{\varepsilon}{\varepsilon/kT} < kT, \qquad 9.8.2 $$

so the mean energy is always less than the equipartition value, only approaching it asymptotically when T becomes large.

In the case of the Einstein solid the units ε could be taken as empirical quantities measured by

$$ \varepsilon = k\Theta, $$

16

where Θ was a characteristic temperature. Alternatively ε could be calculated from the quantum condition

$$\varepsilon = h\nu,$$

where h is the quantum constant and ν was the frequency of each of the Einstein oscillators. Now, the frequency of oscillation ν of a particle of mass m attached to a fixed point by a spring of constant (force per unit extension) λ is

$$\nu = \frac{1}{2\pi}(\lambda/m)^{\frac{1}{2}}, \qquad\qquad 9.8.3$$

so if we knew the elastic constant which measures the strength of interatomic forces we could in principle calculate ν and hence ε and Θ. Without actually doing so we may note that for a crystal such as diamond, where the particles have small mass m but are strongly bound together, Θ is large. On the other hand a crystal such as mercury, with weak interatomic forces and heavy particles, has a small Θ.

Numerical calculations illustrating these points arc the subject of problem 9.16.2.

§9.9   Reconsideration of the specific heat theory in chapter 1

We now apply the results of the last section to the problem of the non-appearance of certain contributions to the specific heats of gases, which we noted in §§ 1.8 and 1.14.

First, we can account for the omission of vibrational terms from the expression for the thermal energy of diatomic molecules by assuming that the bond between the two atoms is so strong that the mean energy of vibration is much greater than kT. If this is correct then we must expect that there is a characteristic temperature Θ_v given by

$$k\Theta_v = h\nu, \qquad\qquad 9.9.1$$

where ν is the frequency of vibration of the atoms in the direction of their line of centres. ν will be given by an expression with the same form as 9.8.3. At temperatures much less than Θ_v the quantum of energy $k\Theta_v$ is too large to be excited thermally, that is

$$k\Theta_v \gg kT. \qquad\qquad 9.9.2$$

Presumably ν, as determined by the bond strength λ and atomic mass m, is so high for most of the diatomic molecules listed in table 1 (p. 13) that inequality 9.9.2 is satisfied at normal temperatures.

The exception in table 1 is Cl_2, which has an abnormally high specific heat at room temperature. This is explained by chemical data which tell us that Cl_2 is weakly bound, so that the quantum of vibrational energy is small, allowing vibrational modes to be excited at moderate temperatures. On the other hand the specific heat of HCl, which is also weakly bound, corresponds to the equipartition value at room temperature. We may account for this by noting that the interatomic vibration in HCl is really a movement of the light H-atom relative to the immobile heavy Cl-atom. Thus, while λ is small, v is large because the m involved is small. Again, *fig.* 1.3 showed the development of additional degrees of freedom and abnormally high specific heat in H_2 at temperatures over 1000°K. This may also be ascribed to the excitation of vibrations and we may correctly infer that the same effect is observed in other gases if they can be heated to sufficiently high temperatures and their specific heats measured.

By extension of the same argument, we may expect that some of the other contributions to the specific heat may disappear at low temperatures or not appear at all at any temperature. Thus the minimum rotational energy of a diatomic molecule is $h^2/(8\pi^2 I)$, where h is the quantum constant and I is the moment of inertia of the molecule. A simple proof of this result is given in § 9.15, but here it is sufficient to note that the moment of inertia I appears in the denominator in the same way as the mass did in the expression for the quantum of energy of the oscillator. We can thus define yet another characteristic temperature Θ_r by

$$k\Theta_r = h^2/(8\pi^2 I), \qquad\qquad 9.9.3$$

and Θ_r will then be a measure of the temperature at which the quantum effects are obvious. For example, for the hydrogen molecule H_2, the mass of each hydrogen atom is $\simeq 1.7 \times 10^{-27}$ kg, and the spacing between them is 0.75×10^{-10} m. Thus $I \simeq 5 \times 10^{-48}$ kg m², which, with $h/2\pi \simeq 10^{-34}$ J sec and $k = 1.4 \times 10^{-23}$ J deg⁻¹, gives $\Theta_r = 50$°K. As *fig.* 1.3 shows, the molar heat of H_2 rises in the region around 100°K from $\frac{3}{2}R$, which corresponds to translational energy only, to $\frac{5}{2}R$, which corresponds to translation plus the equipartition rotational energy.

For other diatomic gases the characteristic temperatures Θ_r are much lower. For example, for N_2, where the atoms are 14 times heavier than in H_2 and the interatomic spacing about 40% more, we would expect the characteristic temperature to be about $14 \times (1 \cdot 4)^2$ ~ 30 times less. In fact, Θ_r for N_2 is $3°K$. The corresponding change in specific heat is not observable since N_2 becomes liquid at $78°K$ and solid at $64°K$. There are in fact no gases other than H_2 for which the suppression of the rotational contribution to the specific heat can be observed.

Finally, we can dispose of the doubt in §§ 1.6 and 1.14 that rotation about the axis of a diatomic molecule should have been included among the degrees of freedom. At that stage we dismissed it by insisting that our model of a diatomic molecule used only point masses which could have no rotational energy about a line through them. We used the same argument to dismiss the need to take account of rotations of atoms in our monatomic gas. We now see from 9.9.3 that it is the very smallness of the moments of inertia of atoms about their centres which forbids such rotational motion to be excited. Thus nearly all the mass of an atom is located in its nucleus, which has a radius of $\sim 10^{-15}$ m, so the corresponding moment of inertia is $\sim 10^{10}$ times less than that for molecular rotation and the characteristic temperature $\sim 10^{10}$ times higher. Similarly, if we calculate the moment of inertia of the electron cloud round the nucleus, we are dealing with masses about 10^3 times less than atoms, rotating at distances of the same order as atomic or molecular sizes. The moments of inertia are thus $\sim 10^3$ times less than for molecular rotations and the characteristic temperatures some thousand times greater, that is several thousand degrees. This is a good estimate of the temperatures required to excite the electrons in atoms or molecules.

§ 9.10   Free energy of mixing

We begin by calculating the entropy of mixing for an arbitrary solid consisting of N_A atoms of type A and N_B atoms of type B, situated at random on $(N_A + N_B)$ lattice sites. We then apply our results to the case where one of the types of atoms is a vacant lattice site, that is a non-atom.

The number of ways of arranging the $(N_A + N_B)$ atoms – one and only one to each site – is

$$w = \frac{(N_A + N_B)!}{N_A! \, N_B!}, \qquad\qquad 9.10.1$$

which is the number of permutations of all the sites divided by the numbers of permutations of each of the sets of indistinguishable atoms. The entropy of mixing is thus, from 9.3.1,

$$S_m = k \ln w = k \ln \frac{(N_A + N_B)!}{N_A! N_B!} , \qquad 9.10.2$$

and, expressing the logarithms by Stirling's formula (§ 12.5) we have

$$S_m = k N_A \ln \frac{N_A + N_B}{N_A} + k N_B \ln \frac{N_A + N_B}{N_B} .$$

Now write $N_A + N_B = N$ so that

$$N_A = cN \quad \text{and} \quad N_B = (1-c)N ,$$

where c is the concentration of A-type atoms. This gives

$$S_m = -Nk\{c \ln c + (1-c) \ln (1-c)\} \qquad 9.10.3$$

$$= -R\{c \ln c + (1-c) \ln (1-c)\} , \qquad 9.10.4$$

if N is Avogadro's number. Since $c < 1$, both logarithms are negative quantities, so $S_m > 0$.

S_m, the entropy of mixing, is strictly speaking the entropy of mixing at $0°K$. At other temperatures there may be a further contribution to the entropy due to changes in the way vibrational energy is distributed amongst the atoms of types A and B. Obviously, the more like the atoms are to each other the less possibilities there will be for changes in thermal entropy to be produced by differences in mixing. If, however, the binding between atoms of the same kind is very different from the binding between atoms of different kinds then the arrangement of atoms will affect the distribution of energy amongst them. In an extreme case, to be discussed in § 9.12, the atoms surrounding a vacant lattice site vibrate at a different frequency from the other atoms, so the units of energy they receive will be different and the resulting distribution over all atoms will be a function not only of temperature but also of the concentration of vacant lattice sites.

The function $S_m(c)$ given by equation 9.10.4 is shown in *fig.* 9.3. The maximum of S occurs at $c = 0.5$ and is

$$S_{max} = R \ln 2 \simeq 0.7 R .$$

At the ends, where $c \rightarrow 0$ and $c \rightarrow 1$, the function $S(c)$ rises very steeply so that a small change in concentration involves a large change in entropy. This may be taken as a statistical confirmation of the well-known fact that it is difficult to extract the last traces of impurities from an almost pure substance.

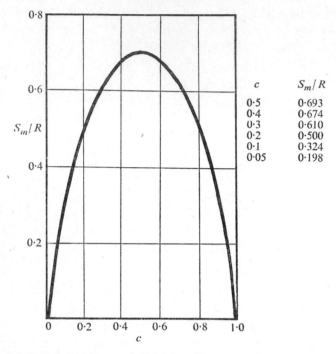

c	S_m/R
0·5	0·693
0·4	0·674
0·3	0·610
0·2	0·500
0·1	0·324
0·05	0·198

Figure 9.3. Variation of entropy of mixing S_m with concentration c.

§ 9.11 Vacant lattice sites in crystals

We saw in § 9.2 that, since bonds have to be broken to remove an atom from its site in a crystal, the energy of a crystal containing a vacant site is higher (less negative) than that of a perfect crystal. The work to produce a single vacancy is called its *formation energy* E_f, and since this is positive it is clear that the less vacancies a crystal contains the lower is its energy. However, the introduction of vacancies leads to an increase in entropy since the extra lattice points allow additional ways of arranging the atoms; so, on entropy grounds alone, it is better for the crystal to have many vacancies and in the limit to vaporise. The equilibrium number of vacancies is obtained as usual by balancing energy against entropy.

The free energy of a crystal containing Nc vacancies and $N(1-c)$ atoms at temperature T is

$$F = NcE_f - TS, \qquad\qquad 9.11.1$$

where S is the entropy produced by mixing Nc vacancies with $N(1-c)$ atoms. Equation 9.10.3 gives for this entropy of mixing:

$$S = -Nk\{c \ln c + (1-c) \ln (1-c)\} + NcS_{th}, \qquad 9.11.2$$

where S_{th} is the change of the thermal entropy produced by introducing one vacancy. We shall calculate this in § 9.12.

Equation 9.11.1 for the free energy then becomes

$$F = NcE_f + NkT\{c \ln c + (1-c)\ln(1-c)\} - TNcS_{th}.$$

$$9.11.3$$

Equilibrium is given by the condition for F to be a minimum, that is

$$\frac{\partial F}{\partial c} = 0,$$

or $E_f + kT \ln c - kT \ln (1-c) - TS_{th} = 0.$ 9.11.4

The other two terms arising from the differentiation of $c \ln c$ and $(1-c) \ln (1-c)$ cancel each other.

Now, numerical estimates will show the concentration c of vacancies is never greater than 10^{-3} or 10^{-4} at the highest temperatures at which a solid remains solid. Thus $1-c \sim 1$ and $\ln (1-c) \sim 0$; so, solving for c, we have

$$c = e^{S_{th}/k} e^{-E_f/kT}. \qquad 9.11.5$$

This formula is very similar in form to 5.9.5, which told us that the fraction of atoms, existing in the vapour phase in equilibrium with a solid or liquid, is proportional to exp $(-$ energy$/kT)$. While formation of vacancies is indeed a sort of internal evaporation, the common feature of both equations is that each gives the fraction of atoms which have enough thermal energy to change state; alternatively, each gives the probability that a given atom will be found in the state of higher energy.

Formula 9.11.5 can be tested by experiment. In principle, all that has to be done is to measure the temperature variation of some quantity which depends on c; examples are electrical resistivity and thermal expansion. Unfortunately, only a small part of the temperature variation of both these quantities is due to vacancies and it is necessary to subtract out or otherwise eliminate the other effects. The best modern method is to measure directly the relative thermal expansion $(\Delta l/l)$ of a rod when its temperature is raised to a given value. At the same time the change in interatomic spacing $(\Delta a/a)$ is measured by X-ray crystallography. $\Delta a/a$ is not affected by the presence of vacancies while $\Delta l / l$ depends both on the concentration of vacancies and on the change in lattice spacing $\Delta a / a$. It can be shown that the concentration of vacancies at the given temperature is

$$c = 3\left\{\frac{\Delta l}{l} - \frac{\Delta a}{a}\right\}. \qquad 9.11.6$$

Given c, E_f and also S_{th} can be calculated.

TABLE 17 : formation energies and entropies of vacancies in metals

metal	$T_m(°K)$	E_f(eV)	S_{th}/k	$E_f \times 10^4 / T_m$
Al	933	0·75±0·07	2·4	8·1
Cu	1356	1·17±0·11	∼1·5	8·5
Ag	1233	1·09±0·1	∼1·5	8·8
Au	1336	0·94±0·09	1	7·0

Table from A. C. Damask and G. J. Dienes *Point Defects in Metals* Gordon and Breach, New York, 1963.

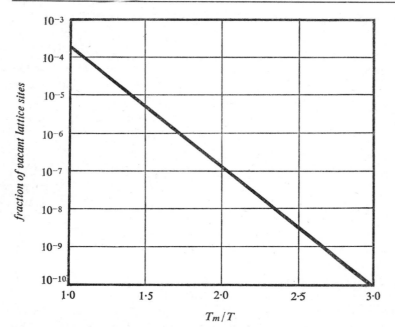

Figure 9.4. Equilibrium vacancy concentrations for the noble metals, Cu, Ag, Au, *at various temperatures relative to their melting points.*

Table 17 gives a few values of E_f and S_{th} for various metals obtained by this method, while *fig.* 9.4 shows the variation of c with T for the noble metals. It will be noted that E_f/T_m, where T_m is the absolute melting temperature, is roughly constant for all the metals listed, and for this reason it is possible to use the same curve of c against T_m/T for all the noble metals. Thus, vacancy concentrations obey a law of corresponding states such that c is approximately the same for all metals of similar structure at the same reduced temperature T/T_m; this suggests that melting is a process closely associated with vacancy production, that is with breaking of bonds. Another law of corresponding states arose in the discussion of specific heats in § 9.6, where we saw that c_V, the molar heat, is the same for all crystals at reduced temperature T/Θ, Θ being a characteristic temperature for the material but not proportional to the melting temperature.

§ 9.12   Thermal entropy of defects

From remarks in §§ 9.10 and 9.11 we expect that there should be a contribution to the entropy, owing to changes in the distribution of thermal quanta when foreign atoms or vacancies are introduced. We illustrate this by calculating the quantity S_{th} used in equation 9.11.2.

Suppose we have Nc vacancies and N occupied lattice sites. We then distribute quanta over the atoms, that is over $3N$ oscillators; obviously we cannot give energy to the vacancies since in our model they represent oscillators which are not there. However, due to the presence of the vacancies, not all the $3N$ oscillators are indistinguishable, since those which surround vacancies are less firmly bound than the others and will have a lower frequency of vibration. If an atom has z nearest neighbours then there are Ncz atoms immediately surrounding vacancies.

Now, on the Einstein model, where all atoms oscillate with the same frequency v, the quanta of energy which are to be distributed over the oscillators are given by (9.8.3)

$$\varepsilon = hv = \frac{h}{2\pi}(\lambda/m)^{\frac{1}{2}} = k\Theta,$$

where λ is a spring constant measuring the restoring force on an atom of mass m when displaced by unit distance. Thus, if λ is different for some atoms, then their frequency of oscillation v will be different from that of the others and we could ascribe a different characteristic temperature Θ_v to them. Assuming that the z atoms around each vacancy vibrate with frequency v', where $v' < v$, we have $3Ncz$ oscillators with frequency v' and $3N(1-cz)$ oscillators with frequency v.

If there are to be significant numbers of vacancies, then *fig.* 9.4 shows that the temperature must be high enough to assume equipartition. Thus, the $3Ncz$ oscillators share energy $3NczkT$ and the $3N(1-cz)$ oscillators share energy $3N(1-cz)kT$; so, using equation 9.5.6, the thermal entropy S_v of the crystal containing Nc vacancies is

$$S_v = 3Nk(1-cz)\left\{1+\ln\frac{kT}{hv}\right\}+3Nkcz\left\{1+\ln\frac{kT}{hv'}\right\}, \qquad 9.12.1$$

whereas the thermal entropy of the crystal, ignoring the effect of the vacancies, is

$$S = 3Nk\left\{1+\ln\frac{kT}{hv}\right\}. \qquad 9.12.2$$

Subtracting 9.12.2 from 9.12.1 we obtain the part of the thermal entropy which is due to the vacancies:

$$S_v - S = 3Nkcz \ln (v/v')$$
$$= Nkc \ln (v/v')^{3z}, \qquad 9.12.3$$

whence the quantity S_{th}, defined in 9.11.2 as the thermal entropy per vacancy, is obtained by dividing $S_v - S$ by Nc:

$$S_{th} = k \ln (v/v')^{3z}. \qquad 9.12.4$$

Since $v > v'$, $S_{th} > 0$, so the factor $e^{S_{th}/k}$ in the expression (9.11.5) for c is greater than 1. Thus, taking account of thermal entropy leads to an increase in the estimated number of vacancies. In fact, using 9.12.4, we obtain for the concentration of vacancies

$$c = (v/v')^{3z} \exp (-E_f/kT). \qquad 9.12.5$$

The vibration frequency of an atom adjacent to a vacancy is unlikely to be very much lower than that of an atom entirely surrounded by other atoms, but the factor $(v/v')^{3z}$ may still be significant since $3z$ may be a large number; for example, $3z = 36$ for a close-packed lattice where each atom has 12 nearest neighbours. From table 17, it appears that S_{th}/k for metals is about 1·5, which corresponds to a fivefold increase in concentration, but to only about 5% change of frequency.

§ 9.13 Free energy of a solid solution

We already have formula 9.10.3 for the entropy of mixing of a solid solution consisting of N_A ($= Nc$) A-type atoms and N_B ($= N(1-c)$) B-type atoms. To decide whether the equilibrium arrangement will be a random mixture, two separate regions of A- and B-type atoms, or something intermediate, we have also to know the energies of the various distributions.

Let us first simplify the problem by assuming that we need only take account of interactions between nearest-neighbour atoms. Call the binding energy between two A-type atoms ϕ_{AA}, meaning that ϕ_{AA} is the work to increase the distance between the two A atoms from the nearest-neighbour distance to infinity. If we follow the usual convention and take the energy of the free atoms as zero, then ϕ_{AA} is negative, and the more negative it is the stronger is the bond. Similarly the binding energy between two B atoms is ϕ_{BB} and between an A-type and a B-type atom it is ϕ_{AB}. We assume that none of these quantities is affected by any change in the other neighbours. We finally assume that all ϕ are independent of temperature. To calculate the total energy of all the bonds we then need to know the numbers of A–A bonds, B–B bonds and A–B bonds.

Consider any atom: it has z nearest neighbours. In a structure consisting of close-packed spheres, $z = 12$. If the nature of the nearest neighbours is determined by pure chance then on the average the atom considered will have zc A-type neighbours and $z(1-c)$ B-type neighbours. Thus each of the Nc A-type atoms has on the average zc A-type neighbours and $z(1-c)$ B-type neighbours, so there are Nc^2z bonds joining A-type atoms to A-type atoms and $Ncz(1-c)$ bonds joining A-type atoms to B-type atoms. Similarly if we consider the bonds round B-type atoms we find that there are $Nz(1-c)^2$ B–B bonds and $Nz(1-c)c$ B–A bonds.

The total of all bonds is thus $Nz(c^2 + 2c(1-c) + (1-c)^2) = Nz$, which is twice the number there should be, since, by our method of considering each atom in turn, we have counted each bond from both ends. Correcting for this we have:

the number of A–A bonds is $\frac{1}{2}Nc^2z$;

the number of B–B bonds is $\frac{1}{2}N(1-c)^2z$;

the number of A–B bonds is $Nc(1-c)z$.

The energy of all the bonds is thus

$$U = \tfrac{1}{2}Nc^2 z\phi_{AA} + Nc(1-c)z\phi_{AB} + \tfrac{1}{2}N(1-c)^2 z\phi_{BB}$$
$$= \tfrac{1}{2}Nz\{c^2\phi_{AA} + 2c(1-c)\phi_{AB} + (1-c)^2\phi_{BB}\}, \qquad 9.13.1$$

where, since we have taken no account of thermal energy, U is the total energy of the alloy at $0°K$.

Introducing the quantity

$$\phi_m = \phi_{AB} - \tfrac{1}{2}(\phi_{AA} + \phi_{BB}), \qquad 9.13.2$$

the expression for U becomes

$$U = \tfrac{1}{2}Nz\{c\phi_{AA} + (1-c)\phi_{BB} + 2c(1-c)\phi_m\}. \qquad 9.13.3$$

ϕ_m is an energy of mixing and is the amount by which the energy of the mixed bond exceeds the average of two bonds between atoms of the same kind. To see the significance of ϕ_m, we consider a few special cases, showing the results in *fig.* 9.5. For definiteness we assume throughout that $\phi_{AA} < \phi_{BB}$.

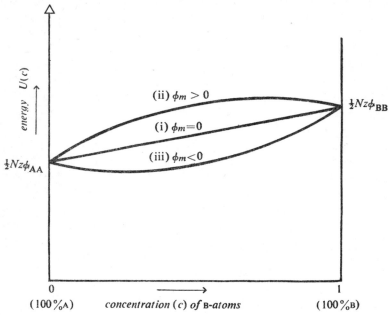

Figure 9.5. Variation of binding energy of a solid solution with composition.

(i) $\phi_m = 0$, that is $\phi_{AB} = \tfrac{1}{2}(\phi_{AA} + \phi_{BB})$.

The total energy then varies linearly with concentration c. From energy considerations alone, any arrangement of the atoms in this alloy would be equally stable. For example, the energy of a homogeneous mixture of equal numbers of A- and B-atoms is the same as if the mixture precipitated out as pure crystals of A and pure crystals of B (a *heterogeneous mixture*). §9.10 showed that the homogeneous mixture has greater entropy.

(ii) $\phi_m > 0$, that is $\phi_{AB} > \frac{1}{2}(\phi_{AA} + \phi_{BB})$.

The graph of $U(c)$ is a parabola (*fig.* 9.5) situated above the straight line of case (i). Here energy considerations suggest that the homogeneous mixture is less stable than a heterogeneous mixture of the pure components. This is what we should have expected, since ϕ_{AA}, ϕ_{BB}, and ϕ_{AB} are all negative; therefore, the condition $\phi_{AB} > \frac{1}{2}(\phi_{AA} + \phi_{BB})$ means that the binding between unlike atoms is less strong than between like atoms. Once again entropy considerations may change this conclusion.

(iii) $\phi_m < 0$, that is $\phi_{AB} < \frac{1}{2}(\phi_{AA} + \phi_{BB})$.

Here the graph of $U(c)$ (*fig.* 9.5) is a parabola lying everywhere under the straight line joining $\frac{1}{2}Nz\phi_{AA}$ to $\frac{1}{2}Nz\phi_{BB}$. From the form of $U(c)$, and also since the inequality $\phi_{AB} < \frac{1}{2}(\phi_{AA} + \phi_{BB})$ means that the binding between unlike atoms is stronger than between like atoms, it is clear that this case favours the formation of homogeneous mixtures. Since entropy considerations also favour homogeneous mixtures, the condition $\phi_m < 0$ thus gives homogeneity without further ado.

These examples suggest that we should separate out those contributions to the energy which depend linearly on c and which are the same whether the components are separated or mixed, and those which depend on the fact that the components are mixed. The latter are all included in the quantity

$$\Delta U_m = Nzc(1-c)\phi_m, \qquad\qquad 9.13.4$$

which is the change of energy produced by mixing; ΔU_m is sometimes called the *heat of solution* and, as we have seen, may be positive or negative. If we separate the energy in this way, we can include thermal energy amongst the terms which are not affected by mixing for, on the Einstein model, each atom vibrates independently and is not affected by the nature of its neighbours. Thus expression 9.13.4 for ΔU_m can be used at any temperature.

§ 9.14   Alloy phases

Expression 9.10.3 for the increase of entropy produced by mixing two components is,

$$S_m = -Nk\{c \ln c + (1-c) \ln (1-c)\}. \qquad 9.14.1$$

Like the expression for the energy obtained in § 9.13, this was derived without taking account of temperature. We saw in § 9.5 that the thermal entropy was obtained by calculating the number of ways in which thermal energy could be distributed over the atoms, so that, on our model, in which each atom vibrates independently, the number of distributions will depend on the concentration of each component, but not on whether the two types of atom occur in separate crystals or are mixed up. Thus our expression for S_m can be used at any temperature.

The change in free energy ΔF produced by mixing is therefore

$$\Delta F = \Delta U_m - T S_m$$
$$= Nzc(1-c)\phi_m + NkT\{c \ln c + (1-c) \ln (1-c)\},$$
$$9.14.2$$

where ϕ_m was defined by 9.13.2. Introducing the parameter p defined by

$$p = kT/z\phi_m,$$

we obtain

$$\Delta F = Nz\phi_m[c(1-c) + p\{c \ln c + (1-c) \ln (1-c)\}].$$
$$9.14.3$$

ϕ_m is a measure of the tendency to form an ordered structure in the sense that ϕ_m large and negative keeps atoms of one kind together; hence p measures the relative importance of the disordering effect of temperature and the ordering effect of ϕ_m. We have already seen that when $\phi_m < 0$, the homogeneous mixture is stable on both energy and entropy grounds but, when $\phi_m > 0$, energy and entropy act in opposite directions. Thus the interesting cases are those where $p > 0$.

Figs. 9.6 and 9.7 give ΔF as a function of c for various positive values of the parameter p.

When $p = 0$, which corresponds to very large ϕ_m or very low temperature, the entropy plays no part and $\Delta F = \Delta U_m$. $\Delta F(c)$ is therefore a parabola as shown and for any value of c, that is any proportions of the constituents, a heterogeneous mixture of the pure substances has lower free energy than a homogeneous mixture. We say that the substances are mutually insoluble in the solid phase.

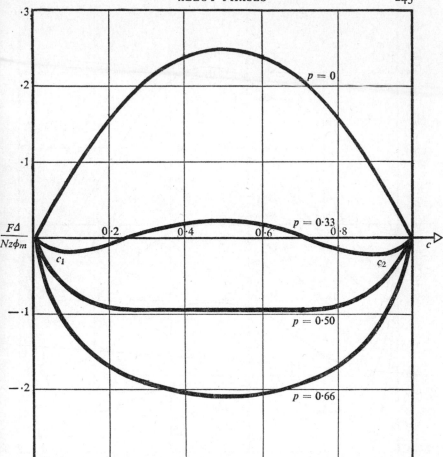

Figure 9.6. Free energy of a solid solution as a function of composition for some values of the parameter $p = kT/z\phi_m$.

When $p > 0.5$, the entropy term is predominant and, for any composition c, the homogeneous mixture has lower free energy and is stable relative to pure crystals of the separate components. Thus, if the temperature can be raised high enough and if the two components are similar atoms, there should be a complete range of solid solutions of one in the other. Naturally there are complications in practice: the necessary temperature may be above the melting point or some factors other than binding energy or entropy may inhibit solubility.

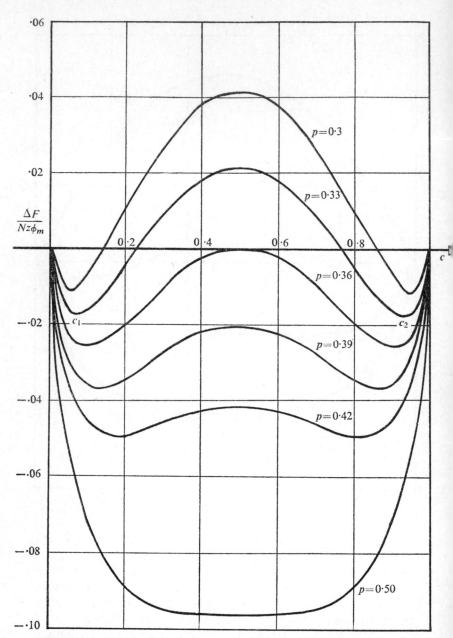

Figure 9.7. Free energy of a solid solution as a function of composition. The curves correspond to some specially interesting values of the parameter $p = kT/z\phi_m$.

The most interesting curves of $\Delta F(c)$ are those for which there are two minima. Some of these are shown on an enlarged scale in *fig.* 9.7. Consider, for example, the curve for $p = 0.33$ in *fig.* 9.6 or 9.7. At concentrations less than the left-hand minimum c_1, the free energy of the mixture is less than the free energy of the separate components. The solid solution is thus stable. At concentrations between c_1 and c_2 the free energy follows a parabola-shaped curve above the straight line joining c_1 and c_2, that is above the common tangent. Throughout this region, the lowest free energy is obtained by a mixture of components of compositions c_1 and c_2. For example, for an alloy with composition c_3, the proportions of the components would be given by

$$\frac{\text{amount of component } c_1}{\text{amount of component } c_2} = \frac{\text{length } c_3 c_2}{\text{length } c_1 c_3}. \qquad 9.14.4$$

The equilibrium state of an alloy with composition between c_1 and c_2 is a mixture of crystals having compositions c_1 and c_2, while for alloys with compositions less than c_1 or greater than c_2, the actual composition is stable. The points c_1 and c_2 are thus the solubility limits of each component in the other. To find the values of c_1 and c_2 we differentiate ΔF with respect to c and equate to zero. Thus

$$\frac{\partial \Delta F}{\partial c} = Nz\phi_m[1 - 2c + p\{\ln c - \ln(1-c)\}]$$

$$= 0 \quad \text{when} \quad c = c_1.$$

This gives

$$\ln \frac{c_1}{1-c_1} = -\frac{1-2c}{p}$$

or
$$\frac{c_1}{1-c_1} = \exp\left\{-\frac{(1-2c_1)z\phi_m}{kT}\right\}. \qquad 9.14.5$$

Solving 9.14.5 we obtain c_1 and $1-c_1$, which, since the $\Delta F(c)$ curve is symmetrical, is c_2. If, however, we assume that $c_1 \ll 1$, which means that solubility is low, we can obtain an explicit formula for c_1, namely

$$c_1 = \exp\left\{-\frac{z\phi_m}{kT}\right\}. \qquad 9.14.6$$

Thus, once again, equilibrium is a balance between the ordering effect (in the sense defined above) of the interatomic forces, and the

17

disordering effect of temperature. We may further conclude from 9.14.5 that solubility increases with temperature, for, at high temperatures, the exponential tends to unity and the points c_1 and c_2 move together until, if other conditions are favourable, there is a continuous range of solid solutions.

We shall not pursue the theory of alloys further except to give a reminder that our example was highly idealised. It is not accurate to consider interactions between nearest-neighbour atoms only, and only a few pairs of atoms are so much alike that we can say it is equally probable that any lattice site is occupied by one or other. Even when the crystal structures of the components are the same, inclusion of these complications makes the $\Delta F(c)$ curve unsymmetrical; then the rule that the common tangent to the $\Delta F(c)$ curve determines the compositions of the terminal solid solutions is still valid, but the points of tangency are no longer minima of the $\Delta F(c)$ curve. We have likewise made no reference to the possibility of ordering of a homogeneous alloy except to avoid the use of the words 'disordered' and 'random' for the states of maximum entropy. Thus, if ϕ_{AB} is numerically greater, that is more negative, than $\frac{1}{2}(\phi_{AA} + \phi_{BB})$, energy considerations will favour what we called a *homogeneous* alloy but not a *random* alloy, since each A-atom will attempt to surround itself with B-atoms and vice versa. If the proportions of A- and B-atoms are suitable this could result in a high degree of order such as is found in NaCl. The entropy, however, while favouring the tendency to mix the A-and B-atoms, opposes ordering, since the requirement that the A- and B-atoms should alternate reduces the number of possible arrangements.

§ 9.15 Appendix : elementary quantum theory

An excellent account of the elementary quantum theory known as Bohr's theory or the 'older quantum theory' is to be found in M. Born *Atomic Physics* Blackie, London, 1965 chapter 5. This theory is more than adequate for our purpose in § § 9.8 and 9.9.

In this theory, the angular momentum of a rotating system turns out to be quantized in units of $h/2\pi$. Thus, a molecule rotating with angular frequency ω about an axis with respect to which it has moment of inertia I, has angular momentum $I\omega$, so

$$I\omega = nh/2\pi,$$

where n is a whole number. This equation defines the allowed values of ω, which are thus a uniformly spaced series. The energies of the allowed rotary motions are given by the values of $\frac{1}{2}I\omega^2$, that is by the values of $\frac{1}{2}\frac{n^2h^2}{(2\pi)^2I}$, and the minimum energy to excite rotation is thus $h^2/(8\pi^2 I)$, as quoted in § 9.9 and used in 9.9.3. The same formula was used later in § 9.9 to estimate the energies required to excite changes in the rates at which electrons move round the nucleus.

§ 9.16 Problems

1. Justify the estimates of U and pV given in § 9.2. Take the cases of a metal, an ionic crystal (NaCl), a valence crystal (diamond), a molecular crystal (I_2) and a rare gas crystal (Ne).

2. Calculate the vibration frequencies v of the atoms in the solids listed in table 16, assuming that each is an Einstein solid. In each case compare the value of v with that obtained from equation 9.8.3. Assume that λ can be estimated from Young's modulus E by remembering that λ is the force per unit extension, that is

$$\lambda = F/x, \qquad 9.16.1$$

where F is the force which stretches a bond in a one-dimensional atomic chain by distance x. In the same chain, E is the force per unit area which produces unit strain. Thus, taking the cross-sectional area of the atomic chain to be $\sim a^2$ where a is the interatomic distance, we have

$$E = \frac{F/a^2}{x/a} = \frac{F/a}{x}. \qquad 9.16.2$$

so that, combining 9.16.1 and 2,

$$\lambda = Ea. \qquad 9.16.3$$

E and a can be obtained from tables, as also can m.

3. Show that fig. 9.7 is correct in indicating that the minima of the graphs of $\Delta F(c)$ come closer together as p increases in the range $0 < p < 0.5$, coalescing when $c = 0.5$. What does this mean physically?

§ 9.17 Further reading

An excellent elementary account of the equilibrium, entropy, and thermal properties of crystals is

A. H. Cottrell *Theoretical Structural Metallurgy* Arnold, London, 1965.

A good general textbook is

D. K. C. MacDonald *Introductory Statistical Mechanics for Physicists* Wiley, New York and London, 1963.

Chapter 10

RATE PROCESSES

One of the commonest problems in physics is that of calculating the rate at which a process takes place. An example of this occurred in chapter 2 when we found that the rates of transport of energy, momentum and matter in perfect gases should vary with the square root of the absolute temperature. Usually, however, the theory of rate processes concerns itself with cases where the rate is determined by the probability that particles can surmount an energy barrier.

§ 10.1 Barrier jumping

Let us reconsider a problem already discussed in § 5.9, that of the rate at which molecules evaporate from a solid or a liquid. We know that a molecule in a condensed phase is attracted by the other molecules, for that is why the condensed phase sticks together; so, in order to escape or evaporate, the molecule has to acquire sufficient energy to overcome these attractions. We have to calculate the probability that a molecule can acquire the necessary energy, which, of course, must be much greater than the mean thermal energy or the solid would disintegrate. On the other hand the only energy available is thermal energy, which, as we know from chapter 5, is not equally distributed over the particles in a system. The problem therefore becomes that of calculating the fraction of molecules which have the necessary energy to surmount the barrier of attractions.

We have already (§ 5.9) obtained one solution of this problem when calculating the fraction of molecules which had energies greater than U_0 or x-components of velocity greater than v_0, where $\frac{1}{2}mv_0^2 = U_0$. The result was (5.9.4)

$$\eta = nA(kT/2\pi m)^{\frac{1}{2}} e^{-U_0/kT}, \qquad 10.1.1$$

where η, the number escaping per second, has been written for $\Gamma'A$ as used in 5.9.4, A being the area of the liquid surface.

In 10.1.1, the pre-exponential factor is the rate at which molecules strike the surface; the exponential expresses the probability that a

molecule has sufficient energy to jump over the barrier represented by
the attractive forces.

§ 10.2   The Arrhenius equation : activation energy

An equation like 10.1.1 is called an *Arrhenius equation* after S. Arrhenius
(1889), who found that the rates of many chemical reactions
could be described by an equation of the form

$$\eta = B\, e^{-E/RT}. \hspace{4cm} 10.2.1$$

Here η is the *rate* at which the process takes place and B is a parameter which has the dimensions of a frequency and is referred to as
the *frequency factor*. B may be a constant or may, as in 10.1.1, vary
slowly with temperature–slowly, that is, in comparison with the
exponential. The quantity E is called the *activation energy*; in 10.2.1 it
is the energy to take one mole over the energy barrier. In 10.1.1 the
activation energy U_0 refers to one molecule and is the energy to
remove one molecule from the liquid surface to the vapour.

Experimentally, E can be measured by measuring the rate at which
the reaction takes place. We might, for example, measure how
much liquid (η) evaporates in a given time at each of a series of
temperatures. If the Arrhenius equation is valid we shall find that a
plot of $\ln \eta$ against $1/T$ will give a straight line, the equation of
which is

$$\ln \eta = \ln B(T) - (E/R)(1/T), \hspace{2.5cm} 10.2.2$$

and the slope of which is $-E/R$ or $-U_0/k$. If E is not much
greater than RT or if the accuracy of measurement is high, deviations
from the straight line may be observed due to the term in $B(T)$. In
practice such deviations are rarely detectable.

If absolute measurements of η are available, the pre-exponential
factor is obtainable from the intercept of the extrapolated line on
the $\ln \eta$ axis, but determination of E in this way does not require
absolute measurements of number of molecules or of equilibrium
concentrations. For example, E for evaporation or sublimation might
be measured by finding the relative amounts of material deposited
from a constant area of surface on to a chilled plate of constant
area at a constant distance from the surface. Such an experiment
does not provide the data necessary to measure the pre-exponential
factor, which involves the geometry of the arrangement, nor does it
reveal if E is constant or a linear function of T. For if

$$E = E' - \alpha T,$$

where α is a constant, then the term in $\exp(\alpha T/RT)$ disappears into the pre-exponential factor.

§ 10.3   Formation energy

Equation 10.2.1, the Arrhenius equation which describes the rate at which some process occurs, is mathematically similar to certain equations which describe equilibrium states. For example, we saw in § 9.11 that the equilibrium concentration c of vacant lattice sites in a solid is

$$c = C \, e^{-E_f/kT}, \qquad\qquad\qquad 10.3.1$$

where C is a quantity which may be a slowly varying function of T but which does not involve the time. E_f is sometimes called an activation energy, but this is unwise since it does not measure the rate at which the equilibrium state is attained. We shall call it a *formation energy*. It frequently happens that the formation energy is the same as the activation energy, as in the example below, but this is not necessary. Again it may happen that an experimentally measured activation energy, as defined by equation 10.2.1, is really the sum of a true activation energy and a formation energy; such a case is discussed in § 10.9.

§ 10.4   Evaporation and vapour pressure : Trouton's rule

In discussing solids in chapter 9 (in particular § 9.13) we introduced the binding energy as the energy required to remove one atom from the solid and take it away to such a distance that it no longer interacted with the other atoms. We took the free atom as being the zero of energy so that the binding energy was a negative quantity; the more negative it was the stronger was the binding. A similar definition of binding energy can be made for a liquid. It is then in accord with this definition as well as with convention to say that the energy of a molecule in the vapour phase is U_0 above that of one on the surface of the liquid or solid and that U_0 is a positive quantity.

We can then write down the ratio of the probabilities P_v that a molecule is in the vapour and P_s that it is bound to the surface of the solid or liquid. For simplicity we assume that an atom remains bound to the surface until it is a distance δ away, where δ is of the order of the interatomic distance, and that its potential energy on the surface is $-U_0$. At any distance greater than δ from the surface, its potential energy is zero. Then, if V is the volume of the vapour phase we obtain,

$$\frac{P_v}{P_s} = \frac{V}{A\delta} e^{-U_0/kT}, \qquad 10.4.1$$

where A is the area of the surface. This equation means that the relative probability of finding the molecule in the respective volumes is equal to the ratio of the volumes multiplied by the Boltzmann factor, which gives the relative probability that it is in one or other of the energy states.

Now, in equilibrium, the relative probability P_v/P_s is equal to the ratio of the numbers of molecules in the vapour (n_v) and in the surface layer (n_s), that is

$$\frac{n_v}{n_s} = \frac{V}{A\delta} e^{-U_0/kT}, \qquad 10.4.2$$

or the number per unit volume n_v/V in the vapour is given by

$$\frac{n_v}{V} = \frac{n_s'}{\delta} e^{-U_0/kT}, \qquad 10.4.3$$

where n_s' is the number of molecules per unit area of the surface. Now, by the definition of density, the equilibrium vapour density ρ is

$$\rho = m\frac{n_v}{V} = \frac{mn_s'}{\delta} e^{-U_0/kT}; \qquad 10.4.4$$

so, since neither n_s' nor δ should depend on temperature, we see that the temperature dependence of the equilibrium vapour density is measured by the Boltzmann factor $\exp(-U_0/kT)$, where U_0 can be called the formation energy of a vapour molecule.

Thus, in the case of evaporation of a simple substance, the activation energy which describes the rate of approach to equilibrium (10.1.1) is the same as the formation energy which describes the equilibrium concentration (10.4.4). In fact the two equations are the same, since the equilibrium vapour density is reached when the number of molecules leaving the surface is equal to the number returning from the vapour. From 10.1.1 the number evaporating per unit area per second is

$$\eta/A = n(kT/2\pi m)^{\frac{1}{2}} e^{-U_0/kT}, \qquad 10.4.5$$

whereas the number of vapour molecules striking unit area of the surface per second is, from 5.8.24,

$$\Gamma = (n_v/V)(kT/2\pi m)^{\frac{1}{2}}. \qquad 10.4.6$$

n_v/V is given by 10.4.3, so

$$\Gamma = (n_s'/\delta)(kT/2\pi m)^{\frac{1}{2}} e^{-U_0/kT}. \qquad 10.4.7$$

If we now assume that every vapour molecule which strikes the surface is trapped there and cannot bounce off, then Γ is the number of molecules returning per second to unit area of the surface. In equilibrium then

$$\Gamma = \eta/A, \qquad 10.4.8$$

which requires equations 10.4.5 and 10.4.7 to be the same. This in turn requires

$$n = n_s'/\delta, \qquad 10.4.9$$

which is, of course, correct, since δ was defined as the thickness of the surface layer. δ need not appear in the equations for equilibrium vapour pressure, for, since $\eta/A = \Gamma$, we may equate the expressions in 10.4.5 and 10.4.6, and obtain

$$n_v/V = n\, e^{-U_0/kT}.$$

Multiplying both sides by m we then have immediately that, *if the liquid evaporates as stable molecules,*

$$\rho_v = \rho_l\, e^{-U_0/kT} = \rho_l\, e^{-L/RT}, \qquad 10.4.10$$

where ρ_v and ρ_l are the densities of vapour and liquid respectively and L is the latent heat of vaporization.

In this form the relation is not of much use, but we may write

$$\rho_v = mp/kT,$$

where p is the pressure at temperature T and the vapour is assumed to behave as a perfect gas. We also write

$$\rho_l = m/v,$$

where v is the volume occupied by one molecule of the liquid. Making these substitutions, 10.4.10 becomes

$$p = (kT/v)\, e^{-L/RT},$$

which gives a formula for the temperature variation of the pressure of the saturated vapour.

Now, when a function consists of the product of a power and an exponential, the exponential takes charge of the variation (§ 12.8), so we may write

$$p = a \exp(-L/RT), \qquad 10.4.11$$

where $a(= kT/v)$ is approximately constant and would really be constant if the volume v occupied by one molecule in the liquid were directly proportional to temperature. Moreover, remembering that the exponential is the important part, we may take v as being the same for all simple liquids; thus a is a constant for all liquids. If we go further and take p as the pressure at the boiling point T_b, that is one atmosphere, we have

$$L/RT_b = \text{constant for all vapours,} \qquad 10.4.12$$

which expresses the empirical result known as *Trouton's rule*.

By experiment, for many vapours, $L/T_b \simeq 21$ cal/gm-mole deg, and it is in this form that Trouton's rule is usually quoted. It seems better, however, to quote values of the non-dimensional parameter L/RT_b, which should thus be about 10. Some values of L/RT_b for a variety of substances are given in table 18.

TABLE 18 : L/RT_b for various substances

substance	L (MJ/kg-mole)	T_b (°K)	L/RT_b
He	0·093	4·3	2·5
H$_2$	0·93	20·4	5·4
O$_2$	6·9	90	9·0
Cl$_2$	19·3	240	9·6
benzene C$_6$H$_6$	31	353	10·4
Na	98	1,155	10·1
Hg	60	630	11·3
H$_2$O	42	373	13·0
acetic acid CH$_3$COOH	24·5	391	7·5

Here, the five substances in the middle are typical of normal vapours where our assumptions turn out to be more-or-less justified. The first two are molecules consisting only of the lightest elements where, as we saw in §§ 1.14 and 9.8–9, classical statistics are not enough and should be replaced by quantum statistics. The last two are examples of substances where the liquid and vapour phases are in very different states of association; thus in liquid water the molecules are joined by strong hydrogen bonds which have to be broken during evaporation. Consequently, the latent heat of vaporization of water is abnormally high and Trouton's constant similarly high. The opposite state of affairs seems to obtain in the case of acetic acid, possibly because the vapour is not broken up into single molecules.

§ 10.5 Rate-limiting processes

It is not necessary that the activation energy describing the rate of approach to equilibrium should be the same as the formation energy describing an equilibrium state. Two simple, if rather artificial, examples will illustrate this.

First, suppose we replace the assumption (10.4.8) that every vapour molecule incident on the liquid surface is trapped there. Instead, let us see what happens if molecules are trapped only if they are moving sufficiently fast–say with x-component of velocity greater than some value v_x'. Slower molecules are supposed to bounce off again. The effect of this assumption, which may or may not be physically sound, is that the rate of return of molecules from the vapour is reduced, since now only a fraction of those incident on the surface are condensed there. Since in equilibrium the rates of evaporation and condensation are equal, this new restriction must affect the equilibrium rate of evaporation and the equilibrium vapour pressure.

The rate at which vapour molecules strike unit area of the surface and are held there is, by an obvious extension of 10.4.6 and 10.4.7,

$$\Gamma = \frac{n_v}{V} \cdot \frac{\displaystyle\int_{v_x'}^{\infty} v_x \, e^{-mv_x^2/2kT} \, dv_x}{\displaystyle\int_{-\infty}^{\infty} e^{-mv_x^2/2kT} \, dv_x}$$

$$= \frac{n_v}{V}\left(\frac{kT}{2\pi m}\right)^{\frac{1}{2}} e^{-mv_x'^2/2kT}$$

$$= \frac{n_v}{V}\left(\frac{kT}{2\pi m}\right)^{\frac{1}{2}} e^{-U_0'/kT}, \qquad\qquad 10.5.1$$

where U_0' has been written for $\frac{1}{2}mv_x'^2$. In equilibrium η/A (10.1.1) must equal Γ, so, equating them, we obtain for n_v

$$(n_v/V) = n \, e^{-U_0/kT} \, e^{U_0'/kT}$$

$$= n \, e^{-(U_0 - U_0')/kT}. \qquad\qquad 10.5.2$$

The equilibrium vapour density is thus increased by a factor $\exp(U_0'/kT)$, while the formation energy for a vapour molecule has been reduced from U_0 to $U_0 - U_0'$. We may represent this on an energy diagram (*fig.* 10.1). In order to escape from the liquid, a molecule has

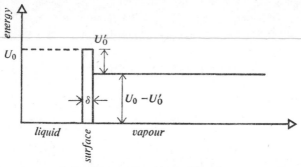

Figure 10.1. *Energy relationships at a hypothetical liquid-vapour interface.*

to pass over an energy barrier of height U_0; this governs the rate of approach to equilibrium and is the activation energy which would be measured in the non-equilibrium experiment suggested in § 10.2. The equilibrium vapour density is determined by the formation energy $U_0 - U_0'$. The energy U_0' can be looked on as a barrier which the vapour molecules have to surmount to return to the liquid.

Probably a more credible physical model would be one where the slower vapour molecules were captured by the liquid while the faster bounce off. If we denote by v_x'' the maximum x-component of velocity which can be captured it is easy to show that the equilibrium vapour pressure is increased by a factor $1/(1 - \exp\{-\frac{1}{2}mv''^2/kT\})$, which is more awkward to deal with and interpret in terms of an activation energy. Experiment shows that neither model corresponds to reality as well as that in § 10.4.

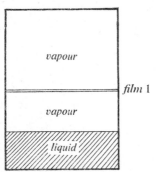

Figure 10.2. *To illustrate the distinction between the equilibrium state and the rate at which it is attained.*

For our second example suppose that the evaporating liquid has a thin cover over it and a few centimetres above it (*fig.* 10.2). The cover might be a very thin film of metal or plastic. If the film is permeable to the vapour then the *equilibrium* vapour pressure on both sides of it is the same, and is determined by the formation energy U_0 as used in the last section. Again, the rate of approach to equilibrium vapour pressure in the region above the liquid and under the film is determined by the same U_0.

Now assume that to pass through the covering film, a molecule must surmount an energy barrier of height U (*fig.* 10.3), where

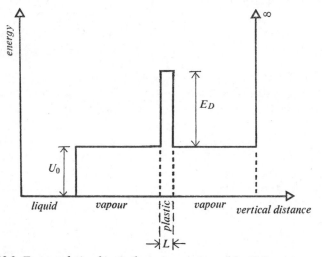

Figure 10.3. *Energy relationships in the various regions of fig.* 10.2.

$U \gg kT$. As in the model for evaporation (*fig.* 10.1), this barrier determines the time taken to reach equilibrium in the space above it by limiting the rate at which molecules can pass through. By analogy with 10.1.1 this rate is proportional to $\exp(-U/kT)$ and therefore strongly dependent on U: consider, for example, two films, one of material for which $U_1 = \frac{1}{2}$ eV, the other with $U_2 = 1$ eV, these, as shown in § 10.9, being reasonable energies for atomic processes. At room temperature, where $kT \sim 1/40$ eV, the ratio of the rates at which the vapour would pass through the respective films is

$$\frac{\Gamma_1}{\Gamma_2} = \frac{e^{-U_1/kT}}{e^{-U_2/kT}} = \frac{e^{-20}}{e^{-40}} = e^{20} \simeq 10^9.$$

Thus, if, with the first film, the vapour pressure built up to a given fraction of the equilibrium value in 1 sec, the time to reach the same pressure with the second is about 30 years. If a material existed for which the activation energy barrier was much higher than 1 eV, then under these conditions equilibrium might never be reached even in geological time.

The conclusion is that the rates of thermally activated processes are strongly dependent on activation energy. Two further consequences of this are worthy of note.

(i) Where there are several energy barriers of different heights all to be crossed in some process, the highest barrier effectively limits the rate of the process. Thus, in our model, suppose both films are inserted as shown in *fig.* 10.4. The space between them will fill

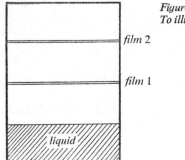

Figure 10.4.
To illustrate rate-limiting processes.

film 2

film 1

liquid

with vapour in a few seconds via barrier U_1. This time is quite negligible compared with the years it will take to fill the space above, via barrier U_2, so that the time of filling this space is essentially the same whether or not barrier U_1 is present. Similarly, if the barriers are transposed so that U_2 is nearer the liquid, the rate at which both spaces are filled depends only on U_2. The highest barrier represents the *rate-limiting process*.

(ii) When there are many energy barriers of the same height to be crossed in some thermally activated process, then the number of barriers influences the rate much less than does their height.

To see this second point, suppose that the molecule passes through the film by the process of solid state diffusion. This process will be discussed in § 10.9, but we may anticipate the results by noting that atoms or molecules diffuse through solids by jumping over each atom in turn, each jump requiring the crossing of an energy barrier;

the solid as seen by the diffusing atom is therefore a series of equal barriers, the number of which is proportional to the thickness. We further anticipate the experimental result that the diffusion coefficient as defined by §§ 2.8, 6.2 and 6.3 is given by

$$D = D_0 \, e^{-E_D/kT},$$

where D_0 is a constant having the dimensions of cm^2/sec and E_D is the activation energy for diffusion. The rate at which the vapour passes by diffusion through the film is then proportional to D/L (§ 6.7), where L is the thickness of the film and thus proportional to the number of energy barriers.

Consider the ratio of the rates of transmission, Γ and Γ', through two films of thickness L and L' made of materials for which the activation energies for diffusion are E_D and $E_{D'}$ respectively. We have

$$\frac{\Gamma}{\Gamma'} = \frac{D_0}{D_0'} \frac{L'}{L} \exp\left(-\{E_D - E_{D'}\}/kT\right).$$

Now by theory (§ 6.3) and experiment (§ 10.9), D_0 is nearly the same for all solids. Equating $D_0 = D_0'$ and taking $E_{D'} = \frac{1}{2}eV$ and $E_D = 1$ eV, which are the same barrier heights as before, and reasonable estimates of activation energies (table 19) for diffusion, we have at room temperature ($kT \simeq 1/40$ eV)

$$\frac{\Gamma}{\Gamma'} = \frac{L'}{L} \exp(-20)$$

$$\simeq \frac{L'}{L} \times 10^{-9}.$$

Thus, if the rates of transmission are to be equal at room temperature, the film having lower activation energy can be 10^9 thicker than that with higher activation energy: a succession of millions of low barriers is no more effective as a rate limiter than one barrier twice as high.

The above example has the advantage of dealing with barriers of physically obvious thickness, though the numerical quantities inserted are somewhat arbitrary. In chemical kinetics, the barrier widths are, like the small barrier in *fig.* 10.1, of molecular size and therefore all of the same order of thickness, though perhaps not very different in height. The same arguments can easily be used to show that the highest barrier, even if not more than a few per cent higher than the next, represents the rate-limiting process.

§ 10.6   Activated states

We may make the conclusions of the last section a little more general
and obtain some more useful results by postulating a mechanism by
which particles cross energy barriers. Suppose we have a system of
particles each of which can exist in one of 3 energy states E_0, E_0' and
E_1 as shown in *fig.* 10.5. E_0' is assumed to be greater than E_0 or E_1,

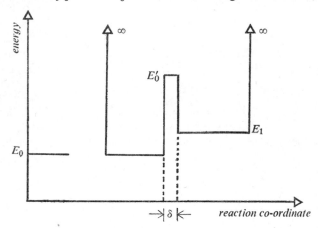

Figure 10.5. *System with two energy minima reported by an energy barrier.*

and both $E_0' - E_0$ and $E_0' - E_1$ are assumed to be much greater than
kT; if not, we are not dealing with a problem involving thermal
activation or barrier jumping. The relationship of E_0 and E_1 is
arbitrary. We make the further assumption that particles in state E_0'
are in thermal equilibrium with particles in the other states. We shall
call E_0 the initial state and consider the rate at which particles pass
over the *activated state* E_0' to arrive at the final state E_1.

One of the simplest examples of such a set of states–simplest to
visualise that is–is the one we shall examine in § 10.9. Here atoms
are changing place within a solid; the initial and final states are the
ordinary lattice sites and the activated state is one where the atoms
changing place squeeze past each other or climb over each other, to
make the change. Another example comes from chemistry where a
simple reaction, such as

$$A_2 + B_2 \rightarrow 2AB,$$

may be thought of as a collision process, where sufficiently energetic
molecules of A_2 and B_2 collide and stick together to form activated

complexes A_2B_2 which then break up to form two AB-type molecules. In both examples the activated states are seen to be unstable, breaking down with very small displacements in one direction–the direction which leads from the energy hump to a stable state. We may measure the *reaction co-ordinate* as a length in this direction, which we take as the x-axis. A configuration which is stable for displacements in all directions but one suggests a saddle, and is thus frequently referred to as a *saddle point*.

If, as we assumed, the activated complexes are in thermal equilibrium with the other particles of the system, then the number of complexes per unit volume, having x-components of velocity between v_x and $v_x + dv_x$, is

$$n(v_x)dv_x = A\, e^{-m^* v_x^2 / 2kT}\, dv_x,$$

where A is a constant and m^* is the effective mass of the complex. The mean velocity of the complexes in the direction of increasing x is then the quantity $\overrightarrow{v_x}$ in § 1.15 or the quantity $|\,\overline{v_x}\,|$ used in the footnote on p. 132, that is

$$|\overline{v_x}| = \frac{\displaystyle\int_0^\infty v_x\, e^{-m^* v_x^2 / 2kT}\, dv_x}{\displaystyle\int_{-\infty}^\infty e^{-m^* v_x^2 / 2kT}\, dv_x}$$

$$= (kT / 2\pi m^*)^{\frac{1}{2}}.$$

The mean time τ which a complex takes to cross the barrier is then $\delta / |\,\overline{v_x}\,|$, where δ is the width of the barrier. τ is also the mean lifetime of an activated complex, and, if n_0' is the number of complexes per unit volume in the activated state E_0', then the rate at which transitions are made over the barrier from state E_0 to state E_1 is n_0' / τ.

Now we know that in equilibrium

$$n_0' = n_0\, e^{-(E_0' - E_0)/kT}, \qquad\qquad 10.6.1$$

so the rate at which particles cross the barrier is

$$\Gamma = (n_0 / \delta)(kT / 2\pi m^*)^{\frac{1}{2}} \exp\{-(E_0' - E_0)/kT\}, \qquad 10.6.2$$

which is essentially the same as 10.1.1. We need not for the moment define $E_0' - E_0$ more carefully, leaving it till (in § 10.9) a specific example shows that the difference in entropy of the initial and activated states may have to be taken into consideration, that is that the energies involved in 10.6.1–2 are free energies as defined in § 8.4.

In this form it is easy to see that if a system goes through a series of states, passing over a series of barriers, then the frequency factors will be all much the same since δ will always be of molecular dimensions and m^* of the order of magnitude of molecular masses. Thus, once again, the heights of the barriers alone determine the relative rates at which successive barriers are crossed.

§ 10.7 Detailed balancing

Suppose we have a system with three energy minima $E_0 = 0$, E_1 and E_2 separated by maxima E_0' and E_1' as shown in *fig.* 10.6. We assume

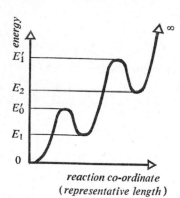

Figure 10.6. *System with three energy minima separated by barriers.*

$E_1' > E_0' > E_1 > 0$ and $E_1' > E_2 > 0$. The relationship of E_2 and E_1 is arbitrary. We further assume that all E_i and E_i', *as well as their differences*, are large compared with kT; as in § 10.6, this is necessary for our problem to be one of thermal activation or barrier jumping. The infinite energies indicated to the left of point E_0 and to the right of E_2 imply that particles have zero probability of leaving the system.

Denote now by n_0, n_1 and n_2 the numbers per unit volume of particles instantaneously in the respective states and write down expressions for the rate of change of each of these numbers: first, for $\dfrac{dn_0}{dt}$ we have

$$\frac{dn_0}{dt} = -n_0 v_0\, e^{-E_0'/kT} + n_1 v_1\, e^{-(E_0' - E_1)/kT}, \qquad 10.7.1$$

where each term on the right-hand side is an expression of the same form as in 10.6.2, the first term giving the number leaving state E_0 in unit time over the barrier E_0', the second giving the rate of return

18

from state E_1 over the barrier ($E'_0 - E_1$). In each case the quantity v_i has the dimensions of a frequency: it is the number of times per second that a given particle in state E_i attempts to jump the barrier; the exponential gives the fraction of successful attempts.

Continuing to write expressions for $\dfrac{dn_i}{dt}$ we have:

$$\frac{dn_1}{dt} = -n_1 v_1\, e^{-(E'_0 - E_1)/kT} + n_1 v_1\, e^{-(E'_1 - E_1)/kT} +$$

$$+ n_0 v_0\, e^{-E'_0/kT} + n_2 v_2\, e^{-(E'_1 - E_2)/kT}, \qquad 10.7.2$$

and $\qquad \dfrac{dn_2}{dt} = n_1 v_1\, e^{-(E'_1 - E_1)/kT} - n_2 v_2\, e^{-(E'_1 - E_2)/kT}. \qquad 10.7.3$

We now simplify these expressions by using the result (§ 10.6) that the v_i are not likely to be very different from each other; in particular, not nearly so different as the exponentials of which examples were given above. We thus take

$$v_0 = v_1 = v_2 = v. \qquad 10.7.4$$

We next note that state E_1 is fed with particles from E_0 over the barrier E'_0 at a rate $n_0 v\, e^{-(E'_0)/kT}$ and depleted at the rate $n_1 v\, e^{-(E'_0 - E_1)/kT}$. If equilibrium were attained then

$$\frac{n_1}{n_0} = e^{-E_1/kT}, \qquad 10.7.5$$

so that these rates would be equal. Then, for every transition tending to disturb equilibrium, there is an inverse process and equilibrium is maintained by each process and its inverse occurring with equal frequency. This is a very special case of the apparently general *principle of detailed balancing*. Again, since $n_1 \ll n_0$, the traffic between states E_2 and E_1 via the barrier E'_1 is very much less than that between E_0 and E_1 via E'_0. This traffic over E'_1 is given by the second and fourth terms of 10.7.2, which may thus be neglected in comparison with the other two. The result is that equilibrium is attained between E_1 and E_0 independently of the existence of E_2.

Replacing n_1 by $n_0\, e^{-E_1/kT}$ in 10.7.3, we have

$$\frac{1}{v}\frac{dn_2}{dt} = n_0\, e^{-E'_1/kT} - n_2\, e^{-(E'_1 - E_2)/kT}, \qquad 10.7.6$$

which tells us that the rate of change of population in state E_2 is governed solely by its own energy and by the height of the barrier

E_1', that is the height of the higher of the two barriers. Equation 10.7.6 further shows that the equilibrium condition

$$\frac{dn_2}{dt} = 0$$

requires

$$\frac{n_2}{n_0} = e^{-E_2/kT}, \qquad 10.7.7$$

which, like 10.7.5, assures us that the equilibrium distribution between the two states is determined only by their relative energies, and is independent of the existence of other states.

The above demonstration is capable of extension to greater numbers of states and can be made more rigorous. The general results for an equilibrium situation are:

(i) there is detailed balance between any two states;

(ii) the rate of transfer of particles between states depends only on the height of the highest barrier between them and is independent of the heights of intermediate barriers or states;

(iii) the relative concentration of particles in any two states depends only on their relative energy; it is independent of the existence of other states.

§ 10.8 Boltzmann's proof of the energy distribution law

In §§ 5.7–8 the distribution of energy amongst particles was derived by consideration of the relative probability of various configurations. We now give an alternative proof based on the results obtained in § 10.7.

Exactly as in § 5.7, suppose that representative points, representing gas molecules, are placed in cells each corresponding to a definite energy. Let the number of points in the cell with energy E_i be n_i, where we do not assume any relationship between n_i and E_i. We now return temporarily to the gas of colliding, but otherwise non-interacting, particles represented by the Σn_i points and suppose that particles, with energy E_i and E_j respectively, collide, as in §§ 5.7–8, scattering their representative points into new energy cells $E_{i'}$ and $E_{j'}$. Conservation of energy requires

$$E_i + E_j = E_{i'} + E_{j'} \qquad 10.8.1$$

or $\qquad E_{i'} - E_i = E_j - E_{j'}. \qquad 10.8.2$

The number of transitions from E_i and E_j to $E_{i'}$ and $E_{j'}$ is proportional to the number of collisions between molecules with energies E_i and E_j, that is to $n_i n_j$, and to the probability that the particle with energy E_j can jump the barrier to the higher energy state $E_{j'}$. We may write this transition rate as $P n_i n_j$, where P involves a frequency factor v_{ij} and a transition probability for which we do not assume an expression meantime. Similarly the rate of transition in the reverse direction from $E_{i'}$ and $E_{j'}$ to E_i and E_j is $P' n_{i'} n_{j'}$.

The proof that $P = P'$ is essentially what Boltzmann (1910) proved in his H-theorem. Boltzmann's proof involves a careful examination of collision processes between gas molecules and, as mentioned in § 5.11, rather obscures its own object. Basically, however, it argues that an observer travelling with the centre of mass of particles with velocities v_i and v_j (and energies E_i and E_j) would see their collision and subsequent separation with velocities $v_{i'}$ and $v_{j'}$ (and energies $E_{i'}$ and $E_{j'}$) as completely equivalent to the inverse situation where particles with velocities $v_{i'}$ and $v_{j'}$ collide and change to v_i and v_j. Boltzmann's proof continues by showing that a gas, for which $P \neq P'$, is not in equilibrium but that if left to itself will change in such a way as to make $P \to P'$.

With $P = P'$ we now have

$$n_i n_j = n_{i'} n_{j'}, \qquad\qquad 10.8.3$$

the n_i being functions of energy and subject to the subsidiary condition expressed by equation 10.8.1. These equations are functional equations and their solution can be found by methods of mathematical analysis. It is easy to see, however, by substitution, that an acceptable solution is

$$n_i = n_0 \, e^{-\beta E_i}, \qquad\qquad 10.8.4$$

where n_0 and β are constants. The rest of the proof, showing that

$$\beta = 1/kT, \qquad\qquad 10.8.5$$

follows exactly as in § 5.8.

Suppose, however, that we felt justified in using the results of § 10.7, having obtained them by methods which did not assume knowledge of equations 10.8.4–5. We would then have the quantities P and P' as the products of frequency factors v and exponentials; thus

$$P = v_{ij} \exp\left\{ -(E_{i'} - E_i)/kT \right\}$$
$$P' = v_{i'j'} \exp\left\{ -(E_j - E_{j'})/kT \right\},$$

where we have taken

$$E_{i'} > E_i \quad \text{and} \quad E_j > E_{j'},$$

which is in accord with 10.8.2. Now v_{ij} and $v_{i'j'}$ are simply collision frequencies, which, as shown in §2.2, depend only on the relative velocities of the particles and are therefore equal by the centre-of-mass argument above. The exponential factors are equal by the conservation of energy condition 10.8.2. Thus once again $P = P'$.

§10.9   A thermally activated process : diffusion in solids

In §6.3 the coefficient D of diffusion in a solid was shown to be

$$D = \tfrac{1}{6}a^2 v, \qquad\qquad 10.9.1$$

where a for the case considered, that of a simple-cubic crystal, was the interatomic spacing of nearest-neighbour atoms, that is the length of the edge of the cubic unit cell, and v was the frequency at which atoms jumped to neighbouring lattice sites. The coefficient $\tfrac{1}{6}$ was derived on the assumption that jumps of length a could take place either perpendicular to, or in the direction of the concentration gradient. In the former case the jumps were ineffective in transporting material; in the latter case atoms were transported distances $\pm a$. If the lattice is not simple-cubic but is, for example, face-centred-cubic, then it is customary to adapt equation 10.9.1 so that a remains the length of the edge of the cubic unit cell. In this case, there are 12 possible jumps an atom can make, corresponding to a move into the position of any of its 12 nearest neighbours. *Fig.* 10.7 indicates a few of these jumps.

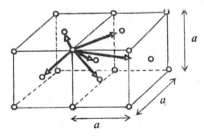

Figure 10.7. *Diffusion jumps in a face-centred-cubic lattice.*

If the concentration gradient is parallel to a cube edge, four of these jumps are ineffective, while the remainder are of length $a/\sqrt{2}$ in the direction at 45° to the concentration gradient, that is, they are effectively of length $\frac{1}{2}a$. Four of these effective jumps are up-gradient and four down-gradient. Then by exactly the same arguments as were used to derive equations 6.3.3–5 we have that the net flux Γ is

$$\Gamma = \tfrac{4}{12}\frac{a}{2}vn(x) - \tfrac{4}{12}\frac{a}{2}vn(x+\tfrac{1}{2}a)$$

$$= -\tfrac{1}{3}\left(\frac{a}{2}\right)^2 v\left\{\frac{n(x+\tfrac{1}{2}a)-n(x)}{\tfrac{1}{2}a}\right\}$$

$$= -\tfrac{1}{12}a^2 v\frac{dn}{dx}\,; \qquad\qquad 10.9.2$$

so that, for a face-centred-cubic lattice,

$$D = \tfrac{1}{12}a^2 v, \qquad\qquad 10.9.3$$

a being the cube edge dimension.

It is however the main object of this chapter to interpret the factor v. This we do by noting that atom movements in solids are believed to be due to exchange of atoms with vacant lattice sites; so the first requirement for an atom to jump is that there exists a vacancy, as defined in § 9.11, in a neighbouring site. Thus

$$v \propto c, \qquad\qquad 10.9.4$$

where c is the fraction of vacancies or the probability that a given site is vacant. Again v will be proportional to the number of possible jumps, that is to the number of nearest neighbours or the co-ordination number z, that is

$$v \propto z. \qquad\qquad 10.9.5$$

Finally, a jumping atom in a crystal has to overcome some sort of energy barrier in order to move from its stable lattice site. In terms of the activated states defined in § 10.6, we may picture this barrier-jumping process as one where an atom has moved from its lattice site into a metastable position or saddle-point from which it may fall back to its old site or forward into a new site. The energy of a crystal containing an atom in an activated state will be higher by an amount E_m than that of the same crystal without the activated state. The entropy will likewise be different because, following § 9.12, we expect an increase in thermal entropy in a crystal containing defects. We denote this entropy difference by S_m, whereupon the jump frequency will be proportional to the rate at which barriers of height $E_m - TS_m$ are crossed at temperature T; that is

$$v \propto \exp\{-(E_m - TS_m)/kT\}. \qquad\qquad 10.9.6$$

Collecting all the relations 10.9.4–6 we may write for the jump frequency

$$v = v_a zc \exp\left(S_m/k\right) \exp\left(-E_m/kT\right), \qquad 10.9.7$$

where v_a has the dimensions of a frequency and can be thought of as the frequency of vibration of atoms in the activated states. We would expect v_a to be somewhat higher than, though of the same order of magnitude as, the vibration frequency of an atom in a stable lattice site.

We now introduce into 10.9.7 the formula 9.11.5 for the concentration c of vacant lattice sites:

$$c = \exp\left(S_f/k\right) \exp\left(-E_f/kT\right), \qquad 10.9.8$$

where S_f has here been written for the thermal entropy of formation of vacancies. Using now equations 10.9.1 or 10.9.3, we have for the diffusion coefficient

$$D = \alpha z v_a a^2 \exp\left(S_f/k\right) \exp\left(S_m/k\right) \exp\left(-E_D/kT\right), \quad 10.9.9$$

where $\quad E_D = E_f + E_m,$ $\qquad\qquad\qquad\qquad$ 10.9.10

and α is a numerical constant, which we saw to be $\frac{1}{12}$ for a face-centred-cubic lattice.

If the diffusion coefficients are measured at various temperatures by the methods described in § 6.3 it is found that the relation between D and T is expressed by a relation of the form

$$D = D_0 \exp\left(-E_D/kT\right), \qquad 10.9.11$$

which is in agreement with 10.9.9 if

$$D_0 = \alpha z v_a a^2 \exp\left(S_f/k\right) \exp\left(S_m/k\right). \qquad 10.9.12$$

Some measured values of D_0 and E_D are given in table 19, from which it appears that for self-diffusion in many metals $D_0 \sim 1$ cm^2/sec. Now, for face-centred-cubic crystals, $\alpha = \frac{1}{12}$, $z = 12$, $a^2 \simeq 10^{-15}$ cm^2, and (from table 17) $\exp\left(S_f/k\right) \simeq 3$–5. S_m/k is not known but, by analogy with considerations of S_f/k, should not be large, perhaps of the order of unity. If so, $\exp\left(S_m/k\right) \sim 2$–3. Hence $v_a \sim 10^{14}$ sec^{-1}, a value somewhat higher than the Einstein or Debye frequencies for atomic vibration (table 16, p. 229). This is what we were led to expect when we identified v_a with the vibration frequency of an atom in a saddle-point configuration.

TABLE 19 : diffusion data for some solids

	D_0 (cm^2/sec)	E_D (eV)	E_f (eV)	E_m (eV)
self-diffusion in metals				
Ag in Ag	0·40	1·91	1·09	0·82 [1]
Cu in Cu	0·20	2·05	1·17	0·88 [1]
Ni in Ni	1·30	2·90	—	—
tracer diffusion [2] in metals				
Cu in Ag	1·2	2·00	1·09	0·91 [3]
Ag in Cu	0·63	2·01	1·17	0·84 [3]
gases in solids				
H$_2$ in neoprene	9·00	0·40	—	—
H in Pd	~0·25	0·44	—	—

[1] from independent measurement; note that experiment confirms equation 10.9.10.
[2] the first element named is the tracer, diffusing in very small quantities into the bulk crystal of the second named element.
[3] by calculation, assuming equation 10.9.10.

§ 10.10   A barrier jumping process : the junction transistor

While it is outside the scope of this book to discuss electrical conduction processes, we may indicate how the ideas of barrier jumping explain the observed form of the current/voltage characteristics of semiconductor rectifying junctions.

Consider a typical semiconducting crystal, for definiteness one of silicon. This element is tetravalent and crystallizes in the diamond-type lattice shown in *fig.* 10.8, each atom having four nearest neighbours. It is assumed that the four valence electrons are fully occupied in forming the four bonds with neighbour atoms and are not available to conduct electricity. Each bond thus is formed by two electrons and the crystal is really one large chemical molecule and is an insulator. In fact, thermal activation will break a small fraction of the bonds, releasing electrons to take part in electrical conductivity, which, since it occurs in pure material, is called *intrinsic conductivity*. We shall largely ignore this contribution to the conductivity except to point out that the breaking of a bond contributes

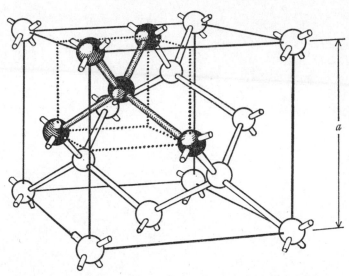

Figure 10.8. *The diamond type lattice which is the crystal structure of silicon.*
This three-dimensional sketch shows how each atom forms four bonds with
its nearest neighbours (after W. Shockley Electrons and Holes in Semiconductors
D. Van Nostrand Company, Inc., Princeton, New Jersey, 1950).

not only an electron free to move throughout the crystal but also a
bond which is one electron short. The missing electron can be replaced
by another from a neighbouring complete bond, which in turn
becomes one short. Thus the state of being one electron short can
also travel throughout the crystal and can be thought of as the movement of a positive particle in the opposite direction to that taken by
the electrons which attempt to complete the broken bonds. This
state of being one electron short is called a *positive hole* and the
imaginary particles with this name contribute to the electrical
conductivity as shown in *fig.* 10.9.

Now suppose that a small fraction of the tetravalent silicon atoms
are replaced by atoms of a pentavalent impurity, say arsenic. Each
pentavalent atom contributes 5 valence electrons of which 4 are
required to form the bonds of the diamond-type lattice, while the
fifth is normally free to conduct electricity. Thus, the impurities turn
the crystal into a conductor–though a poor conductor compared
with metals, since there are few free electrons. It is called an *extrinsic*
semiconductor and, since the conductivity is by negatively charged
particles, it is called *n*-type.

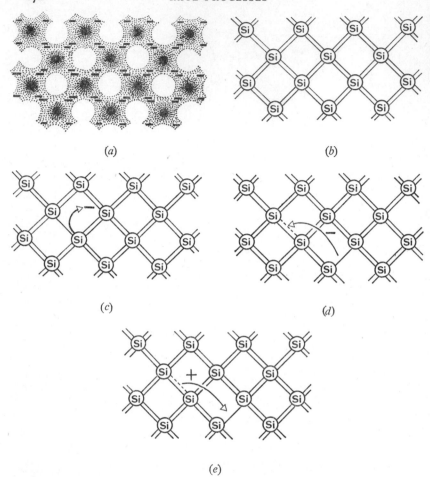

(a)   *(b)*

(c)   *(d)*

(e)

Figure 10.9. *Simplified two-dimensional drawing of the bonds in silicon. In (a)
the two electrons in each bond are shown as clouds of negative charge. In (b)
the bonds are further simplified to appear as lines, one for each electron. In
(c) one bond is broken by thermal agitation giving a free electron available to
conduct electricity. In (d) the missing electron has been replaced by another
leaving a different bond broken. (e) shows that this is the same as if the
missing bond had moved in the opposite direction. (after W. Shockley* Electrons
and Holes in Semiconductors *D. Van Nostrand Company, Inc., Princeton,
New Jersey,* 1950).

Similarly, if some of the silicon atoms in the pure crystal are
replaced by trivalent impurities such as gallium, one bond per
impurity atom will be an electron short. As we have seen the state of

being an electron short can move about the crystal as if it were a positive charge carrier. The resulting extrinsic conductivity is said to be *p*-type. *n*- and *p*-type conductivities are illustrated in *fig.* 10.10.

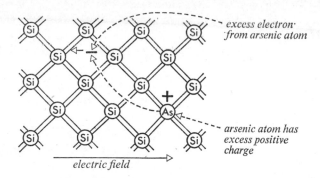

excess electron· from arsenic atom

arsenic atom has excess positive charge

electric field

(*a*)   *n-type conductivity*

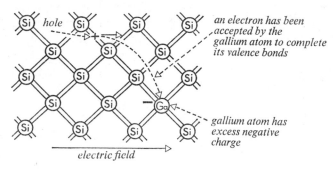

an electron has been accepted by the gallium atom to complete its valence bonds

gallium atom has excess negative charge

electric field

(*b*)   *p-type conductivity*

Figure 10.10. *Impurity conductivity in silicon crystals* (*after W. Shockley* Electrons and Holes in Semiconductors *D. Van Nostrand Company, Inc., Princeton, New Jersey, 1950*).

If a piece of *n*-type material is brought into close contact with a piece of *p*-type material, we have the rectifying device known as a *p-n* junction. Before setting out to discover why such a device has rectifying properties we may note that the contact has to be so close that both *p*- and *n*-material are parts of the same silicon crystal: a possible method of manufacture might be to diffuse in tri- and pentavalent impurities from opposite ends of a pure intrinsic crystal of silicon. Alternatively one type of impurity, say trivalent gallium, might be diffused in, in quantities large enough to swamp the effect of pentavalent impurity already present in the crystal. In either case the importance of diffusion in technological processes is illustrated.

When the p-type and n-type materials are in contact it may be expected that those electrons in the n-type material which are surplus to bond requirements will begin to move to the p-type material to complete the deficient bonds there. The same process can be thought of as a movement of holes from p-type to n-type to mop up the excess electrons in the n-type material. Whichever way we look at it, or even if we think of it as if both processes were going on simultaneously, the result is to leave excess positive charges on the impurity ions of the n-type material and excess negative charges on the impurities of the p-type material. Electrostatic attraction will then bring the exchange of electrons and holes to a standstill.

In the boundary region between n-type and p-type all bonds will be complete and there will be no excess electrons; the boundary region is thus effectively intrinsic material and, on our assumptions, a non-conductor with a strong electrostatic field across it, as shown in *fig.* 10.11*a*. The resemblance to a capacitor will be apparent, for there are positively and negatively charged plates separated by a region of non-conducting dielectric. Each plate is joined to the next part of the circuit by an electrical conductor.

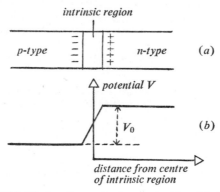

Figure 10.11(*a*). *The junction region in a p-n rectifier.* (*b*) *Variation of potential in the junction region.*

We now consider the motion of charged particles up and down the potential hill shown in *fig.* 10.11*b*. Positive holes with charge $+q$ coming from the p-type material will see the potential hill in the conventional direction as shown, that is they have to acquire energy qV_0 to climb it. Electrons with charge $(-q)$ from the n-type material also see a hill to climb in order to reach the negatively charged p-type material. This hill is of height $(-q)(-V_0)$, that is the same as for holes. Since we are used to dealing with a conventional current of positive charge carriers, which in an ordinary conductor flow down the conventional potential gradient, we may use the fact that we now have such particles and conveniently restrict the subsequent discussion to the movement of positive holes, remembering that the total current is carried by both holes and electrons.

In equilibrium there will be a small flow of holes up the potential hill from the p-type material to the n-type, where they will recombine with electrons in the manner we saw before. The resultant current is called the recombination current i_r. This flow will be balanced by drift of those holes which are generated by the intrinsic process in the n-type material and which diffuse down the potential hill to the p-type. This is called the generation current i_g and in equilibrium

$$i_r = i_g.$$

The equilibrium process may be likened to that of evaporation of molecules up an energy step and their subsequent return, as discussed in § 10.4. The rate-limiting process will be the ascent of the potential hill and will thus involve a factor $e^{-qV_0/kT}$, where V_0 is the height of the hill.

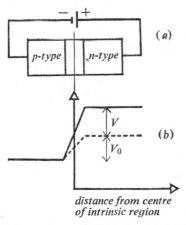

Figure 10.12(a). n-type material biased positively with respect to the p-type. (b) The height of the potential hill is increased.

If now the n-type material is made positive with respect to the p-type, for example by applying a battery as shown in *fig.* 10.12, the height of the energy hill is increased by qV, where V is the applied potential difference. The recombination current is thus reduced by a factor $e^{qV/kT}$, while the generation current is unchanged, that is

$$i_r(V) = i_g e^{-qV/kT}. \qquad\qquad 10.10.1$$

The net hole current i_p across the junction is the difference between the recombination and generation currents:

$$i_p = i_r - i_g = i_g(e^{-qV/kT} - 1). \qquad\qquad 10.10.2$$

If the bias is reversed so that the height of the potential hill is reduced from V_0 to $V_0 - V$, the holes are faced with a smaller hill and the recombination current is increased from the equilibrium value by a factor $e^{qV/kT}$. The generation current is again unchanged so that, with the bias in this direction,

$$i_p = i_g(e^{qV/kT} - 1). \qquad\qquad 10.10.3$$

This equation includes 10.10.2 if V is taken as positive when the p-type material is biased positively with respect to the n-type, and V is taken as negative with the reverse bias. Equation 10.10.3 shows that if qV is large and positive the net current through the device is large and rises exponentially with V. If qV is large and negative the net current reaches a saturation value $-i_g$.

The electron current flowing through the device behaves in exactly the same way, since an applied voltage which increases the height of the hill for holes also increases it for electrons, and an applied voltage which lowers the hill does so for charge carriers of both signs. The total hole and electron current is thus given by

$$i = i_s(e^{qV/kT} - 1), \qquad\qquad 10.10.4$$

where i_s is the sum of the two generation currents and $-i_s$ is the saturation current which is obtained when the n-type material is heavily biased positively relative to the p-type.

Fig. 10.13 shows the form of the theoretical function 10.10.4, which is in general agreement with curves obtained by experiments on p-n junction rectifiers.

Equation 10.10.4 and *fig.* 10.13 illustrate a feature of solid-state rectifiers, namely that they do not rectify small voltages. Thus, if $qV \ll kT$, the exponential can be expanded giving

$$i = i_s(qV/kT), \qquad\qquad 10.10.5$$

that is, a current directly proportional to the applied potential difference. This is the property of an ohmic conductor.

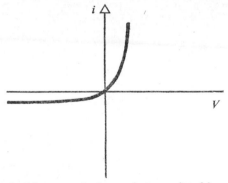

Figure 10.13. *Graph of the current / voltage relation predicted for a p-n junction by equation* 10.10.4.

§ 10.11 Problems

1. The following readings of the variation of vapour pressure (p) with temperature (T) of water were made by observing the temperature at which water boiled at each pressure. Show that these readings are consistent with the idea that evaporation is a thermally activated process. Calculate the activation energy and estimate its accuracy.

TABLE 20 : boiling point of water at various pressures

$T°C$	100·0	94·5	91·9	86·9	77·5	62·9	46·6
p (mm Hg)	760	623	596	470	325	175	82

2. The results in table 21 were obtained by L. W. Barr (Ph.D. Thesis, Edinburgh 1959) in his work on diffusion of antimony into copper carried out by the method described in § 6.3 and problem 7.22.3. Use these results to show that the diffusion coefficient D fits an equation of the form given in 10.9.11:

$$D = D_0 \exp\left(-E_D/kT\right).$$

Show that $D_0 = (0·38 \pm 0·12)$ cm^2 sec^{-1} and that the activation energy E_D is

$$E_D = 1·83 \pm 0·03 \text{ eV/atom}.$$

TABLE 21 : diffusion of antimony into copper

temperature $T(°C)$	diffusion coefficient $D(cm^2 sec^{-1})$
600	9.73×10^{-12}
653	4.53×10^{-11}
706	1.43×10^{-10}
758	4.46×10^{-10}
806	9.73×10^{-10}
859	2.70×10^{-9}
898	4.81×10^{-9}
955	1.14×10^{-8}
1,002	2.27×10^{-8}

§ 10.12   Further reading

The classical treatise on rate processes is

S. Glasstone, K. J. Laidner and H. Eyring *The Theory of Rate Processes* McGraw-Hill, New York and London, 1941.

Much of this book is written at a level suitable for elementary reading.

Chapter 11

FLUCTUATIONS

§ 11.1   Assemblies of discrete entities

This book is about the properties of matter as predicted by statistical treatment of models consisting of large numbers of discrete entities. In many of the results, the fact that the entities were discrete did not appear, any random effects being smoothed out by averaging over large numbers. In this way values were obtained for the average pressure of a gas, for the specific heats of gases and solids and for the conditions for phase equilibrium.

We have, however, met with effects due to the random behaviour of individual entities. These included fluctuations in the length of free paths (§ 4.7), diffusion (§ 6·2) due to random motion of individual atoms, Brownian motion (§ 6.9), and the theory of random errors (§ 7.4). In § 5·5 we obtained a formula for the probable deviations from the most probable distribution of molecules between two halves of their container, and in § 7.2 the same formula was applied to predict the accuracy of a random sample. We shall pursue the theory of fluctuations no further than to generalise some of our existing results and point out a few more applications.

§ 11.2   Deviations from the mean : the binomial distribution

It is convenient to use the methods of § 4.6 to calculate the relative probabilities of deviations from the mean. We can then apply the results to a problem of counting individual particles similar to that discussed in § 4.8 and answering the question: if the mean counting rate is $\bar{n}$ per minute, what is the probability that we shall observe exactly n counts in a given minute? The same result can be applied to the mean number of molecular impacts with a wall–that is to the mean pressure–with the question: can we observe pressure fluctuations?

Suppose, as in § 4.6, that we have a bag containing a large number of balls most of which are white, but a small fraction p are red. We assume as before that p is kept constant either by replacing drawn balls or by having the numbers of both colours so large that the extracted balls make no difference. The probability of drawing a red ball is then p and the mean number $\bar{n}$ of red balls obtained in N draws is

$$\bar{n} = Np. \tag{11.2.1}$$

The probability of drawing exactly n red balls in N draws is then, by § 3.4,

$$F(n) = p^n(1-p)^{N-n}\,{}^N C_n, \tag{11.2.2}$$

that is, the probability $F(n)$ is equal to the product of the independent probabilities of n events with probability p, and $(N-n)$ events with probability $(1-p)$, multiplied by the number of ways in which the n and $N-n$ events can be arranged. $F(n)$ is the *binomial distribution*.

The same formula as 11.2.2 would have been obtained if, as in § 5.2, we had been putting balls into two boxes, one with probability p, the other with probability $1-p$. In this case the formula would represent the probability that exactly n balls out of N had been put in the box with probability p, the remaining $N-n$ going in the other box. Since the probability that a ball or molecule goes into a small volume v, part of a larger volume V, is $p = v/V$ (§5.2), our present calculation is a generalisation of § 5.5 to the case $p \neq \frac{1}{2}$.

Fig. 11.1 shows the relative probabilities of drawing 0, 1, 2, . . . red balls from a bag containing a large number of balls one quarter of which are red. *Fig.* 11.1a refers to the case when 10 balls in all are drawn, *fig.* 11.1b to the case when 100 balls are drawn. In *fig.* 11.1a the most probable number of red balls is 2 out of 10, though 3 is only slightly less probable. The mean is, of course, 2.5. In *fig.* 11.1b, the mean and most probable values are both 25 out of 100. Two other points about *figs.* 11.1a and b are important: first, the histogram for the larger $\bar{n}$ is almost symmetrical about the mean, that for small $\bar{n}$ is very skew. The second point relates to the width of the two histograms: when $\bar{n} = 2\cdot5$ the width is small in absolute terms but large relative to $\bar{n}$; when $\bar{n} = 25$ the width is greater but is now small relative to $\bar{n}$.

For completeness we quote now general results for the probability of deviations from the mean; that is, for the quantities $(\overline{\Delta n})^2$ and $\overline{\delta^2}$, where

$$\Delta n = n - \bar{n} \tag{11.2.3}$$
$$(= q \text{ as used in } \S 5.5)$$

and

$$\overline{\delta^2} = \overline{(\Delta n)^2}/(\bar{n})^2 \tag{11.2.4}$$
$$(= \overline{q^2}/(\bar{n})^2 \text{ as used in } \S 5.5).$$

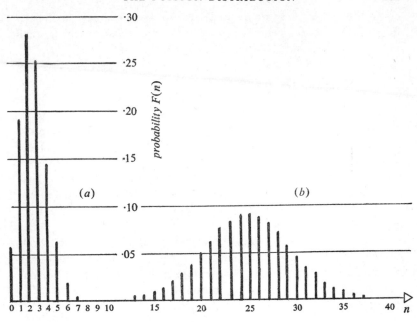

Figure 11.1. *The binomial distribution*
$F(n) = (\tfrac{1}{4})^n(\tfrac{3}{4})^{N-n}\,{}^N C_n$, *for* (a) $N = 10$, (b) $N = 100$.

In § 5.5 these quantities were calculated for the special case of $p = \tfrac{1}{2}$. General results valid for any $p \leqslant 1$ are

$$\bar{n} = Np, \qquad\qquad\qquad 11.2.5$$

$$\overline{(\Delta n)^2} = Np(1-p), \qquad\qquad 11.2.6$$

and $\qquad \overline{\delta^2} = \overline{(\Delta n)^2}/(\bar{n})^2 = (1-p)/\bar{n}. \qquad 11.2.7$

$(\overline{\delta^2})^{\tfrac{1}{2}}$, the root-mean-square deviation from the mean, or standard deviation, occurred also in the theory of errors, where we saw (§ 7·5) that it was a measure of the width of the curve. This is the mathematical confirmation of the observed relative widths of the two distributions in *fig.* 11.1.

The general formulae, 11.2.5–7, the proofs of which are left as problem 11.5.1, are of limited use in physics, where p usually satisfies, or can be arranged to satisfy, the requirement $p \ll 1$.

§ 11.3 The Poisson distribution

A formula for $F(n)$, less intractable than 11.2.2, can be obtained if we assume that $p \to 0$ but that $\bar{n}$, given by 11.2.1, remains finite. Such conditions are likely to be realised in physics: for example, in density fluctuations we are generally interested in fluctuations in a small volume v of the total volume of gas V, so that

$$p = v/V \ll 1.$$

Again, in the counting of nuclear particles, we may find that the mean number $\bar{n}$ arriving per unit time may have any value, depending on the nature of the source. This is treated mathematically by considering a model similar to that in § 4.8, where the random occurrence of such events is controlled by a superhuman fate who draws balls from a bag at regular intervals—a white ball means no event, a red ball means that a particle arrives. The probability of drawing a red ball, or the fraction of red balls in the bag, can be reduced indefinitely, while still maintaining a mean rate $\bar{n}$ per unit time, if the drawing is imagined to be fast enough.

It is convenient to deal separately with the cases where $\bar{n}$ is a large number, as in the case of molecular impacts on a wall, and where $\bar{n}$ is small, as may be the case in counting. In the case of $\bar{n} \sim 1$ we may write down the probabilities of observing 0, 1, 2, 3 events (red balls) in N draws. These are from 11.2.2:

$$F(0) = (1-p)^N,$$

$$F(1) = p(1-p)^{N-1}\frac{N}{1},$$

$$F(2) = p^2(1-p)^{N-2}\frac{N(N-1)}{1\times 2},$$

$$F(3) = p^3(1-p)^{N-3}\frac{N(N-1)(N-2)}{1\times 2\times 3},$$

$$\text{11.3.1}$$

and so on. Now, if N is very large, $N \simeq N-1 \simeq N-2$, etc., so for $n \ll N$ we may write

$$F(n) = \frac{(Np)^n}{n!}(1-p)^{N-n}$$

$$= \frac{\bar{n}^n}{n!}(1-p)^{N-n}.$$

If $p \ll 1$, as was already assumed, we may further approximate to $F(n)$ by writing

$$F(n) = \frac{\bar{n}^n}{n!}(1-p)^N$$

$$= \frac{\bar{n}^n}{n!}\left(1-\frac{\bar{n}}{N}\right)^{\bar{n}(N/\bar{n})}.$$

$$\text{11.3.2}$$

It is shown in § 12.4 that

$$\lim_{M \to \infty} \left(1 - \frac{1}{M}\right)^{xM} = e^{-x},$$

so our final formula for $F(n)$ is

$$F(n) = \frac{\bar{n}^n}{n!} e^{-\bar{n}}. \qquad 11.3.3$$

This is the *Poisson distribution*. It is as well to restate in words what it implies, taking the concrete case of balls in a bag. If repeated drawings of a large sample N of balls are made and the mean number of red balls in each sample is $\bar{n}$, then if $\bar{n} \ll N$, the probability that the sample contains exactly n red balls is $F(n)$ given by expression 11.3.3. We note:

(i) Since the number in each sample is large, n could in principle be large, but the relative probabilities fall off rapidly as n tends to large values. In fact, from 11.3.3

$$\frac{F(n+1)}{F(n)} = \frac{\bar{n}}{n+1} \to 0 \quad \text{as} \quad n \to \infty.$$

We may also see this directly from 11.2.2 since our assumptions imply that $p \ll 1$.

(ii) $F(n)$ is normalised, that is,

$$\sum_{n=0}^{\infty} F(n) = 1. \qquad 11.3.4$$

We may see this from 11.2.2 since the $F(n)$ are the terms in the binomial expansion of $\{p + (1-p)\}^N$. In this case, the summation is from 0 to N. All terms for which $n > N$ are zero. Alternatively, using expression 11.3.3 for $F(n)$, we have:

$$\sum_{n=0}^{\infty} F(n) = e^{-\bar{n}} \left\{ 1 + \frac{\bar{n}}{1} + \frac{\bar{n}^2}{1 \times 2} + \cdots \right\}$$
$$= e^{-\bar{n}} e^{\bar{n}} = 1.$$

(iii) If $\bar{n}$ is an integer then the most probable value n_m of n is $\bar{n}$. This is since

$$\frac{F(\bar{n})}{F(\bar{n}+1)} = \frac{\bar{n}^{\bar{n}}}{\bar{n}!} \cdot \frac{(\bar{n}+1)!}{\bar{n}^{\bar{n}+1}} = \frac{\bar{n}+1}{\bar{n}} > 1.$$

Similarly

$$\frac{F(\bar{n}+1)}{F(\bar{n}+2)} > 1, \quad \frac{F(\bar{n})}{F(\bar{n}-1)} > 1,$$

and so on.

This is a generalisation of the results in §§ 5.2–4 where we showed that the most probable distribution of gas molecules in space is that where equal volumes contain equal numbers of molecules.

If $\bar{n}$ is not an integer then $F(\bar{n})$ is not defined and the most probable value of n is then one of the integers on either side of $\bar{n}$.

(iv) The mean value of n is of course $\bar{n}$. It is however instructive to prove it using expression 11.3.3 for $F(n)$. We have

$$\text{mean } n = \sum_{n=0}^{\infty} nF(n)$$

$$= \sum_{n=1}^{\infty} nF(n) = e^{-\bar{n}} \sum_{n=1}^{\infty} \bar{n} \cdot \frac{\bar{n}^{n-1}}{(n-1)!}.$$

Now write $n' = n-1$, which gives

$$\text{mean } n = \bar{n} \, e^{-\bar{n}} \sum_{n'=0}^{\infty} \frac{\bar{n}^{n'}}{n'!}$$

$$= \bar{n},$$

since $\quad e^{-\bar{n}} \sum_{n'=0}^{\infty} \frac{\bar{n}^{n'}}{n'!} = \sum_{n'=0}^{\infty} F(n') = 1.$

(v) The same technique as in (iv) may be used to calculate the mean-square fluctuation from the mean. This is

$$\overline{(\Delta n)^2} = \overline{(\bar{n}-n)^2}$$

$$= (\bar{n})^2 - 2\overline{n\bar{n}} + \overline{n^2}$$

$$= (\bar{n})^2 - 2(\bar{n})^2 + \overline{n^2}$$

$$= \overline{n^2} - (\bar{n})^2. \qquad 11.3.5$$

Rather than calculate $\overline{n^2}$ it is easier to calculate $\overline{n(n-1)}$ and use

$$\overline{n^2} = \overline{n(n-1)} + \bar{n}. \qquad 11.3.6$$

Thus

$$\overline{n(n-1)} = \sum_{n=0}^{\infty} n(n-1)F(n)$$

$$= e^{-\bar{n}} \sum_{n=2}^{\infty} \frac{\bar{n}^2 \bar{n}^{n-2}}{(n-2)!}.$$

Writing $n' = n-2$, then gives

$$\overline{n(n-1)} = \bar{n}^2 \, e^{-\bar{n}} \sum_{n'=0}^{\infty} \frac{\bar{n}^{n'}}{n'!}$$

$$= (\bar{n}^2). \qquad 11.3.7$$

Then from 11.3.5–7 we have
$$\overline{(\Delta n)^2} = \bar{n},$$ 11.3.8
which agrees with 11.2.6 for the case of $p \ll 1$.

§ 11.4 The normal distribution

We can show the symmetry of the distribution for large $\bar{n}$ by expanding formula 11.3.3 for $F(n)$ by use of Stirling's formula (§ 12.5). By this formula
$$\ln (n!) = n \ln n - n,$$ 11.4.1
provided n is large. Then
$$\ln F(n) = n \ln \bar{n} - \bar{n} - n \ln n + n$$
$$= -n \ln (n/\bar{n}) + (n - \bar{n}).$$
Writing now
$$\varepsilon = n - \bar{n},$$ 11.4.2
so that ε is the deviation from the mean, we obtain
$$\ln F(n) = -(\bar{n} + \varepsilon) \ln \frac{\bar{n} + \varepsilon}{\bar{n}} + \varepsilon$$

$$= -(\bar{n} + \varepsilon) \ln \left(1 + \frac{\varepsilon}{\bar{n}}\right) + \varepsilon.$$

Since we are interested in small deviations from the mean we may assume $\varepsilon \ll \bar{n}$ and expand the logarithm, obtaining
$$\ln F(n) = -(\bar{n} + \varepsilon)\left(\frac{\varepsilon}{\bar{n}} - \frac{\varepsilon^2}{2\bar{n}^2} + \ldots\right) + \varepsilon$$

$$\simeq -\frac{\varepsilon^2}{2\bar{n}},$$ 11.4.3

neglecting terms in $\varepsilon^3/(\bar{n})^3$ and higher powers. Thus for $F(n)$ we obtain
$$F(n) = e^{-\varepsilon^2/2\bar{n}} = e^{-(n-\bar{n})^2/2\bar{n}},$$ 11.4.4
which is of course symmetrical about $n = \bar{n}$.

In this form $F(n)$ is not normalised, the normalisation having been lost by use of approximation 11.4.1 for $\ln n!$, rather than the better approximation 12.5.5. We can, however, readily renormalise by treating n as a continuous variable.

If n is large, the probabilities that we obtain $n+1$, $n+2$, ... red balls are almost the same as the probabilities of obtaining n. Moreover, the probability of obtaining between n and $n+dn$ is proportional to dn and also to $F(n)$; thus, defining $F(n) \, dn$ as this probability, we have
$$F(n)dn = C \, e^{-(n-\bar{n}^2)/2\bar{n}} dn,$$

where C is a constant later to be used for normalisation. The probability of obtaining between n_1 and n_2 red balls is then

$$C\int_{n_1}^{n_2} F(n)dn = C\int_{n_1}^{n_2} e^{-(n-\bar{n})^2/2\bar{n}} \, dn.$$

Now, the variable n must lie between 0 and N, or the variable ε between $-\bar{n}$ and $N-\bar{n}$. Thus

$$C\int_0^N e^{-(n-\bar{n})^2/2\bar{n}} \, dn = C\int_{-\bar{n}}^{N-\bar{n}} e^{-\varepsilon^2/2\bar{n}} \, d\varepsilon = 1. \qquad 11.4.5$$

Since, however, we have already assumed that $N \gg \bar{n} \gg 1$, and since the form of the integrand shows that it must be very small when n is greatly different from $\bar{n}$, there will be no great error in assuming that the limits of integration are $+\infty$ and $-\infty$. Thus

$$C\int_{-\infty}^{\infty} e^{-\varepsilon^2/2\bar{n}} \, d\varepsilon = 1, \qquad 11.4.6$$

whence, using the value of the integral given in § 12.6, we obtain

$$C = (2\pi\bar{n})^{-\frac{1}{2}}, \qquad 11.4.7$$

so that the normalised form of $F(n)$ is

$$F(n) = (2\pi\bar{n})^{-\frac{1}{2}} e^{-(n-\bar{n})^2/2\bar{n}}. \qquad 11.4.8$$

11.4.8 is the *normal* or *Gaussian distribution*, which we have already met in connection with the random walk (§ 6.1) and the theory of errors (§ 7.5). Its shape has been shown in *figs.* 5.2, p. 118 and 5.5, p. 131, where the similarity to *fig.* 11.1*b*, p. 281, is obvious.

§ 11.5 Density fluctuations

The formulae in §§ 11.3–4 can be applied to the distribution of molecules in space. Thus if v is a volume, small compared with the total volume of gas, the mean number of molecules in v is

$$\bar{n} = nv, \qquad 11.5.1$$

where n is as usual the mean number per unit volume. The probability that the volume v will contain exactly n molecules is then given by equation 11.4.8 if $\bar{n}$ is large, and by 11.3.3 if $\bar{n}$ happens to be small either because v is very small or the pressure very low. In either case the mean-square fluctuation is

$$\overline{(\Delta n)^2} = \bar{n} = nv. \qquad 11.5.2$$

Thus, if v is large or the density is high, the fluctuations will be large, but the relative fluctuation, $(\overline{\delta^2})^{\frac{1}{2}}$, defined by

$$\overline{\delta^2} = \overline{(\Delta n)^2}/(\bar{n})^2, \qquad 11.5.3$$

will be small. In a given volume, the relative fluctuation will increase inversely as the square root of the pressure. Thus, to take a numerical example, a volume of $(1\ \mu m)^3$ of gas contains about 10^7 molecules at N.T.P., and this number fluctuates by $(10^7)^{\frac{1}{2}}$ or about $\frac{1}{30}\%$. If the pressure is reduced by a factor of 10^3, that is to about 1 torr, the relative fluctuation increases by a factor of $(10^3)^{\frac{1}{2}}$, that is to about 1%; while in a vacuum of 1 millitorr the relative fluctuation approaches 30%.

These pressure fluctuations can be observed directly. For example, if the optical amplification system of a galvanometer is sufficiently sensitive, movements of the suspension due to fluctuations of the pressure on various parts of it can be detected. This is, of course, one of the manifestations of the phenomenon we have discussed under the name of Brownian motion. Again, it is observed that gases at low pressures scatter light because density fluctuations in regions of the order of magnitude of a wavelength ($\sim 1\ \mu m$) result in changes of refractive index. In gases near to their critical point, that is under conditions when they cannot be treated as perfect, these fluctuations become specially large and give rise to a characteristic opalescence.

If the conduction electrons in metals are thought of as forming an electron gas, similar considerations show that the electron density will be subject to local fluctuations. The electron movements which produce these fluctuations and smooth them out again are equivalent to random electric currents, which can be detected and amplified. This is the origin of Johnson noise which is one of the factors limiting the useful amplification of electronic equipment.

§ 11.6   Fluctuations in beams of particles

One of the classic experiments to show that nuclear disintegrations take place at random intervals has already been discussed in § 4.8, and described in problem 4.11.5. In the analysis of the counting records by Rutherford, Geiger and Bateman (1910) counts were made of the numbers of α-particles which produced scintillations on a fluorescent screen in periods of $7\frac{1}{2}$ sec. In all, 10,097 particles were counted in 2,608 periods, giving an average $\bar{n}$ of 3·87 per period. The numbers of occasions on which $n = 0, 1, 2, \ldots$ scintillations were observed in a single period were recorded and compared with the number calculated from equation 11.3.3 with $\bar{n} = 3·87$. In every case, agreement was within the expected sampling error or root-mean-square deviation from the expected number. The actual experimental results are given in problem 11.7.3.

Recent applications of the same technique have been to study the emission of photons from light sources. Results show that the numbers of photons emitted in equal time intervals from traditional sources, such as tungsten lamps, are distributed according to the Poisson law (11.3.3), showing that emission is random and that there is no correlation between the emission from one atom and from another. The distribution of photons from lasers shows deviations from the simple Poisson law.

A final example of the influence of random effects in particle beams is the phenomenon of shot noise in electronic valves. Suppose the mean current through the valve is $\bar{i}$: in time t a charge $\bar{i}t$ will be transported, made up of $\bar{n}$ electrons each with charge q, so that

$$\bar{i}t = \bar{n}q.$$ 11.6.1

If these electrons are emitted at random from the cathode, then the emission of any one has no influence on the emission of another, so the number $\bar{n}$ will vary from interval to interval, the fraction of intervals in which actual numbers n are emitted being given by formula 11.3.3 or 11.4.8. The mean-square fluctuation is

$$\overline{(\Delta n)^2} = \overline{(n-\bar{n})^2} = \bar{n}.$$ 11.6.2

Multiplying throughout 11.6.2 by q^2, where q is the electronic charge, converts numbers of electrons to charge and gives

$$q^2\overline{(\Delta n)^2} = \bar{n}q^2$$
$$= \bar{i}qt,$$ 11.6.3

so that, superposed on the steady-rate charge transport, there is transport of random charge. The relative importance of the random current or shot noise increases as the mean current falls, in agreement with 11.5.3. Shot noise is a further limitation of the ability of electronic devices to produce useful amplification of small signals.

§ 11.7 Problems

1. Prove formulae 11.2.5–7. To do this, use the formula for $F(n)$ in 11.2.2 which is true for all $p \leqslant 1$, but do not change the binomial into an exponential, since this requires the assumption that $p \ll 1$. First check that

$$\sum_{n=0}^{N} F(n) = 1.$$

Then write, similarly to § 5.4,

$$\bar{n} = \sum_{n=0}^{N} nF(n) = \sum_{n=1}^{N} nF(n)$$

$$= Np \sum_{n=1}^{N} \frac{(N-1)!}{(n-1)![(N-1)-(n-1)]!} \times p^{n-1}(1-p)^{[(N-1)-(n-1)]}.$$

Replacing $N-1$ by N' and $n-1$ by n', result 11.2.5 follows in the same way as it did in the calculation of $\bar{n}$ with the restricted form of $F(n)$ in § 11.3. Similarly evaluate

$$\overline{n(n-1)} = \sum_{n=0}^{N} n(n-1)F(n)$$

and use the two results in problem 3.12.7. In the present notation these are

$$\overline{n^2} = \overline{n(n-1)} + \bar{n}$$

and $\qquad \overline{(\Delta n)^2} = \overline{n^2} - (\bar{n})^2,$

2. (i) Two lamp posts are exactly 250 m apart. In an experiment, similar to that suggested in § 7.2, this distance is measured by driving a car past the lamp posts on 10 randomly-occurring occasions. Show that the probabilities that the distance-measuring device will indicate a change of integral kilometre on $n = 0, 1, 2, \ldots$ occasions, are (to three decimal places):

n	0	1	2	3	4	5	6	7	8 or 9 or 10
probability	0·056	0·188	0·282	0·251	0·145	0·058	0·016	0·003	0·000

(ii) If the car in (i) is driven past the same lamp posts 100 times, show that the relative probabilities that a new kilometre is recorded on n occasions are

n	23	24	25	26	27
probability relative to $F(\bar{n})$	0·935	0·988	1·000	0·963	0·879

The answers to (i) are the ordinates plotted in *fig.* 11.1*a*. The answers to (ii) give the relationship between the ordinates on either side of the maximum in *fig.* 11.1*b*, and show that this curve, for all its appearance of symmetry is not quite symmetrical. If logarithms of factorials up to 100! are available it can be shown that

$$F(\bar{n}) = F(25) = 0·09.$$

3. In Rutherford and Geiger's experiments on the emission of α-particles from polonium described in problem 4.11.5 the numbers of α-particles arriving in successive intervals of $7\frac{1}{2}$ sec were recorded. Table 22 gives the numbers of intervals in which 0, 1, 2, . . . particles were counted. Analyse the results by the method described in § 11.6 and due to Rutherford, Geiger and Bateman (*Phil. Mag.* **20,** 698 (1910)), and complete the table. Show that the assumption of random emission is justified.

TABLE 22 : counting statistics for α-particles

number of α-particles in a $7\frac{1}{2}$ sec interval	number of intervals observed	theoretical values
0	57	54
1	203	210
2	383	
3	525	
4	532	
5	408	
6	273	
7	139	
8	45	
9	27	
10	10	
11	4	
12	0	
13	1	
14	1	

total number of particles	10,097
number of intervals	2608
average number per interval	3·87

---

§ 11.8 Further reading

The following book has a great many ingenious elementary accounts of fluctuation phenomena:

D. K. C. MacDonald *Noise and Fluctuations: an introduction* Wiley, New York and London, 1962.

Chapter 12

MATHEMATICAL FORMULAE AND METHODS

In this chapter we list a few mathematical proofs and formulae which are useful in statistical physics. Proofs and rules, where given, are designed for physical convenience and clarity rather than mathematical rigour.

§ 12.1   The integrals $\int_a^b x^n e^{-\alpha x}\, dx$

These first appear in § 4.1.

By elementary integration

$$\int_a^b e^{-\alpha x}\, dx = -\frac{1}{\alpha}[e^{-\alpha x}]_a^b$$

$$= \frac{1}{\alpha}(e^{-\alpha a} - e^{-\alpha b}).\qquad\qquad 12.1.1$$

$$\int_a^b x\, e^{-\alpha x}\, dx = -\frac{1}{\alpha}[x\, e^{-\alpha x}]_a^b + \frac{1}{\alpha}\int_a^b e^{-\alpha x}\, dx$$

by integration by parts. Then proceeding as in 12.1.1, we obtain:

$$\int_a^b x\, e^{-\alpha x}\, dx = \frac{a}{\alpha}e^{-\alpha a} - \frac{b}{\alpha}e^{-\alpha b} + \frac{1}{\alpha^2}(e^{-\alpha a} - e^{-\alpha b}),\qquad 12.1.2$$

and so on for $\int_a^b x^2 e^{-\alpha x}\, dx$ etc. The expressions are much simpler if the limits of integration are 0 or ∞.

§ 12.2   Differentiation under the integral sign

The integrals of § 12.1 and many others in statistical physics are readily evaluated by differentiation under the integral sign. Thus

$$\int_a^b x\, e^{-\alpha x}\, dx = -\frac{\partial}{\partial \alpha}\int_a^b e^{-\alpha x}\, dx$$

$$= -\frac{\partial}{\partial \alpha}\left\{\frac{1}{\alpha}(e^{-\alpha a} - e^{-\alpha b})\right\}$$

$$= \frac{a}{\alpha}e^{-\alpha a} - \frac{b}{\alpha}e^{-\alpha b} + \frac{1}{\alpha^2}(e^{-\alpha a} - e^{-\alpha b}),\qquad 12.2.1$$

as obtained in 12.1.2. Once again the work is simplified if either of the limits of integration is 0 or ∞.

Differentiation under the integral sign, that is writing

$$\frac{\partial}{\partial \alpha}\int_a^b f(\alpha,x)dx = \int_a^b \frac{\partial}{\partial \alpha}f(\alpha,x)dx,$$

is safe if α does not depend on x, a, or b and the function $f(\alpha,x)$, is well behaved in the range $a \leqslant x \leqslant b$. All the functions in this book satisfy these requirements.

§ 12.3 Logarithmic differentiation

An even shorter method for dealing with the commonly occurring integral quotients, for example 4.1.8, is

$$\frac{\int_a^b x\,e^{-\alpha x}\,dx}{\int_a^b e^{-\alpha x}\,dx} = -\frac{\partial}{\partial \alpha}\ln\int_a^b e^{-\alpha x}\,dx$$

$$= -\frac{\partial}{\partial \alpha}\ln\left\{\frac{1}{\alpha}(e^{-\alpha a}-e^{-\alpha b})\right\}. \qquad 12.3.1$$

This expression can be simplified if the upper limit b is ∞ when, remembering that

$$\ln(e^x) = x, \qquad\qquad 12.3.2$$

we have

$$\frac{\int_a^\infty x\,e^{-\alpha x}\,dx}{\int_a^\infty e^{-\alpha x}\,dx} = \frac{\partial}{\partial \alpha}\ln \alpha - \frac{\partial}{\partial \alpha}(-\alpha a)$$

$$= \frac{1}{\alpha}+a. \qquad\qquad 12.3.3$$

When $a = 0$, as in the case of 4.1.8, the expression further simplifies to give

$$\frac{\int_0^\infty x\,e^{-\alpha x}\,dx}{\int_0^\infty e^{-\alpha x}\,dx} = -\frac{\partial}{\partial \alpha}\ln\int_0^\infty e^{-\alpha x}\,dx$$

$$= -\frac{\partial}{\partial \alpha}\ln\frac{1}{\alpha}$$

$$= -\frac{\partial}{\partial \alpha}\ln \alpha$$

$$= \frac{1}{\alpha}. \qquad\qquad 12.3.4$$

In dealing with integrals such as 4.2.1, which contain exponentials in the form $\exp(-x/x_0)$, it is usually quicker to write

$$x_0 = 1/\alpha$$

and substitute back when the evaluation is complete.

§ 12.4   The exponential as the limit of a binomial

Equation 4.6.4 requires us to prove

$$\lim_{n\to\infty}\left(1+\frac{x}{n}\right)^n = e^x.$$

(i) *Formal proof:* consider the differential coefficient defined by

$$f'(0) = \lim_{t\to 0}\frac{f(t)-f(0)}{t} \qquad\qquad 12.4.1$$

and apply it to the function

$$f(t) = \ln(1+xt). \qquad\qquad 12.4.2$$

We have

$$f'(t) = \frac{d}{dt}\cdot f(t) = \frac{x}{1+xt}$$

so $f'(0) = x$.

By 12.4.1

$$f'(0) = \lim_{t\to 0}\frac{\ln(1+xt)-0}{t} = x.$$

Now put $t = \dfrac{1}{n}$ and obtain

$$\lim_{n\to\infty} n\ln\left(\overline{1+\frac{x}{n}}\right) = x,$$

or $$\lim_{n\to\infty}\ln\left(1+\frac{x}{n}\right)^n = x$$

so $$\lim_{n\to\infty}\left(1+\frac{x}{n}\right)^n = e^x. \qquad\qquad 12.4.3$$

(ii) *Informal proof:* use the binomial theorem to write

$$\left(1+\frac{x}{n}\right)^n = 1+n\frac{x}{n}+\frac{n(n-1)}{2!}\frac{x^2}{n^2}+\frac{n(n-1)(n-2)}{3!}\frac{x^3}{n^3}+\cdots.$$

$$12.4.4$$

Now

$$e^x = 1 + x + \frac{x^2}{2!} + \frac{x^3}{3!} + \ldots \ldots$$ 12.4.5

If $n \to \infty$, then, in every term in series 12.4.4, fractions of the type

$$\frac{n(n-1)(n-2)\ldots(n-r+1)}{n^r} \to 1,$$

so that the series 12.4.4 and 12.4.5 become equal term by term.

(iii) *Corollaries of* (i) *and* (ii) are

$$\lim\left(1 + \frac{1}{n}\right)^n = e,$$ 12.4.6

$$\lim\left(1 - \frac{1}{n}\right)^n = e^{-1}.$$ 12.4.7

The latter result is the one used in 4.6.4.

§ 12.5 Stirling's formula

The formula for $\ln(N!)$ valid for large N is

$$\ln N! = N \ln N - N.$$ 12.5.1

Informal proof: by definition of the integral as the limit of a sum we have

$$\int_a^b f(x)dx = \lim_{h\to 0} h\{f(a+h) + f(a+2h) + \ldots + f(a+nh)\},$$

12.5.2

where $a + nh = b$

or $n = (b-a)/h.$

We note here the comparison between this limit and the process for calculating the area under the curve $f(x)$ by adding up the areas of n rectangular strips each of width h (see *fig.* 12.1).

Now, in equation 12.5.2, if we take $a = 1, f(x) = \ln x$ and $h = 1$, and assume that the expression is valid even though $h \nrightarrow 0$, then

$$\int_1^{n+1} \ln x \, dx = \ln 2 + \ln 3 + \ldots + \ln(n+1).$$ 12.5.3

The left-hand side of this equation is

$$\int_1^{n+1} \ln x \, dx = [x \ln x - x]_1^{n+1}$$

$$= (n+1)\ln(n+1) - n.$$

The right-hand side is $\ln (n+1)!$ Thus
$$\ln (n+1)! = (n+1) \ln (n+1) - n$$
or, writing $n+1 = N$,
$$\ln N! = N \ln N - N + 1. \qquad 12.5.4$$
Now if N is a large number, $N \ln N \gg N \gg 1$, so the 1 can be neglected in equation 12.5.4 giving the required approximate value 12.5.1.

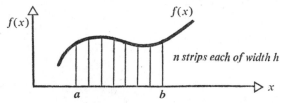

Figure 12.1.
$$\int_a^b f(x)\, dx = \textit{area of n rectangular strips of width } h = (b-a)/n.$$

This proof conceals the significance of the requirement that N or n is large, which has vanished into the assumptions involved in the derivation of 12.5.3 from 12.5.2. A more accurate proof gives
$$\ln N! = N \ln N - N + \tfrac{1}{2} \ln (2\pi N) + \text{terms of order } N^{-1}.$$
$$12.5.5$$
In general, the simpler formula 12.5.1 suffices in statistical physics. Exceptions arise, however, if it is required to take an antilogarithm to obtain $N!$, for then, from 12.5.5,
$$N! = (2\pi N)^{\frac{1}{2}} (N/e)^N, \qquad 12.5.6$$
while the corresponding formula from 12.5.1 would omit the factor $(2\pi N)^{\frac{1}{2}}$. This complication was concealed in § 5.6, where it was hidden in the normalisation constant C_3.

§ 12.6   The 'error integrals'
Integrals of the type
$$I_n = \int_0^{\infty} x^n e^{-hx^2}\, dx, \qquad 12.6.1$$
where n is a positive integer require separate treatment for n odd and n even. The easier case is n odd. Thus, by elementary integration,
$$I_1 = \int_0^{\infty} x\, e^{-hx^2}\, dx = \frac{1}{2h}, \qquad 12.6.2$$

whence, using the methods of § 12.2,

$$I_3 = \int_0^\infty x^3\, e^{-hx^2}\, dx = -\frac{\partial}{\partial h} \int_0^\infty x\, e^{-hx^2}\, dx$$

$$= -\frac{\partial}{\partial h}\left(\frac{1}{2h}\right) = \frac{1}{2h^2}, \qquad\qquad 12.6.3$$

$$I_5 = \int_0^\infty x^5\, e^{-hx^2}\, dx = -\frac{\partial}{\partial h} \int_0^\infty x^3\, e^{-hx^2}\, dx$$

$$= \frac{1}{h^3}, \qquad\qquad 12.6.4$$

and so on.

When n is even we have

$$I_0 = \int_0^\infty e^{-hx^2}\, dx = \tfrac{1}{2} \int_{-\infty}^\infty e^{-hx^2}\, dx, \qquad\qquad 12.6.5$$

by the symmetry of the function e^{-hx^2} shown in *fig.* 5.5. Now

$$\int_{-\infty}^\infty e^{-x^2}\, dx = \pi^{\frac{1}{2}}, \qquad\qquad 12.6.6$$

which is a result worth remembering.

Proof: write

$$I = \int_{-\infty}^\infty e^{-x^2}\, dx = \int_{-\infty}^\infty e^{-y^2}\, dy,$$

since a definite integral is a function of its limits only, not of the variable of integration. So

$$I^2 = \int_{-\infty}^\infty \int_{-\infty}^\infty e^{-x^2}\, e^{-y^2}\, dx\, dy$$

$$= \int_{-\infty}^\infty \int_{-\infty}^\infty e^{-(x^2+y^2)}\, dx\, dy.$$

The limits on the double integral indicate that the integration is over the whole (x,y) plane. Now change to polar co-ordinates, writing

$$x = r \cos \theta$$

and $$y = r \sin \theta,$$

so that the integrand becomes e^{-r^2}. The element of area in polar (r,θ) co-ordinates is $r\,dr\,d\theta$, so that

$$I^2 = \int_0^\infty \int_0^{2\pi} e^{-r^2} r\,dr\,d\theta$$

$$= [\theta]_0^{2\pi} \int_0^\infty e^{-r^2} r\,dr$$

$$= 2\pi[-\tfrac{1}{2} e^{-r^2}]_0^\infty$$

$$= \pi,$$

so $\qquad I = \int_{-\infty}^{\infty} e^{-x^2}\,dx = \pi^{\frac{1}{2}}.$

Writing $h^{\frac{1}{2}}x$ for x we have immediately

$$I_0 = \int_0^\infty e^{-hx^2}\,dx = \tfrac{1}{2}\int_{-\infty}^{\infty} e^{-hx^2}\,dx = \tfrac{1}{2}\left(\frac{\pi}{h}\right)^{\frac{1}{2}}. \qquad 12.6.7$$

Then, using the technique of differentiation under the integral,

$$I_2 = \int_0^\infty x^2 e^{-hx^2}\,dx = -\frac{\partial}{\partial h}\int_0^\infty e^{-hx^2}\,dx$$

$$= -\frac{\partial}{\partial h}\left(\frac{1}{2}\frac{\pi^{\frac{1}{2}}}{h^{\frac{1}{2}}}\right) = \frac{1}{4}\frac{\pi^{\frac{1}{2}}}{h^{\frac{3}{2}}}. \qquad 12.6.8$$

$$I_4 = \int_0^\infty x^4 e^{-hx^2}\,dx = -\frac{\partial}{\partial h}\int_0^\infty x^2 e^{-hx^2}\,dx = \frac{3}{8}\frac{\pi^{\frac{1}{2}}}{h^{\frac{5}{2}}}, \qquad 12.6.9$$

and so on.

As an alternative to differentiation under the integral we may write

$$\int_0^\infty x^2 e^{-hx^2}\,dx = \int_0^\infty x\lceil x\,e^{-hx^2}\rceil dx \qquad 12.6.10$$

and then integrate by parts.

For a distribution $n(v)dv = Av^2 e^{-\mu v^2}dv$, as in § 5.10, where A is independent of v, the mean $\bar{v}$ is

$$\bar{v} = \frac{\displaystyle\int_0^\infty Av^3 e^{-\mu v^2}\,dv}{\displaystyle\int_0^\infty Av^2 e^{-\mu v^2}\,dv} = \frac{2}{(\pi\mu)^{\frac{1}{2}}} \qquad 12.6.11$$

and the mean square $\overline{v^2}$ is

$$\overline{v^2} = \frac{\displaystyle\int_0^\infty Av^4 e^{-\mu v^2}\,dv}{\displaystyle\int_0^\infty Av^2 e^{-\mu v^2}\,dv} = \frac{3}{2\mu}, \qquad 12.6.12$$

MATHEMATICAL FORMULAE AND METHODS

both by use of formulae 12.6.2–9.

Alternatively, logarithmic differentiation (§ 12.3) gives

$$\overline{v^2} = -\frac{\partial}{\partial \beta} \ln \int_0^\infty v^2 e^{-\mu v^2} \, dv$$

$$= -\frac{\partial}{\partial \mu} \ln \left(\frac{\pi^{\frac{1}{2}}}{4}\right)\frac{1}{\mu^{\frac{3}{2}}}$$

$$= \tfrac{3}{2}\frac{\partial}{\partial \mu} \ln \mu = \frac{3}{2\mu}. \tag{12.6.13}$$

§ 12.7 The error functions

The function

$$\text{erf } x = \frac{2}{\pi^{\frac{1}{2}}} \int_0^x e^{-x^2} \, dx \tag{12.7.1}$$

was defined by 5.10.11 as the *error function*. The function from which it was derived (5.10.10) is called the *complementary error function*:

$$\text{erfc } x = \frac{2}{\pi^{\frac{1}{2}}} \int_x^\infty e^{-x^2} \, dx. \tag{12.7.2}$$

When $x \gg 1$ there is a useful approximation:

$$\text{erfc } x = \frac{1}{\pi^{\frac{1}{2}}x} e^{-x^2}. \tag{12.7.3}$$

Problem 5.15.4 shows that, if high accuracy is not required, the condition $x \gg 1$ is not very severe.

§ 12.8 'The exponential takes charge'

The mathematical formulation of this saying is that, given $n > 0$,

$$\lim_{x \to \infty} (x^{-n} e^x) = \infty, \tag{12.8.1}$$

that is e^x tends to infinity faster than any power of x.

Informal proof: write

$$e^x = 1 + x + \frac{x^2}{2!} + \frac{x^3}{3!} + \cdots$$

so that there are always powers of x higher than the nth.

Similarly

$$\lim_{x \to \infty} (x^n e^{-x}) = 0 \tag{12.8.2}$$

and

$$\lim_{x \to \infty} (x^{-n} \ln x) = 0, \tag{12.8.3}$$

the latter limit meaning that any positive power of x tends to infinity faster than $\ln x$.

Physical quantities do not tend to infinity but the physical consequences of these mathematical formulae are easy to see since n, the power to which any physical quantity is raised is never greater than about 4, seldom greater than 3. Thus convergence or divergence under the influence of the exponential is rapid. Take, for example, formulae 5.9.4 and 10.4.5 for the rates of evaporation:

$$\Gamma = CT^{\frac{1}{2}} e^{-L/RT},$$

where C is a constant and L the latent heat of vaporisation. This can be written

$$\ln \Gamma = \ln C' + \tfrac{1}{2} \ln \frac{T}{T_b} - \left(\frac{L}{RT_b}\right)\frac{T_b}{T},$$

where T_b is the absolute boiling point. We know from Trouton's rule (§ 10.4) that $L/RT_b \sim 10$, so a 10% change of T, at temperatures near T_b, changes the logarithm term by 5%, but the T_b/T term by 100%. Halving the temperature similarly changes the logarithmic term by 35%, the T_b/T term by a factor of 20. At temperatures much less than T_b the difference in behaviour of the terms corresponding to $T^{\frac{1}{2}}$ and $\exp(-T_b/T)$ is still more striking.

§ 12.9 Permutations and combinations

The number of ways of choosing n things from N

$= $ no. of combinations of N things n at a time

$$= {}^N C_n = \frac{N!}{n!(N-n)!} = {}^N C_{N-n}. \qquad 12.9.1$$

This is also the number of ways of arranging N things, n of one kind and indistinguishable, $N-n$ of another kind and indistinguishable. Thus the probability of n heads in N tosses of a coin is

$$P(n) = (\tfrac{1}{2})^N {}^N C_n \qquad 12.9.2$$

$= $ probability of $(N-n)$ heads and n tails.

If we have N boxes and n indistinguishable balls, then

(i) if each box can contain either one ball or no ball, the number of ways of distributing the balls over the boxes is

$$w = \frac{N!}{(N-n)!n!}, \qquad 12.9.3$$

that is the number of arrangements of $(N-n)$ empty boxes and n full ones, the same situation as 12.9.1.

(ii) if there is no restriction on the number of balls in any box, then the number of ways in which the balls can be distributed over the boxes is

$$w = \frac{(N+n-1)!}{(N-1)!n!}.$$ 12.9.4

Proof: write $B_1\ B_2\ B_3 \ldots$ for the boxes

$$b_1\ b_2\ b_3 \ldots \text{ for the balls}$$

and take the series $B_1 b_1 b_2 B_2 b_3 B_3 B_4 \ldots$ to mean that box [1] contains balls b_1, b_2; box [2] contains ball b_3; box [3] contains no ball, and so on. Then w is calculated as follows: the first term can be chosen in N ways since it must represent a box; the remaining $(N+n-1)$ terms can be arranged in any order, so the number of permutations is $N(N+n-1)!$. This has to be divided by $N!n!$, since the order of filling the boxes is irrelevant and the balls are indistinguishable.

Generally it is the logarithm of expression 12.9.4 which is required, in which case, since N and n are both $\gg 1$, it is irrelevant whether w is written as in 12.9.4 or as

$$w = \frac{(N+n)!}{N!n!}.$$ 12.9.5

12.9.5 is the expression usually quoted for w and is the one used in 9.5.2.

INDEX

INDEX